2007 EDITION

INJURY FACTS®

NATIONAL SAFETY COUNCIL

FORMERLY ACCIDENT FACTS®

The National Safety Council, chartered by an act of Congress, is a nongovernmental, not-for-profit, public service organization with a mission to educate and influence people to prevent accidental injury and death.

Injury Facts®, the Council's annual statistical report on unintentional injuries and their characteristics and costs, was prepared by:

Research and Statistical Services Group
Mei-Li Lin, Executive Director
Alan F. Hoskin, Manager, Statistics Department
Kevin T. Fearn, Sr. Statistical Associate
Kathleen T. Porretta, Production Manager
Sergey Sinelnikov, Research Associate

Questions or comments about the content of *Injury Facts*® should be directed to the Research and Statistics Department, National Safety Council, 1121 Spring Lake Drive, Itasca, IL 60143, or telephone 630-775-2322, or fax 630-285-0242, or E-mail rssdept@nsc.org.

For price and ordering information, visit www.nsc.org or write Customer Relations, National Safety Council, 1121 Spring Lake Drive, Itasca, IL 60143, or telephone 800-621-7619, or fax 630-285-0797.

Acknowledgments
The information presented in *Injury Facts*® was made possible by the cooperation of many organizations and individuals, including state vital and health statistics authorities, state traffic authorities, state workers' compensation authorities, trade associations, Bureau of the Census, Bureau of Labor Statistics, Consumer Product Safety Commission, Federal Highway Administration, Federal Railroad Administration, International Labour Office, International Road Federation, National Center for Health Statistics, National Fire Protection Association, National Highway Traffic Safety Administration, National Transportation Safety Board, National Weather Service, Mine Safety and Health Administration, and the World Health Organization. Specific contributions are acknowledged in footnotes and source notes throughout the book.

Visit the National Safety Council's website:

http://www.nsc.org

Suggested citation: National Safety Council. (2007). *Injury Facts*®, *2007 Edition.* Itasca, IL: Author.

Library of Congress Catalog Card Number: 99–74142

Printed in U.S.A.   ISBN 0–87912–269–2   NSC Press Product No. 02306–0000
978-0-87912-269-0

Unintentional-injury deaths were up 1% in 2005 compared to the revised 2004 total. Unintentional-injury deaths were estimated to total 113,000 in 2005 and 112,000 in 2004.

The resident population of the United States was 296,410,000 in 2005, an increase of 1% from 2004. The death rate in 2005 was 38.1 per 100,000 population — unchanged from 2004 and 12% greater than the lowest rate on record, which was 34.0 in 1992.

The graph on page *v* shows the overall trends in the number of unintentional-injury deaths, the population, and the death rate per 100,000 population. A more complete summary of the situation in 2005 and recent trends is given on page 2.

Changes in the 2007 Edition

Once again, some important improvements have been made to *Injury Facts*. In addition to the changes listed here, there are two new products related to the book. The *Injury Facts Challenge* — an interactive, intranet-based, weekly quiz derived from the content of *Injury Facts*. The *Challenge* helps to build or maintain a safety culture within an organization by providing safety facts and tips and stimulating discussion of safety among employees. *Injury Facts Talks* are Microsoft® PowerPoint® presentations loaded with data from *Injury Facts* that may be used to build safety awareness among various audiences both at work and in the community. For more information on these products, visit the Council's web site (www.nsc.org), call Customer Service at 800-621-7619, or contact your local council.

Look for *new* data on ...

• Traffic safety issues — speeding, distracted driving, motorcycles, large trucks, teen drivers, graduated driver licensing

• Work injuries by nature of injury

• Drowning deaths in bathtubs and swimming pools

• Falls and fall risk factors among the elderly

• Youth risk behavior surveillance

• Nonfatal poisoning exposures by substance

• International fatality data on drownings

• And more

and *updated* or *expanded* data on ...

• General mortality

• Occupational injury and illness incidence rates by industry

• Occupational injury and illness profile data by industry sector

• Workers' compensation claims and costs

• Disasters

• Injuries by income and educational attainment

• Comparing safety of transportation modes

• Highway work zones

• Sports and recreation injuries

• Consumer product-related injuries

• Accidental deaths by state

• And more

Your comments and suggestions to improve *Injury Facts* are welcome. Information on how to contact us is given on page *ii*.

UNINTENTIONAL-INJURY DEATHS, DEATH RATES, AND POPULATION, UNITED STATES, 1903–2005

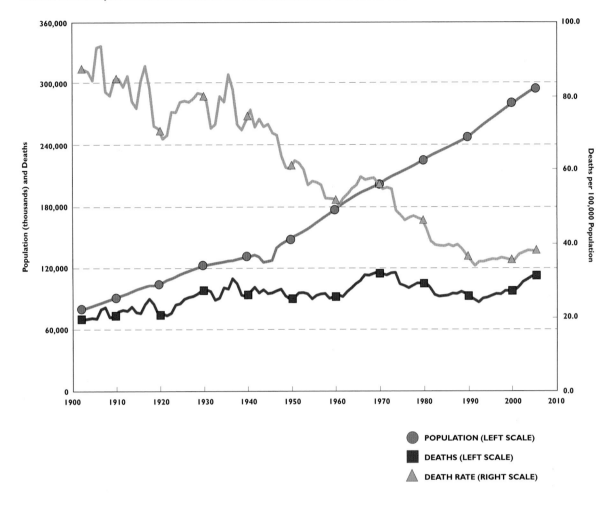

POPULATION (LEFT SCALE)

DEATHS (LEFT SCALE)

DEATH RATE (RIGHT SCALE)

ALL UNINTENTIONAL
INJURIES

INJURY FACTS®

NATIONAL SAFETY COUNCIL

ALL UNINTENTIONAL INJURIES, 2005

Unintentional-injury deaths were up 1% in 2005 compared to the revised 2004 total. Unintentional-injury deaths were estimated to total 113,000 in 2005 and 112,000 in 2004. The 2005 estimate is 3% greater than the 2003 final count of 109,277. The 2005 figure is 30% greater than the 1992 total of 86,777 (the lowest annual total since 1924) and only 3% below the 1969 peak of 116,385 deaths.

The death rate in 2005 was 38.1 per 100,000 population — 12% greater than the lowest rate on record, which was 34.0 in 1992. The 2005 death rate was unchanged from the 2004 revised rate.

Comparing 2005 to 2004, home and work deaths decreased while motor-vehicle and public deaths increased. The population death rate in the home class declined and the rates increased in the motor-vehicle and public classes.

The motor-vehicle death total was up 1% in 2005. The motor-vehicle death rate per 100,000,000 vehicle-miles was 1.54 in 2005, up 0.7% from the revised 2004 rate (1.53) and down 0.6% from the revised 2003 rate of 1.55.

According to the latest final data (2003), unintentional injuries continued to be the fifth leading cause of death, exceeded only by heart disease, cancer, stroke, and chronic lower respiratory diseases. Preliminary death

certificate data for 2004 indicate that unintentional injuries will remain in fifth place.

Nonfatal injuries also affect millions of Americans. In 2004, 33.2 million people — about 1 out of 9 — sought medical attention for an injury and 2.8 million people were hospitalized for injuries. About 28.1 million were treated in hospital emergency departments and about 5.2 million visits to hospital outpatient departments were for unintentional injuries. About 58.4 million visits to physicians' offices were for unintentional injuries.

The economic impact of these fatal and nonfatal unintentional injuries amounted to $625.5 billion in 2005. This is equivalent to about $2,100 per capita, or about $5,500 per household. These are costs that every individual and household pays whether directly out of pocket, through higher prices for goods and services, or through higher taxes.

Between 1912 and 2005, unintentional-injury deaths per 100,000 population were reduced 51% (after adjusting for the classification change in 1948) from 82.4 to 38.1. The reduction in the overall rate during a period when the nation's population tripled has resulted in 5,100,000 fewer people being killed due to unintentional injuries than there would have been if the rate had not been reduced.

ALL UNINTENTIONAL INJURIES, 2005

Class	Deaths	Change from 2004	Deaths per 100,000 Persons	Disabling Injuries[a]
All Classes[b]	113,000	+1%	38.1	24,100,000
Motor-vehicle	45,800	+1%	15.5	2,400,000
Public nonwork	43,442			2,300,000
Work	2,158			100,000
Home	200			(c)
Work	4,961	−1%	1.7	3,700,000
Nonmotor-vehicle	2,803			3,600,000
Motor-vehicle	2,158			100,000
Home	37,000	−8%	12.5	8,900,000
Nonmotor-vehicle	36,800			8,900,000
Motor-vehicle	200			(c)
Public	27,600	+15%	9.3	9,200,000

Source: National Safety Council estimates (rounded) based on data from the National Center for Health Statistics, state departments of health, and state traffic authorities, except for the work figures which are from the Bureau of Labor Statistics, Census of Fatal Occupational Injuries (CFOI). The National Safety Council adopted the CFOI count for work-related unintentional injuries beginning with 1992. See the Glossary for definitions and the Technical Appendix for estimating procedures. Beginning with 1999 data, which became available in 2001, deaths are classified according to the 10th revision of the International Classification of Diseases. Caution should be used in comparing data classified under the two systems.
[a]Disabling beyond the day of injury. Disabling injuries are not reported on a national basis, so the totals shown are approximations based on ratios of disabling injuries to deaths developed by the National Safety Council. The totals are the best estimates for the current year. They should not, however, be compared with totals shown in previous editions of this book to indicate year-to-year changes or trends. See the Glossary for definitions and the Technical Appendix for estimating procedures.
[b]Deaths and injuries above for the four separate classes add to more than the All Classes figures due to rounding and because some deaths and injuries are included in more than one class. For example, 2,158 work deaths involved motor vehicles and are in both the work and motor-vehicle totals and 200 motor-vehicle deaths occurred on home premises and are in both home and motor-vehicle. The total of such duplication amounted to about 2,358 deaths and 100,000 injuries in 2005.
[c]Less than 10,000.

UNINTENTIONAL-INJURY DEATHS BY CLASS, UNITED STATES, 2005

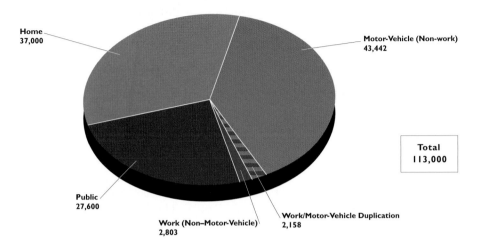

Home
37,000

Motor-Vehicle (Non-work)
43,442

Total
113,000

Public
27,600

Work (Non–Motor-Vehicle)
2,803

Work/Motor-Vehicle Duplication
2,158

UNINTENTIONAL DISABLING INJURIES BY CLASS, UNITED STATES, 2005

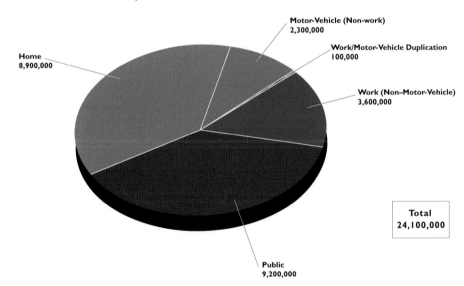

Motor-Vehicle (Non-work)
2,300,000

Work/Motor-Vehicle Duplication
100,000

Home
8,900,000

Work (Non–Motor-Vehicle)
3,600,000

Total
24,100,000

Public
9,200,000

COSTS OF UNINTENTIONAL INJURIES BY CLASS, 2005

The total cost of unintentional injuries in 2005, $625.5 billion, includes estimates of economic costs of fatal and nonfatal unintentional injuries together with employers' uninsured costs, vehicle damage costs, and fire losses. Wage and productivity losses, medical expenses, administrative expenses, and employers' uninsured costs are included in all four classes of injuries. Cost components unique to each class are identified below.

Motor-vehicle crash costs include property damage from motor-vehicle accidents. Work costs include the value of property damage in on-the-job motor-vehicle accidents and fires. Home and public costs include estimated fire losses, but do not include other property damage costs.

Besides the estimated $625.5 billion in economic losses from unintentional injuries in 2005, lost quality of life from those injuries is valued at an additional $3,007.8 billion, making the comprehensive cost $3,633.3 billion in 2005.

Several cost benchmarks were updated for the 2005–2006 edition making 2004 and later costs not comparable to previous years. The method for estimating the number of medically attended injuries by class was revised to use the latest National Health Interview Survey data. Estimated property damage costs in motor-vehicle crashes were rebenchmarked using National Highway Traffic Safety Administration data. The value of a statistical life also was updated, which affects only the comprehensive cost mentioned in the paragraph above.

CERTAIN COSTS OF UNINTENTIONAL INJURIES BY CLASS, 2005 ($ BILLIONS)

Cost	Total[a]	Motor-Vehicle	Work	Home	Public Nonmotor-Vehicle
Total	**$625.5**	**$247.7**	**$160.4**	**$142.3**	**$96.3**
Wage and productivity losses	318.2	88.0	80.0	90.6	64.0
Medical expenses	118.8	34.3	31.3	33.5	21.6
Administrative expenses[b]	117.4	81.9	34.4	7.0	6.9
Motor-vehicle damage	41.3	41.3	1.7	(c)	(c)
Employers' uninsured costs	19.1	2.2	10.7	4.2	2.4
Fire loss	10.7	(c)	2.3	7.0	1.4

Source: National Safety Council estimates. See the Technical Appendix. Cost-estimating procedures were revised extensively for the 1993 edition of Accident Facts®. In general, cost estimates are not comparable from year to year. As additional data or new benchmarks become available, they are used from that point forward. Previously estimated figures are not revised.
[a]Duplication between work and motor-vehicle, which amounted to $21.2 billion, was eliminated from the total.
[b]Home and public insurance administration costs may include costs of administering medical treatment claims for some motor-vehicle injuries filed through health insurance plans.
[c]Not included; see comments above.

COSTS OF UNINTENTIONAL INJURIES BY CLASS, 2005

TOTAL COST $625.5 BILLION

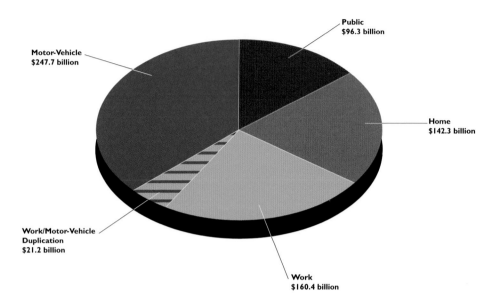

Public
$96.3 billion

Motor-Vehicle
$247.7 billion

Home
$142.3 billion

Work/Motor-Vehicle
Duplication
$21.2 billion

Work
$160.4 billion

COSTS OF UNINTENTIONAL INJURIES BY COMPONENT

Wage and Productivity Losses

A person's contribution to the wealth of the nation usually is measured in terms of wages and household production. The total of wages and fringe benefits together with an estimate of the replacement-cost value of household services provides an estimate of this lost productivity. Also included is travel delay for motor-vehicle accidents.

Medical Expenses

Doctor fees, hospital charges, the cost of medicines, future medical costs, and ambulance, helicopter, and other emergency medical services are included.

Administrative Expenses

Include the administrative cost of public and private insurance, and police and legal costs. Private insurance administrative costs are the difference between premiums paid to insurance companies and claims paid out by them. It is their cost of doing business and is a part of the cost total. Claims paid by insurance companies are not identified separately, as every claim is compensation for losses such as wages, medical expenses, property damage, etc.

Motor-Vehicle Damage

Includes the value of damage to vehicles from motor-vehicle crashes. The cost of normal wear and tear to vehicles is not included.

Employers' Uninsured Costs

This is an estimate of the uninsured costs incurred by employers, representing the dollar value of time lost by uninjured workers. It includes time spent investigating and reporting injuries, giving first aid, hiring and training of replacement workers, and the extra cost of overtime for uninjured workers.

Fire Loss

Includes losses from both structure fires and nonstructure fires such as vehicles, outside storage, crops, and timber.

Work–Motor-Vehicle Duplication

The cost of motor-vehicle crashes that involve persons in the course of their work is included in both classes but the duplication is eliminated from the total. The duplication in 2005 amounted to $21.2 billion and was made up of $4.4 billion in wage and productivity losses, $1.9 billion in medical expenses, $12.8 billion in administrative expenses, $1.7 billion in vehicle damage, and $0.4 billion in employers' uninsured costs.

COSTS OF UNINTENTIONAL INJURIES BY COMPONENT, 2005

TOTAL COST $625.5 BILLION

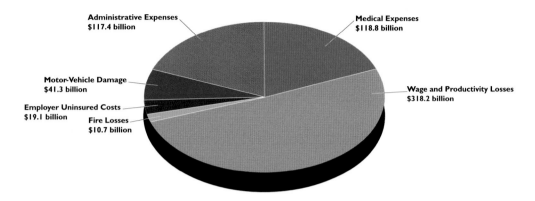

Administrative Expenses
$117.4 billion

Medical Expenses
$118.8 billion

Motor-Vehicle Damage
$41.3 billion

Wage and Productivity Losses
$318.2 billion

Employer Uninsured Costs
$19.1 billion

Fire Losses
$10.7 billion

COST EQUIVALENTS

The costs of unintentional injuries are immense — billions of dollars. Since figures this large can be difficult to comprehend, it is sometimes useful to reduce the numbers to a more understandable scale by relating them to quantities encountered in daily life. The table below shows how the costs of unintentional injuries compare to common quantities such as taxes, corporate profits, or stock dividends.

COST EQUIVALENTS, 2005

The Cost of ...	Is Equivalent to ...
... All Injuries ($625.5 billion)	... 67 cents of every dollar paid in federal personal income taxes, **or** ... 51 cents of every dollar spent on food in the U.S.
... Motor-Vehicle Crashes ($247.7 billion)	... purchasing 440 gallons of gasoline for each registered vehicle in the U.S., **or** ... more than $1,200 per licensed driver.
... Work Injuries ($160.4 billion)	... 31 cents of every dollar of corporate dividends to stockholders, **or** ... 11 cents of every dollar of pre-tax corporate profits, **or** ... exceeds the combined profits reported by the 16 largest Fortune 500 companies.
... Home Injuries ($142.3 billion)	... a $87,000 rebate on each new single-family home built, **or** ... 42 cents of every dollar of property taxes paid.
... Public Injuries ($96.3 billion)	... a $10.5 million grant to each public library in the U.S., **or** ... a $92,300 bonus for each police officer and firefighter.

Source: National Safety Council estimates.

DEATHS DUE TO UNINTENTIONAL INJURIES, 2005

TYPE OF EVENT AND AGE OF VICTIM

All Unintentional Injuries

The term "unintentional" covers most deaths from injury and poisoning. Excluded are homicides (including legal intervention), suicides, deaths for which none of these categories can be determined, and war deaths.

	Total	Change from 2004	Death Rate[a]
Deaths	113,000	+1%	38.1

Motor-Vehicle Accidents

Includes deaths involving mechanically or electrically powered highway-transport vehicles in motion (except those on rails), both on and off the highway or street.

	Total	Change from 2004	Death Rate[a]
Deaths	45,800	+1%	15.5

Poisoning

Includes deaths from drugs, medicines, other solid and liquid substances, and gases and vapors. Excludes poisonings from spoiled foods, salmonella, etc., which are classified as disease deaths.

	Total	Change from 2004	Death Rate[a]
Deaths	20,900	+5%	7.1

Falls

Includes deaths from falls from one level to another or on the same level. Excludes falls in or from transport vehicles, or while boarding or alighting from them.

	Total	Change from 2004	Death Rate[a]
Deaths	17,700	+1%	6.0

Choking

Includes deaths from unintentional ingestion or inhalation of food or other objects resulting in the obstruction of respiratory passages.

	Total	Change from 2004	Death Rate[a]
Deaths	4,600	+2%	1.6

See footnotes on page 9.

Drowning

Includes nontransport-related drownings such as those resulting from swimming, playing in the water, or falling in. Excludes drownings in floods and other cataclysms, which are classified to the cataclysm, and boating-related drownings.

	Total	Change from 2004	Death Rate[a]
Deaths	3,600	0%	1.2

Age	0–4	5–14	15–24	25–44	45–64	65–74	75+
Deaths	500	300	650	800	850	200	300

Fires, flames, and smoke

Includes deaths from exposure to fires, flames, and smoke, and from injuries in fires--such as falls and struck by falling objects. Excludes burns from hot objects or liquids.

	Total	Change from 2004	Death Rate[a]
Deaths	3,100	−14%	1.0

Age	0–4	5–14	15–24	25–44	45–64	65–74	75+
Deaths	240	190	120	600	850	450	650

Mechanical Suffocation

Includes deaths from hanging and strangulation, and suffocation in enclosed or confined spaces, cave-ins, or by bed clothes, plastic bags, or similar materials.

	Total	Change from 2004	Death Rate[a]
Deaths	1,400	0%	0.5

Age	0–4	5–14	15–24	25–44	45–64	65–74	75+
Deaths	550	80	70	300	210	70	120

Natural Heat or Cold

Includes deaths resulting from exposure to excessive natural heat and cold (e.g., extreme weather conditions).

	Total	Change from 2004	Death Rate[a]
Deaths	900	−10%	0.3

Age	0–4	5–14	15–24	25–44	45–64	65–74	75+
Deaths	30	10	40	180	260	130	250

All Other Types

Most important types included are: firearms, struck by or against object, machinery, electric current, and air, water, and rail transport.

	Total	Change from 2004	Death Rate[a]
Deaths	15,000	−1%	5.1

Note: Category descriptions have changed due to adoption of ICD-10. See Technical Appendix for comparability.
[a]Deaths per 100,000 population.
[b]Deaths per 100,000 population in each age group.
[c]Death rate less than 0.05.

Age	0–4	5–14	15–24	25–44	45–64	65–74	75+
Deaths	40	260	1,300	2,700	3,100	1,400	6,200

LEADING CAUSES OF DEATH

Unintentional injuries are the fifth leading cause of death overall and first among persons in age groups from 1 to 44. By single years of age, unintentional injuries are the leading cause from 1 to 41.

Causes are ranked for both sexes combined. Some leading causes for males and females separately may not be shown. Beginning with 1999 data, deaths are classified according to the 10th revision of the *International Classification of Diseases*. See the Technical Appendix for comparability.

DEATHS AND DEATH RATES BY AGE AND SEX, 2003

Cause	Number of Deaths			Death Rates[a]		
	Total	Male	Female	Total	Male	Female
All Ages[b]						
All Causes	**2,448,288**	**1,201,964**	**1,246,324**	**841.8**	**840.2**	**843.3**
Heart disease	685,089	336,095	348,994	235.5	234.9	236.1
Cancer (malignant neoplasms)	556,902	287,990	268,912	191.5	201.3	182.0
Stroke (cerebrovascular disease)	157,689	61,426	96,263	54.2	42.9	65.1
Chronic lower respiratory diseases	126,382	60,714	65,668	43.5	42.4	44.4
Unintentional injuries	**109,277**	**70,532**	**38,745**	**37.6**	**49.3**	**26.2**
Motor-vehicle	44,757	30,655	14,102	15.4	21.4	9.5
Poisoning	19,457	13,176	6,281	6.7	9.2	4.2
Falls	17,229	8,910	8,319	5.9	6.2	5.6
Choking[c]	4,272	2,222	2,050	1.5	1.6	1.4
Fires and flames	3,369	1,948	1,421	1.2	1.4	1.0
All other unintentional injuries	20,193	13,621	6,572	6.9	9.5	4.4
Diabetes mellitus	74,219	35,438	38,781	25.5	24.8	26.2
Influenza and pneumonia	65,163	28,778	36,385	22.4	20.1	24.6
Alzheimer's disease	63,457	18,335	45,122	21.8	12.8	30.5
Nephritis and nephrosis	42,453	20,481	21,972	14.6	14.3	14.9
Septicemia	34,069	14,987	19,082	11.7	10.5	12.9
Under 1 Year						
All Causes	**28,025**	**15,902**	**12,123**	**695.2**	**770.8**	**615.9**
Congenital anomalies	5,621	3,020	2,601	139.4	146.4	132.1
Short gestation, low birth weight, n.e.c.	4,849	2,737	2,112	120.3	132.7	107.3
Sudden infant death syndrome	2,162	1,280	882	53.6	62.0	44.8
Maternal complications of pregnancy	1,710	958	752	42.4	46.4	38.2
Complications of placenta, cord, membranes	1,099	598	501	27.3	29.0	25.5
Unintentional injuries	**945**	**539**	**406**	**23.4**	**26.1**	**20.6**
Mechanical suffocation	558	334	224	13.8	16.2	11.4
Motor-vehicle	145	80	65	3.6	3.9	3.3
Drowning	58	34	24	1.4	1.6	1.2
Choking[c]	61	32	29	1.5	1.6	1.5
Fires and flames	30	9	11	0.7	0.4	0.6
All other unintentional injuries	93	50	53	2.3	2.4	2.7
Respiratory distress	831	492	339	20.6	23.8	17.2
Bacterial sepsis	772	462	310	19.1	22.4	15.7
Neonatal hemorrhage	649	384	265	16.1	18.6	13.5
Diseases of the circulatory system	591	331	260	14.7	16.0	13.2
1 to 4 Year						
All Causes	**4,965**	**2,826**	**2,139**	**31.5**	**35.1**	**27.8**
Unintentional injuries	**1,717**	**1,048**	**669**	**10.9**	**13.0**	**8.7**
Motor-vehicle	621	353	268	3.9	4.4	3.5
Drowning	456	301	155	2.9	3.7	2.0
Fires and flames	224	131	93	1.4	1.6	1.2
Choking[c]	88	57	31	0.6	0.7	0.4
Mechanical suffocation	71	44	27	0.5	0.5	0.4
All other unintentional injuries	257	162	95	1.6	2.0	1.2
Congenital anomalies	541	275	266	3.4	3.4	3.5
Cancer (malignant neoplasms)	392	227	165	2.5	2.8	2.1
Homicide	376	202	174	2.4	2.5	2.3
Heart disease	186	89	97	1.2	1.1	1.3
Influenza and pneumonia	163	91	72	1.0	1.1	0.9
Septicemia	85	54	31	0.5	0.7	0.4
Certain conditions originating in the perinatal period	79	43	36	0.5	0.5	0.5
Chronic lower respiratory diseases	55	38	17	0.3	0.5	0.2
Benign neoplasms	51	31	20	0.3	0.4	0.3

See source and footnotes on page 12.

DEATHS AND DEATH RATES BY AGE AND SEX, 2003, Cont.

	Number of Deaths			Death Rates[a]		
Cause	Total	Male	Female	Total	Male	Female
5 to 14 Years						
All Causes	**6,954**	**4,150**	**2,804**	**17.0**	**19.8**	**14.0**
Unintentional injuries	**2,618**	**1,662**	**956**	**6.4**	**7.9**	**4.8**
Motor-vehicle	1,642	1,009	633	4.0	4.8	3.2
Drowning	268	199	69	0.7	0.9	0.3
Fires and flames	215	112	103	0.5	0.5	0.5
Mechanical suffocation	58	50	8	0.1	0.2	0.0
Firearms	49	46	3	0.1	0.2	0.0
All other unintentional injuries	386	246	140	0.9	1.2	0.7
Cancer (malignant neoplasms)	1,076	591	485	2.6	2.8	2.4
Congenital anomalies	386	198	188	0.9	0.9	0.9
Homicide	324	215	109	0.8	1.0	0.5
Heart disease	264	155	109	0.6	0.7	0.5
Suicide	250	194	56	0.6	0.9	0.3
Influenza and pneumonia	147	70	77	0.4	0.3	0.4
Chronic lower respiratory diseases	118	75	43	0.3	0.4	0.2
Benign neoplasms	79	43	36	0.2	0.2	0.2
Septicemia	77	34	43	0.2	0.2	0.2
15 to 24 Years						
All Causes	**33,568**	**24,670**	**8,898**	**81.4**	**116.3**	**44.4**
Unintentional injuries	**15,272**	**11,291**	**3,981**	**37.0**	**53.2**	**19.9**
Motor-vehicle	10,972	7,806	3,166	26.6	36.8	15.8
Poisoning	1,999	1,562	437	4.8	7.4	2.2
Drowning	567	525	42	1.4	2.5	0.2
Falls	230	186	44	0.6	0.9	0.2
Firearms	200	182	18	0.5	0.9	0.1
All other unintentional injuries	1,304	1,030	274	3.2	4.9	1.4
Homicide	5,368	4,624	744	13.0	21.8	3.7
Suicide	3,988	3,381	607	9.7	15.9	3.0
Cancer	1,651	979	672	4.0	4.6	3.4
Heart disease	1,133	718	415	2.7	3.4	2.1
Congenital anomalies	451	272	179	1.1	1.3	0.9
Influenza and pneumonia	224	124	100	0.5	0.6	0.5
Stroke (cerebrovascular disease)	221	116	105	0.5	0.5	0.5
Chronic lower respiratory diseases	191	114	77	0.5	0.5	0.4
Human immunodeficiency virus infection	178	95	83	0.4	0.4	0.4
25 to 34 Years						
All Causes	**41,300**	**28,602**	**12,698**	**103.6**	**141.5**	**64.6**
Unintentional injuries	**12,541**	**9,534**	**3,007**	**31.5**	**47.2**	**15.3**
Motor-vehicle	6,833	5,156	1,677	17.1	25.5	8.5
Poisoning	3,435	2,514	921	8.6	12.4	4.7
Drowning	356	323	33	0.9	1.6	0.2
Falls	285	237	48	0.7	1.2	0.2
Fires and flames	252	154	98	0.6	0.8	0.5
All other unintentional injuries	1,380	1,150	230	3.5	5.7	1.2
Suicide	5,065	4,156	911	12.7	20.6	4.6
Homicide	4,516	3,741	820	11.3	18.5	4.2
Cancer	3,741	1,804	1,937	9.4	8.9	9.9
Heart disease	3,250	2,129	1,121	8.2	10.5	5.7
Human immunodeficiency virus infection	1,588	1,038	550	4.0	5.1	2.8
Diabetes mellitus	657	379	278	1.6	1.9	1.4
Stroke (cerebrovascular disease)	583	314	269	1.5	1.6	1.4
Congenital anomalies	426	233	193	1.1	1.2	1.0
Influenza and pneumonia	373	229	144	0.9	1.1	0.7
35 to 44 Years						
All Causes	**89,461**	**56,435**	**33,026**	**201.5**	**254.8**	**148.4**
Unintentional injuries	**16,766**	**12,003**	**4,763**	**37.8**	**54.2**	**21.4**
Motor-vehicle	6,961	4,984	1,977	15.7	22.5	8.9
Poisoning	6,230	4,166	2,064	14.0	18.8	9.3
Falls	636	525	111	1.4	2.4	0.5
Drowning	462	392	70	1.0	1.8	0.3
Fires and flames	395	257	138	0.9	1.2	0.6
All other unintentional injuries	2,082	1,679	403	4.7	7.6	1.8
Cancer	15,509	6,825	8,684	34.9	30.8	39.0
Heart disease	13,600	9,463	4,137	30.6	42.7	18.6
Suicide	6,602	5,138	1,464	14.9	23.2	6.6
Human immunodeficiency virus infection	5,340	3,884	1,456	12.0	17.5	6.5
Homicide	3,110	2,308	802	7.0	10.4	3.6
Chronic liver disease and cirrhosis	3,020	2,033	987	6.8	9.2	4.4
Stroke (cerebrovascular disease)	2,460	1,283	1,177	5.5	5.8	5.3
Diabetes mellitus	2,049	1,264	785	4.6	5.7	3.5
Influenza and pneumonia	992	560	432	2.2	2.5	1.9

See source and footnotes on page 12.

LEADING CAUSES OF DEATH (CONT.)

DEATHS AND DEATH RATES BY AGE AND SEX, 2003, Cont.

Cause	Number of Deaths			Death Rates[a]		
	Total	Male	Female	Total	Male	Female
45 to 54 Years						
All Causes	**176,781**	**110,682**	**66,099**	**433.2**	**552.2**	**318.4**
Cancer	49,843	25,542	24,301	122.1	127.4	117.0
Heart disease	37,732	27,304	10,428	92.5	136.2	50.2
Unintentional injuries	**15,837**	**11,196**	**4,641**	**38.8**	**55.9**	**22.4**
Motor-vehicle	6,074	4,303	1,771	14.9	21.5	8.5
Poisoning	5,434	3,598	1,836	13.3	17.9	8.8
Falls	1,043	800	243	2.6	4.0	1.2
Fires and flames	526	329	197	1.3	1.6	0.9
Drowning	397	320	77	1.0	1.6	0.4
All other unintentional injuries	2,363	1,846	517	5.8	9.2	2.5
Chronic liver disease and cirrhosis	7,466	5,514	1,952	18.3	27.5	9.4
Suicide	6,481	4,887	1,594	15.9	24.4	7.7
Stroke (cerebrovascular disease)	6,127	3,350	2,777	15.0	16.7	13.4
Diabetes mellitus	5,658	3,341	2,317	13.9	16.7	11.2
Human immunodeficiency virus infection	4,442	3,438	1,004	10.9	17.2	4.8
Chronic lower respiratory diseases	3,537	1,826	1,711	8.7	9.1	8.2
Viral hepatitis	2,259	1,666	593	5.5	8.3	2.9
55 to 64						
All Causes	**262,519**	**156,461**	**106,058**	**943.2**	**1,168.1**	**734.5**
Cancer	95,692	51,927	43,765	343.8	387.7	303.1
Heart disease	65,060	44,522	20,538	233.7	332.4	142.2
Chronic lower respiratory diseases	12,077	6,243	5,834	43.4	46.6	40.4
Diabetes mellitus	10,731	6,044	4,687	38.6	45.1	32.5
Stroke (cerebrovascular disease)	9,946	5,478	4,468	35.7	40.9	30.9
Unintentional injuries	**9,170**	**6,324**	**2,846**	**32.9**	**47.2**	**19.7**
Motor-vehicle	3,958	2,683	1,275	14.2	20.0	8.8
Poisoning	1,370	841	529	4.9	6.3	3.7
Falls	1,220	827	393	4.4	6.2	2.7
Fires and flames	392	254	138	1.4	1.9	1.0
Choking[c]	386	240	146	1.4	1.8	1.0
All other unintentional injuries	1,844	1,479	365	6.6	11.0	2.5
Chronic liver disease and cirrhosis	6,428	4,537	1,891	23.1	33.9	13.1
Suicide	3,843	2,987	856	13.8	22.3	5.9
Nephritis and nephrosis	3,806	2,065	1,741	13.7	15.4	12.1
Septicemia	3,651	1,887	1,764	13.1	14.1	12.2
65 to 74 Years						
All Causes	**413,497**	**231,421**	**182,076**	**2,253.3**	**2,769.0**	**1,821.9**
Cancer	141,248	77,793	63,455	769.7	930.8	635.0
Heart disease	107,263	65,568	41,695	584.5	784.5	417.2
Chronic lower respiratory diseases	29,919	15,333	14,586	163.0	183.5	146.0
Stroke (cerebrovascular disease)	20,708	10,668	10,040	112.8	127.6	100.5
Diabetes mellitus	16,656	8,687	7,969	90.8	103.9	79.7
Unintentional injuries	8,081	4,921	3,160	44.0	58.9	31.6
Motor-vehicle	2,967	1,778	1,189	16.2	21.3	11.9
Falls	2,048	1,209	839	11.2	14.5	8.4
Choking[c]	568	305	263	3.1	3.6	2.6
Fires and flames	419	244	175	2.3	2.9	1.8
Poisoning	403	223	180	2.2	2.7	1.8
All other unintentional injuries	1,676	1,162	514	9.1	13.9	5.1
Nephritis and nephrosis	7,345	3,785	3,560	40.0	45.3	35.6
Influenza and pneumonia	6,831	3,882	2,949	37.2	46.4	29.5
Septicemia	5,970	3,023	2,947	32.5	36.2	29.5
Chronic liver disease and cirrhosis	5,406	3,265	2,141	29.5	39.1	21.4
75 Years and Older[b]						
All Causes	1,391,218	570,815	820,403	7,904.1	8,647.0	7,458.2
Heart disease	456,162	185,900	270,262	2,591.6	2,816.1	2,456.9
Cancer	247,675	122,268	125,407	1,407.1	1,852.2	1,140.1
Stroke (cerebrovascular disease)	117,428	40,094	77,334	667.2	607.4	703.0
Chronic lower respiratory diseases	79,222	36,477	42,745	450.1	552.6	388.6
Alzheimer's disease	58,978	16,370	42,608	335.1	248.0	387.3
Influenza and pneumonia	50,841	20,580	30,261	288.8	311.8	275.1
Diabetes mellitus	38,266	15,605	22,661	217.4	236.4	206.0
Nephritis and nephrosis	27,911	12,651	15,260	158.6	191.6	138.7
Unintentional injuries	**26,330**	**12,014**	**14,316**	**149.6**	**182.0**	**130.1**
Falls	11,654	5,048	6,606	66.2	76.5	60.1
Motor-vehicle	4,584	2,503	2,081	26.0	37.9	18.9
Choking[c]	2,493	1,188	1,305	14.2	18.0	11.9
Fires and flames	717	338	379	4.1	5.1	3.4
Poisoning	456	205	251	2.6	3.1	2.3
All other unintentional injuries	6,426	2,732	3,694	36.5	41.4	33.6
Septicemia	20,478	7,985	12,493	116.3	121.0	113.6

Source: National Safety Council analysis of National Center for Health Statistics mortality data and Bureau of the Census population data.
[a] Deaths per 100,000 population in each age group.
[b] Includes 342 deaths where the age is unknown.
[c] Inhalation or ingestion of food or other objects.

LEADING CAUSES OF NONFATAL UNINTENIONAL INJURIES

Falls are the leading cause of nonfatal unintentional injuries that are treated in hospital emergency departments (ED) according to data from the All Injury Program, a cooperative program involving the National Center for Injury Prevention and Control, CDC, and the Consumer Product Safety Commission. Over eight million people were treated in an ED for fall-related injuries in 2004. Falls were the leading cause of nonfatal injuries for all age groups except 15–24 years old for which struck by or against an object or person was the leading cause. Struck by or against, overexertion, and motor-vehicle crashes involving vehicle occupants were also leading causes for most age groups.

LEADING CAUSES OF NONFATAL UNINTENTIONAL INJURIES TREATED IN HOSPITAL EMERGENCY DEPARTMENTS BY AGE GROUP, UNITED STATES, 2004

Rank	All Ages	Age Group <1	1–4	5–9	10–14	15–24	25–34	35–44	45–54	55–64	65+
1	Falls 8,058,498	Falls 126,281	Falls 888,335	Falls 676,704	Falls 668,589	Struck by/against 980,050	Falls 762,703	Falls 816,521	Falls 791,813	Falls 607,041	Falls 1,850,649
2	Struck by/against 4,430,171	Struck by/against 30,760	Struck by/against 368,104	Struck by/against 404,124	Struck by/against 593,752	Motor-vehicle occupant 914,024	Overexertion 673,076	Overexertion 645,508	Overexertion 423,692	Struck by/against 200,708	Struck by/against 214,235
3	Overexertion 3,279,383	Other bite/sting[a] 12,753	Other bite/sting[a] 145,001	Cut/pierce 115,886	Overexertion 272,797	Falls 869,363	Struck by/against 669,346	Struck by/against 575,089	Struck by/against 393,861	Overexertion 200,451	Motor-vehicle occupant 185,779
4	Motor-vehicle occupant 3,000,866	Fire/burn 11,372	Foreign body 113,084	Pedalcyclist 101,891	Cut/pierce 155,040	Overexertion 739,741	Motor-vehicle occupant 612,446	Motor-vehicle occupant 501,564	Motor-vehicle occupant 363,728	Motor-vehicle occupant 197,296	Overexertion 167,395
5	Cut/Pierce 2,285,191	Foreign body 9,767	Cut/pierce 86,787	Other bite/sting[a] 93,317	Pedalcyclist 140,063	Cut/pierce 498,856	Cut/pierce 440,900	Cut/pierce 398,151	Cut/pierce 296,883	Cut/pierce 164,110	Cut/pierce 122,162
6	Other bite/sting[a] 1,103,257	Other specified[b] 7,979	Overexertion 76,876	Motor-vehicle occupant 74,399	Motor-vehicle occupant 99,353	Other bite/sting[a] 194,493	Other bite/sting[a] 173,843	Other specified[b] 176,427	Other specified[b] 149,760	Other bite/sting[a] 68,461	Other bite/sting[a] 74,395
7	Other specified[b] 820,676	Inhalation/Suffocation 7,801	Fire/burn 57,728	Overexertion 73,980	Unknown/unspecified 95,311	Other specified[b] 158,451	Other specified[b] 142,385	Other bite/sting[a] 153,531	Other bite/sting[a] 117,166	Other specified[b] 59,121	Poisoning 61,888
8	Other transport[c] 623,846	Motor-vehicle occupant 6,992	Other specified[b] 49,446	Foreign body 58,303	Other transport[c] 70,429	Unknown/unspecified 142,089	Other transport[c] 102,175	Poisoning 118,140	Poisoning 92,787	Poisoning 39,802	Other transport[c] 47,822
9	Foreign body 609,493	Cut/Pierce 6,152	Poisoning 47,402	Dog bite 52,568	Other bite/sting[a] 70,286	Other transport[c] 136,800	Foreign body 99,096	Foreign body 89,079	Other transport[c] 67,640	Other transport[c] 33,856	Unknown/unspecified 40,910
10	Unknown/unspecified 589,698	Poisoning 5,814	Unknown/unspecified 47,078	Other transport[c] 49,071	Dog bite 39,265	Poisoning 100,145	Poisoning 90,372	Other transport[c] 82,760	Foreign body 62,703	Foreign body 32,348	Other specified[b] 37,148

All Causes											
Number	27,436,649	2,281,902		1,805,164	2,340,410	5,236,524	4,156,334	3,912,138	3,023,465	1,741,677	2,939,034[d]
Per 1,000 population	93.4	113.7		92.1	110.7	125.6	103.8	88.7	72.6	59.9	81.0[d]

Source: NEISS All Injury Program, Office of Statistics and Programming, National Center for Injury Prevention and Control, CDC, and Consumer Product Safety Commission.
[a] Other than dog bite.
[b] Includes electric current, explosions, fireworks, radiation, animal scratch, etc. Excludes all causes listed in the table and bb/pellet gunshot, drowning and near drowning, firearm gunshot, suffocation, machinery, natural and environmental conditions, pedestrians, and motorcyclists.
[c] Includes occupant of any transport vehicle other than a motor vehicle or motor cycle (e.g., airplane, rail car, boat, ATV, animal rider).
[d] Includes 2,798 cases with age unknown.

LEADING CAUSES OF UNINTENTIONAL-INJURY DEATH BY AGE, 2003

UNINTENTIONAL-INJURY DEATHS BY AGE AND EVENT, UNITED STATES, 2003

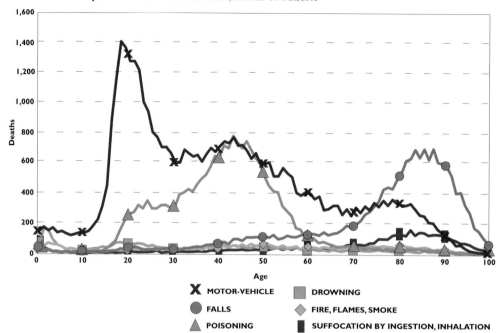

X MOTOR-VEHICLE	DROWNING
● FALLS	◆ FIRE, FLAMES, SMOKE
▲ POISONING	■ SUFFOCATION BY INGESTION, INHALATION

Motor-vehicle crashes, poisonings, falls, choking (suffocation by inhalation or ingestion of food or other object), fires and flames, drownings, and mechanical suffocation were the seven leading causes of unintentional-injury death in the United States in 2003. The graph above depicts the number of deaths attributed to the top six causes by single years of age through age 99.

In 2003, motor-vehicle crashes were the leading cause of unintentional-injury death for all ages combined and the leading cause of unintentional-injury deaths for each single year of age from 3 to 42, for those aged 45, and again for each single year of age from 48 to 74. Furthermore, for those aged 2 through 33, motor-vehicle crashes caused more deaths than any other injury type or illness, combining to account for 24% of the total for that age range.

The distribution of 2003 motor-vehicle fatalities shows a sharp increase during adolescence, rising from 447 for 15-year-olds to 1,404 for 18-year-olds. The greatest number of motor-vehicle fatalities occurred to persons aged 18 in 2003.

The second leading cause of unintentional-injury death overall in 2003 was poisoning. Poisoning fatalities reached a high of 777 for 43-year-olds and were the leading cause of unintentional-injury death for those aged 43–44 and 46–47. Poisonings were the second leading cause of unintentional-injury death each year of age from 16 to 42, for those aged 45, and again for

each year from 48 to 58. Falls were the third leading cause of unintentional-injury death in the United States in 2003. Falls were the leading cause of unintentional-injury death of persons aged 75 and older and second leading cause from ages 59 through 74 for each year of age; deaths resulting from falls peaked at 697 for individuals age 87.

Choking[a] was the fourth leading cause of unintentional-injury death in 2003. Choking deaths peaked at age 81 with 167 deaths. It was the second leading cause of unintentional-injury death for each year of age 90 and over. The fifth leading cause of unintentional-injury death was fires and flames, which peaked at 67 for 2-year-olds. Fires and flames were the second leading cause of injury death for children ages 8–9.

Drownings were the sixth leading cause of unintentional-injury death in 2003. Fatalities due to drownings were the leading cause of death for children aged 2 and reached a high of 159 for 1-year-olds (the second leading cause for that age). They were also the second leading cause of unintentional-injury death for children and adolescents aged 3, 6–7, and 10–15. Mechanical suffocation was the seventh leading cause overall and the leading cause for infants under 1 year old, with 558 deaths.

Source: National Safety Council tabulations of National Center for Health Statistics data. See the Technical Appendix for ICD-10 codes for the leading causes and comparability with prior years.
[a] *Inhalation or ingestion of food or other objects.*

UNINTENTIONAL-INJURY DEATHS PER 100,000 POPULATION BY AGE AND EVENT, UNITED STATES, 2003

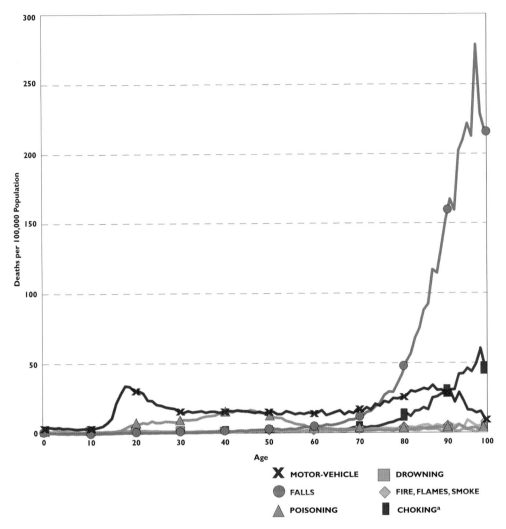

On the basis of deaths per 100,000 population at each age, motor-vehicle death rates in 2003 rose to an initial high of 34.0 for persons 18 years of age. This rate declined to an average of about 15.0 for those aged 30 to 69, then increased to its peak at 34.2 for those 87 years of age.

While motor-vehicle crashes are a significant problem for all ages, deaths resulting from falls for certain older ages have even higher death rates. Beginning at about age 70, the death rate from falls increases dramatically. At age 75, the falls death rate surpasses that for motor-vehicle, with the death rate continuing to rise with increasing age.

The poisoning death rate remains low until about age 16 where it starts to increase up to its peak rate of 16.6 at 46 years of age and then falls again.

Death rates due to choking on inhaled or ingested food or other objects are quite low for most ages. Rates are slightly elevated for infants and toddlers and rise rapidly beginning at about age 68. The death rates for drownings show peaks at very young ages, in the late teens, and again at some very old ages.

The graph above depicts death rates per 100,000 population for the six leading causes of unintentional-injury deaths in 2003 for single years of age through age 99.

Source: National Safety Council tabulations of National Center for Health Statistics data. See the Technical Appendix for ICD-10 codes for the leading causes and comparability with prior years.
a Inhalation or ingestion of food or other objects.

UNINTENTIONAL-INJURY DEATHS
BY SEX AND AGE, 2003

UNINTENTIONAL-INJURY DEATHS BY SEX AND AGE, UNITED STATES, 2003

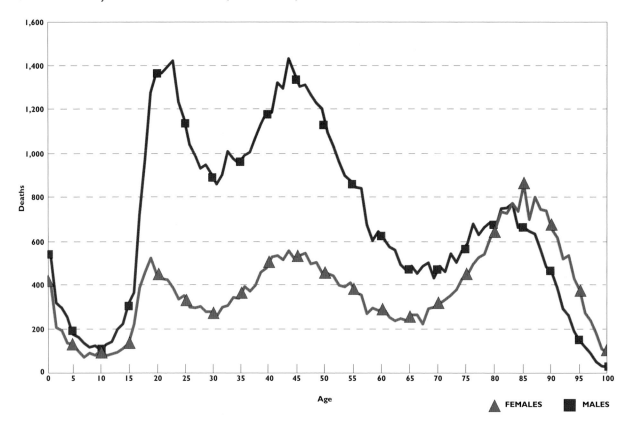

Males incur more deaths due to unintentional injuries than females at all ages from birth to age 82. The difference between the unintentional-injury death totals ranges from 0 at age 83 to 1,036 at age 22. The excess number of deaths for males compared to females is most evident from the late teenage years to the late forties where the gap begins to narrow. Beginning at age 84, deaths of females exceed those of males by as little as 54 deaths to as much as 273 at age 93.

Unintentional-injury deaths are at their lowest level for both sexes from about age 4 to about age 13. For males the highest number of deaths (1,434) occurs at age 43,

with high totals—including another peak of 1,424 deaths for those aged 22—occurring from the late teens until the late forties or early fifties. For females, however, the highest totals occur among the elderly from about age 78 and older. The greatest number of female deaths (860) occurs at age 85.

The graph above shows the number of unintentional-injury deaths in 2003 for each sex by single years of age from under 1 year old to age 99. It is based on death certificate data from the National Center for Health Statistics.

UNINTENTIONAL-INJURY DEATHS PER 100,000 POPULATION BY SEX AND AGE, UNITED STATES, 2003

Throughout the lifespan, males have greater unintentional-injury death rates for each year of age compared to females. The graph above shows the unintentional-injury death rates for males and females by single year of age from under 1 year old to age 99. It is based on National Center for Health Statistics mortality data and U.S. Census Bureau population data.

Death rates for both sexes are lowest from birth until the mid-teenage years where rates rise rapidly. Rates then remain fairly constant until the late sixties where they again rise steadily with increasing age. For comparison, the overall unintentional-injury death rate for all ages and both sexes was 37.6.

ALL DEATHS DUE TO INJURY

MORTALITY BY SELECTED EXTERNAL CAUSES, UNITED STATES, 2001–2003

Type of Accident or Manner of Injury	2003[a]	2002	2001
All External Causes of Mortality, V01–Y89[b]	**166,857**	**164,112**	**160,099**
Deaths Due to Unintentional (Accidental) Injuries, V01–X59, Y85–Y86	**109,277**	**106,742**	**101,537**
Transport Accidents, V01–V99, Y85	**48,071**	**48,366**	**47,288**
Motor-vehicle accidents, V02–V04, V09.0, V09.2, V12–V14, V19.0–V19.2, V19.4–V19.6, V20–V79, V80.3–V80.5, V81.0–V81.1, V82.0–V82.1, V83–V86, V87.0–V87.8, V88.0–V88.8, V89.0, V89.2	**44,757**	**45,380**	**43,788**
Pedestrian, V01–V09	5,991	6,091	6,071
Pedalcyclist, V10–V19	762	767	792
Motorcycle rider, V20–V29	3,676	3,215	3,042
Occupant of three-wheeled motor vehicle, V30–V39	13	21	11
Car occupant, V40–V49	15,797	16,337	14,946
Occupant of pick-up truck or van, V50–V59	4,163	4,286	3,739
Occupant of heavy transport vehicle, V60–V69	442	456	374
Bus occupant, V70–V79	36	43	37
Animal rider or occupant of animal-drawn vehicle, V80	101	118	116
Occupant of railway train or railway vehicle, V81	24	28	26
Occupant of streetcar, V82	2	4	3
Other and unspecified land transport accidents, V83–V89	15,107	15,100	16,036
Occupant of special industrial vehicle, V83	*12*	*15*	*10*
Occupant of special agricultural vehicle, V84	*175*	*149*	*239*
Occupant of special construction vehicle, V85	*20*	*32*	*18*
Occupant of all-terrain or other off-road motor vehicle, V86	*906*	*776*	*751*
Other and unspecified person, V87–V89	*13,994*	*14,128*	*15,018*
Water transport accidents, V90–V94	573	617	591
Drowning, V90, V92	*412*	*413*	*413*
Other and unspecified injuries, V91, V93–V94	*161*	*204*	*178*
Air and space transport accidents, V95–V97	742	653	918
Other and unspecified transport accidents and sequelae, V98–V99, Y85	642	630	586
Other specified transport accidents, V98	*2*	*2*	*1*
Unspecified transport accident, V99	*0*	*1*	*3*
Nontransport Unintentional (Accidental) Injuries, W00–X59, Y86	**61,206**	**58,376**	**54,249**
Falls, W00–W19	17,229	16,257	15,019
Fall on same level from slipping, tripping, and stumbling, W01	*597*	*646*	*564*
Other fall on same level, W00, W02–W03, W18	*3,896*	*3,610*	*2,570*
Fall involving bed, chair, other furniture, W06–W08	*838*	*785*	*734*
Fall on and from stairs and steps, W10	*1,588*	*1,598*	*1,462*
Fall on and from ladder or scaffolding, W11–W12	*417*	*406*	*439*
Fall from out of or through building or structure, W13	*600*	*557*	*580*
Other fall from one level to another, W09, W14–W17	*701*	*766*	*840*
Other and unspecified fall, W04–W05, W19	*8,592*	*7,889*	*7,830*
Exposure to inanimate mechanical forces, W20–W49	2,658	2,727	2,752
Struck by or striking against object, W20–W22	*809*	*864*	*853*
Caught between objects, W23	*136*	*115*	*116*
Contact with machinery, W24, W30–W31	*640*	*652*	*648*
Contact with sharp objects, W25–W29	*99*	*105*	*81*
Firearms discharge, W32–W34	*730*	*762*	*802*
Explosion and rupture of pressurized devices, W35–W38	*30*	*27*	*38*
Fireworks discharge, W39	*11*	*5*	*6*
Explosion of other materials, W40	*147*	*137*	*138*
Foreign body entering through skin or natural orifice, W44–W45	*22*	*23*	*33*
Other and unspecified inanimate mechanical forces, W41–W43, W49	*34*	*37*	*37*
Exposure to animate mechanical forces, W50–W64	171	144	160
Struck by or against another person, W50–W52	*39*	*26*	*45*
Bitten or struck by dog, W54	*32*	*18*	*25*
Bitten or struck by other mammals, W53, W55	*78*	*75*	*65*
Bitten or stung by nonvenomous insect and other arthropods, W57	*12*	*13*	*9*
Bitten or crushed by other reptiles, W59	*0*	*0*	*0*
Other and unspecified animate mechanical forces, W56, W58, W60, W64	*10*	*12*	*16*
Accidental drowning and submersion, W65–W74	3,306	3,447	3,281
Drowning and submersion while in or falling into bath-tub, W65–W66	*332*	*352*	*322*
Drowning and submersion while in or falling into swimming-pool, W67–W68	*515*	*636*	*596*
Drowning and submersion while in or falling into natural water, W69–W70	*1,225*	*1,325*	*1,054*
Other and unspecified drowning and submersion, W73–W74	*1,234*	*1,134*	*1,309*
Other accidental threats to breathing, W75–W84	5,579	5,517	5,555
Accidental suffocation and strangulation in bed, W75	*497*	*509*	*456*
Other accidental hanging and strangulation, W76	*277*	*297*	*279*
Threat to breathing due to cave-in, falling earth and other substances, W77	*46*	*57*	*56*
Inhalation of gastric contents, W78	*393*	*369*	*422*
Inhalation and ingestion of food causing obstruction of respiratory tract, W79	*875*	*819*	*742*
Inhalation and ingestion of other objects causing obstruction of respiratory tract, W80	*3,004*	*2,940*	*3,021*
Confined to or trapped in a low-oxygen environment, W81	*16*	*19*	*20*
Other and unspecified threats to breathing, W83–W84	*471*	*507*	*559*

See source and footnotes on page 19.

ALL DEATHS DUE TO INJURY (CONT.)

MORTALITY BY SELECTED EXTERNAL CAUSES, UNITED STATES, 2001–2003, Cont.

Type of Accident or Manner of Injury	2003[a]	2002	2001
Exposure to electric current, radiation, temperature, and pressure, W85–W99	396	454	431
Electric transmission lines, W85	96	109	83
Other and unspecified electric current, W86–W87	280	322	326
Radiation, W88–W91	0	0	0
Excessive heat or cold of man-made origin, W92–W93	10	10	8
High and low air pressure and changes in air pressure, W94	10	13	13
Other and unspecified man-made environmental factors, W99	0	0	1
Exposure to smoke, fire and flames, X00–X09	3,369	3,159	3,309
Uncontrolled fire in building or structure, X00	2,761	2,533	2,673
Uncontrolled fire not in building or structure, X01	57	53	61
Controlled fire in building or structure, X02	35	35	44
Controlled fire not in building or structure, X03	39	30	41
Ignition of highly flammable material, X04	55	71	53
Ignition or melting of nightwear, X05	3	13	5
Ignition or melting of other clothing and apparel, X06	104	104	125
Other and unspecified smoke fire and flames, X08–X09	315	320	307
Contact with heat and hot substances, X10–X19	88	102	114
Contact with hot tap-water, X11	26	40	57
Other and unspecified heat and hot substances, X10, X12–X19	62	62	57
Contact with venomous animals and plants, X20–X29	94	76	61
Contact with venomous snakes and lizards, X20	2	3	7
Contact with venomous spiders, X21	8	10	5
Contact with hornets, wasps and bees, X23	66	54	43
Contact with other and unspecified venomous animal or plant, X22, X24–X29	18	9	6
Exposure to forces of nature, X30–X39	1,140	1,219	1,100
Exposure to excessive natural heat, X30	273	350	300
Exposure to excessive natural cold, X31	620	646	599
Lightning, X33	47	66	44
Earthquake and other earth movements, X34–X36	32	31	28
Cataclysmic storm, X37	75	63	54
Flood, X38	26	9	35
Exposure to other and unspecified forces of nature, X32, X39	67	54	40
Accidental poisoning by and exposure to noxious substances, X40–X49	19,457	17,550	14,078
Nonopioid analgesics, antipyretics, and antirheumatics, X40	210	222	208
Antiepileptic, sedative-hypnotic, antiparkinsonism, and psychotropic drugs n.e.c., X41	1,205	1,024	763
Narcotics and psychodysleptics [hallucinogens] n.e.c., X42	9,231	8,264	6,509
Other and unspecified drugs, medicaments, and biologicals, X43–X44	7,648	6,884	5,544
Alcohol, X45	373	355	303
Gases and vapors, X46–X47	690	691	656
Other and unspecified chemicals and noxious substances, X48–X49	100	110	95
Overexertion, travel and privation, X50–X57	48	128	137
Accidental exposure to other and unspecified factors and sequelae, X58–X59, Y86	7,671	7,596	8,252
Intentional self-harm, X60–X84, Y87.0, *U03	**31,484**	**31,655**	**30,622**
Intentional self-poisoning, X60–X69	5,462	5,486	5,191
Intentional self-harm by hanging, strangulation, and suffocation, X70	6,635	6,462	6,198
Intentional self-harm by firearm, X72–X74	16,907	17,108	16,869
Other and unspecified means and sequelae, X71, X75–X84, Y87.0	2,480	2,599	2,360
Terrorism, *U03	0	0	4
Assault, X85–Y09, Y87.1, *U01	**17,732**	**17,638**	**20,308**
Assault by firearm, X93–X95	11,920	11,829	11,348
Assault by sharp object, X99	2,049	2,074	1,971
Other and unspecified means and sequelae, X85–X92, X96–X98, Y00–Y09, Y87.1	3,763	3,734	4,067
Terrorism, *U01	0	1	2,922
Event of undetermined intent, Y10–Y34, Y87.2, Y89.9	**5,072**	**4,830**	**4,198**
Poisoning, Y10–Y19	3,700	3,336	2,909
Hanging, strangulation, and suffocation, Y20	108	133	131
Drowning and submersion, Y21	215	259	235
Firearm discharge, Y22–Y24	232	243	231
Exposure to smoke, fire, and flames, Y26	100	99	76
Falling, jumping, or pushed from a high place, Y30	77	103	77
Other and unspecified means and sequelae, Y25, Y27–Y29, Y31–Y34, Y87.2, Y89.9	640	657	539
Legal intervention, Y35, Y89.0	**423**	**384**	**396**
Legal intervention involving firearm discharge, Y35.0	347	300	323
Legal execution, Y35.5	60	67	63
Other and unspecified means and sequelae, Y35.1–Y35.4, Y35.6–Y35.7, Y89.0	16	17	10
Operations of war and sequelae, Y36, Y89.1	**14**	**20**	**17**
Complications of medical and surgical care and sequelae, Y40–Y84, Y88.0–Y88.3	**2,855**	**2,843**	**3,021**

Source: National Center for Health Statistics. Deaths are classified on the basis of the Tenth Revision of "The International Classification of Diseases" (ICD-10), which became effective in 1999.
Note: "n.e.c." means not elsewhere classified. Dashes (—) indicate cause code did not exist.
[a] Latest official figures.
[b] Numbers following titles refer to external cause of injury and poisoning classifications in ICD-10.

DEATHS BY AGE, SEX, AND TYPE

UNINTENTIONAL-INJURY DEATHS BY AGE, SEX, AND TYPE, UNITED STATES, 2003[a]

Age & Sex	Total[b]	Motor-vehicle	Poisoning	Falls	Choking[c]	Fires/Flames	Drowning[d]	Mechanical Suffocation	Natural Heat/Cold	All Types	
										Males	Females
Total	109,277	44,757	19,457	17,229	4,272	3,369	3,306	1,307	893	70,532	38,745
0–4	2,662	766	69	68	149	254	514	629	33	1,587	1,075
5–14	2,618	1,642	61	45	23	215	268	58	4	1,662	956
15–24	15,272	10,972	1,999	230	56	199	567	78	38	11,291	3,981
25–44	29,307	13,794	9,665	921	277	647	818	258	173	21,537	7,770
45–64	25,007	10,032	6,804	2,263	706	918	662	169	262	17,520	7,487
65–74	8,081	2,967	403	2,048	568	419	202	40	103	4,921	3,160
75+	26,330	4,584	456	11,654	2,493	717	275	75	280	12,014	14,316
Males	70,532	30,655	13,176	8,910	2,222	1,948	2,632	909	630		
Females	38,745	14,102	6,281	8,319	2,050	1,421	674	398	263		

Source: National Safety Council tabulations of National Center for Health Statistics mortality data.
[a]Latest official figures.
[b]Includes types not shown separately.
[c]Inhalation or ingestion of food or other objects.
[d]Excludes transport drownings.

Of the 109,277 unintentional-injury deaths in 2003, men accounted for 65% of all deaths. Women had the greatest share of deaths in the 75 and over age group (54% women). By type of accident, men accounted for 80% of all drowning deaths and 52% of deaths due to choking (inhalation or ingestion of food or other object obstructing breathing).

UNINTENTIONAL-INJURY DEATH RATES BY TYPE AND SEX, UNITED STATES, 2003[a]

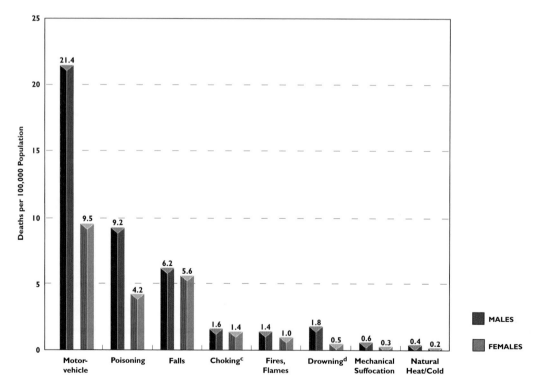

See footnotes in table above.

UNINTENTIONAL-INJURY DEATHS BY MONTH AND TYPE, UNITED STATES, 2003[a]

Month	All Types	Motor-vehicle	Poisoning	Falls	Choking[b]	Fires/ Flames	Drowning[c]	Mechanical Suffocation	Natural Heat/Cold	Struck By/ Against	All Other Types
Total	**109,277**	**44,757**	**19,457**	**17,229**	**4,272**	**3,369**	**3,306**	**1,307**	**893**	**809**	**13,878**
January	8,948	3,226	1,673	1,523	438	479	107	102	165	73	1,162
February	8,094	2,927	1,632	1,310	338	496	107	102	134	53	995
March	8,566	3,307	1,669	1,373	366	322	174	100	66	76	1,113
April	8,606	3,585	1,565	1,342	334	262	223	110	39	69	1,077
May	9,141	3,758	1,705	1,420	332	194	358	99	36	70	1,169
June	9,282	3,915	1,579	1,361	356	179	511	119	58	76	1,128
July	9,922	4,203	1,677	1,366	291	181	627	109	94	78	1,296
August	9,688	4,201	1,598	1,420	310	161	486	97	89	68	1,258
September	8,891	3,855	1,492	1,431	329	193	281	112	24	59	1,115
October	9,379	4,108	1,635	1,478	371	221	173	123	13	72	1,185
November	9,220	3,919	1,572	1,543	369	278	151	113	51	57	1,167
December	9,540	3,753	1,660	1,662	438	403	108	121	124	58	1,213
Average	**9,106**	**3,730**	**1,621**	**1,436**	**356**	**281**	**276**	**109**	**74**	**67**	**1,157**

Source: National Safety Council tabulations of National Center for Health Statistics mortality data.
[a]Latest official figures.
[b]Inhalation or ingestion of food or other object obstructing breathing.
[c]Excludes water transport drownings.

UNINTENTIONAL-INJURY DEATHS BY MONTH AND TYPE, UNITED STATES, 2003[a]

ALL UNINTENTIONAL-INJURY DEATHS

UNINTENTIONAL DROWNING DEATHS

UNINTENTIONAL FIRES AND FLAMES DEATHS

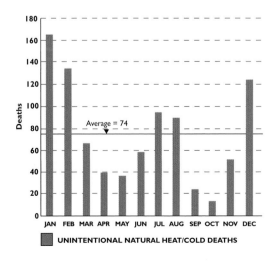

UNINTENTIONAL NATURAL HEAT/COLD DEATHS

See page 98 for motor-vehicle deaths by month.

THE NATIONAL HEALTH INTERVIEW SURVEY, 2004

The National Health Interview Survey, conducted by the National Center for Health Statistics, is a continuous, personal-interview sampling of households to obtain information about the health status of household members, including injuries experienced during the 3 months prior to the interview. Responsible family members residing in the household supplied the information found in the survey. In 2004, interviews were completed for 94,460 persons living in 36,579 households throughout the United States. See page 23 for definitions.

NUMBER OF LEADING EXTERNAL CAUSES OF INJURY AND POISONING EPISODES BY AGE, UNITED STATES, 2004

| | Population[a] (000) | External Cause of Injury and Poisoning (number in thousands) | | | | | | |
		Fall	Transportation[b]	Overexertion	Struck by or Against Person or Object	Cutting-Piercing Instruments	Poisoning[b]	Other Injury Causes[b]
All Ages	**292,416**	**12,030**	**3,690**	**4,763**	**3,852**	**2,844**	**375**	**5,619**
Under 12 years	47,906	2,066	488	(d)	563	331[c]	(d)	1,221
12–17 years	25,351	1,159	297[c]	895	1,036	(d)	(d)	762
18–44 years	112,177	3,362	1,823	2,643	1,427	1,564	195[c]	2,223
45–64 years	70,650	3,229	869	831	625	654	(d)	1,008
65–74 years	18,478	559	(d)	(d)	(d)	(d)	0	249[c]
75 years and over	17,855	1,654	(d)	(d)	(d)	(d)	0	(d)

[a]Civilian noninstitutionalized population
[b]"Transportation" includes motor vehicle, bicycle, motorcycle, pedestrian, train, boat, or airplane. "Poisoning" does not include food poisoning or allergic reaction. "Other Injury Causes" includes fire/burn/scald related, animal or insect bites, machinery, and unknown causes.
[c]Figure does not meet standard of reliability or precision and should be used with caution.
[d]Estimate is not shown because it does not meet standard of reliability or precision.

LEADING EXTERNAL CAUSES OF INJURY AND POISONING EPISODES BY SEX, UNITED STATES, 2004

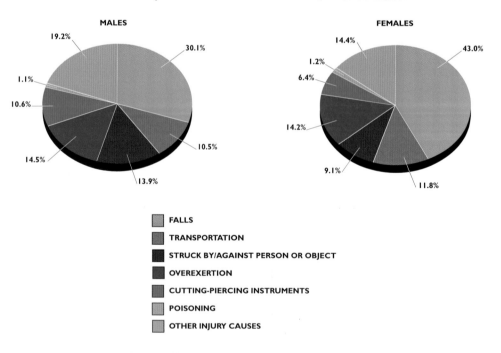

MALES

19.2%
30.1%
1.1%
10.6%
10.5%
14.5%
13.9%

FEMALES

14.4%
43.0%
1.2%
6.4%
14.2%
9.1%
11.8%

- FALLS
- TRANSPORTATION
- STRUCK BY/AGAINST PERSON OR OBJECT
- OVEREXERTION
- CUTTING-PIERCING INSTRUMENTS
- POISONING
- OTHER INJURY CAUSES

Source: Adams, P. F. & Barnes, P. M. (2006, August). Summary health statistics for the U.S. population: National Health Interview Survey, 2004. Vital and Health Statistics, Series 10 (No. 229). Hyattsville, MD: National Center for Health Statistics.

In 2004, an estimated 33.2 million medically consulted injury and poisoning episodes were recorded, of which 52.1% were among males and 47.9% among females. The overall injury rate was 115 episodes per 1,000 population with men (122 per 1,000 men) experiencing higher rates than women (107 per 1,000 women). Most injuries occurred in or around the home (46.0%) followed by injuries on streets, highways and parking lots (13.4%) and injuries at recreational and sport facilities (12.1%).

For the 17.3 million injuries reported by men, the single most common place of injury occurrence was outside the home (22.4%), with injuries inside the home contributing an additional 18.9%. Injuries in public areas, such as schools, hospitals, streets, recreational facilities, industrial and trade areas, and public buildings, together accounted for 50.5% of the total.

Similar to men, about half of injuries among women occurred either in or outside the home environment. However, almost twice as many women got injured inside than outside the home. Streets, parking lots and highways were the third most common location for injuries among women, accounting for 13.8%. The proportion of injuries at recreational and sport facilities was much lower among women (8.1%) than men (15.7%).

The 2004 NHIS injury definitions are listed below for comparability with prior years and other injury figures published in *Injury Facts®*.

NUMBER AND PERCENT OF INJURY EPISODES BY PLACE OF OCCURRENCE AND SEX, UNITED STATES, 2004

Place of Occurrence of Injury Episode	Both Sexes		Male		Female	
	Number of Episodes (000)	Percent	Number of Episodes (000)	Percent	Number of Episodes (000)	Percent
Total episodes[a]	33,173	100%	17,273	100%	15,900	100%
Home (inside)	8,567	25.8	3,258	18.9	5,309	33.4
Home (outside)	6,701	20.2	3,871	22.4	2,830	17.8
School/child care center/preschool	2,598	7.8	1,035	6.0	1,563	9.8
Hospital/residential institution	554	1.7	199[b]	1.2	355[b]	2.2
Street/highway/parking lot	4,449	13.4	2,250	13.0	2,199	13.8
Sport facility/recreation area/lake/river/pool	4,003	12.1	2,709	15.7	1,294	8.1
Industrial/construction/farm/mine/quarry	1,766	5.3	1,441	8.3	325[b]	2.0
Trade/service area	1,314	4.0	729	4.2	585[b]	3.7
Other public building	861	2.6	367[b]	2.1	494	3.1
Other unspecified	2,151	6.5	1,285	7.4	866	5.4

Source: Adams, P. F. & Barnes, P. M. (2006, August). Summary health statistics for the U.S. population: National Health Interview Survey, 2004. Vital and Health Statistics, Series 10 (No. 229). Hyattsville, MD: National Center for Health Statistics.
[a]Numbers and percents may not sum to respective totals due to rounding and unknowns.
[b]Figure does not meet standard of reliability or precision and should be used with caution.

Injury definitions

National Health Interview Survey definitions. The 2004 National Health Interview Survey (NHIS) figures include medically consulted injury and poisoning *episodes* (e.g., call to a poison control center; use of an emergency vehicle or emergency room; visit to a doctor's office or other health clinic; phone call to a doctor, nurse, or other health care professional) that reportedly occurred during the three months prior to the date of the interview and resulted in one or more *conditions*. Injury and poisoning estimates are calculated using only those episodes that occurred five weeks or less before the interview date. This reflects a change from 1997–2003, when the NHIS data contained injury and poisoning episodes that were reported to occur within four months of the interview, and estimates were calculated using a three-month recall period. Also starting in 2004, an imputation procedure was performed for injury and poisoning episodes to assign a date of occurrence if it was not reported. Therefore, figures for 2004 are not comparable to estimates from prior years.

In the 2004 NHIS Injury and Poisoning file, an *injury episode* refers to the traumatic event in which the person was injured one or more times from an external cause (e.g., a fall, a motor vehicle traffic accident). An *injury condition* is the acute condition or the physical harm caused by the traumatic event. Likewise, a *poisoning episode* refers to the event resulting from ingestion of or contact with harmful substances, as well as overdoses or wrong use of any drug or medication, while a *poisoning condition* is the acute condition or the physical harm caused by the event. Each episode must have at least one injury condition or poisoning classified according to the nature-of-injury codes 800-909.2, 909.4, 909.9, 910–994.9, 995.5–995.59, and 995.80–995.85 in the Ninth Revision of the International Classification of Diseases (ICD-9-CM). Poisoning episodes exclude food poisoning, sun poisoning, or poison ivy rashes.

National Safety Council definition of injury. A disabling injury is defined as one that results in death, some degree of permanent impairment, or renders the injured person unable to effectively perform their regular duties or activities for a full day beyond the day of the injury. This definition applies to all unintentional injuries. All injury totals labeled "disabling injuries" in *Injury Facts®* are based on this definition. Some *rates* in the Work section are based on OSHA definitions of recordable cases (see Glossary).

THE NATIONAL HEALTH INTERVIEW SURVEY, 2004 (CONT.)

Approximately one in four medically consulted injury episodes is sustained during leisure activities. Leisure injuries account for more than half of all injury episodes among children under the age of 12 and about one-third of injuries among older adults over 65 years.

More women than men get injured while engaged in leisure activities, working around the house or yard, driving, and attending school, whereas more men than women suffer injuries related to paid work and sports. The charts on this page illustrate these gender differences in terms of percentages and rates.

NUMBER OF INJURY EPISODES BY AGE AND ACTIVITY AT TIME OF INJURY, UNITED STATES, 2004

| | Total[a] | Activity at Time of Injury[b] (number in thousands) | | | | | | |
		Leisure Activities	Working at Paid Job	Sports	Working Around House or Yard	Driving[c]	Attending School	Other[d]
All Ages	**33,173**	**8,935**	**5,324**	**5,103**	**4,831**	**2,534**	**1,069**	**5,238**
Under 12 years	4,816	2,705	0	649	0	169[e]	344[e]	839
12–17 years	4,310	969	(f)	2,264	(f)	(f)	539[e]	256[e]
18–44 years	13,236	2,637	3,704	1,879	1,793	1,497	(f)	1,416
45–64 years	7,314	1,610	1,398	238[e]	1,965	604	(f)	1,594
65–74 years	1,286	316[e]	(f)	0	387[e]	(f)	0	402
75 years and over	2,210	698	(f)	(f)	527	(f)	0	731

[a] Numbers and percents may not sum to respective totals due to rounding and unknowns.
[b] Activity at time of injury and poisoning episodes is based on the question, "What was [person] doing when the injury/poisoning happened?" Respondents could indicate up to two activities.
[c] Driving includes both drivers and passengers.
[d] "Other" includes unpaid work such as housework, shopping, volunteer work, sleeping, resting, eating, drinking, cooking, hands-on care from another person, and other unspecified activities.
[e] Estimates with relative standard errors of greater than 30% and less than or equal to 50% should be used with caution.
[f] Estimates with relative standard errors of greater than 50% are not shown.

PERCENT AND RATES OF INJURY EPISODES BY SEX AND ACTIVITY AT TIME OF INJURY, UNITED STATES, 2004

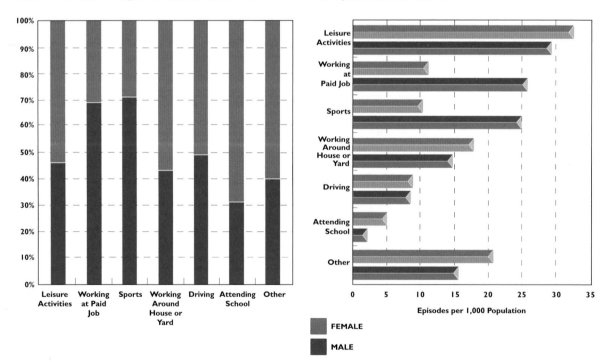

Source: Adams, P.F. & Barnes, P.M. (2006, August). Summary health statistics for the U.S. population: National Health Interview Survey, 2004. Vital and Health Statistics, Series 10 (No. 229). Hyattsville, MD: National Center for Health Statistics.

The NHIS questionnaire includes items that measure two dimensions of socioeconomic status — family income and education — and, thus, provides an opportunity to examine how injuries are distributed across various sub-groups in the U.S. population.

Epidemiological research reveals that position in society plays a role in the occurrence of various illnesses, including heart disease, lung disease, stroke, cancer, hypertension, and diabetes. In general, persons with the highest levels of income and education are healthier than those with median income and education, who, in turn, tend to be in better health than the poor and less educated.[a]

NHIS data indicate that all people are affected by injuries regardless of income or educational attainment, but there is no clear socioeconomic gradient in the injury occurrence rates. Persons with an incomplete college degree have higher rates of medically consulted injuries compared to both college graduates as well as persons who have less than a high-school diploma. Persons with family income less than $20,000 report higher injury rates (134 per 1,000 population) than those whose income is at least $20,000 (116 per 1,000 population).

[a]Banks, J., Marmot, M., Oldfield, Z., Smith, J.P. (2006). Disease and disadvantage in the United States and in England. *Journal of American Medical Association. 295 (17): 2037-2045.*

PERCENTAGES AND RATES OF MEDICALLY CONSULTED INJURIES BY LEVEL OF EDUCATION, UNITIED STATES, 2004

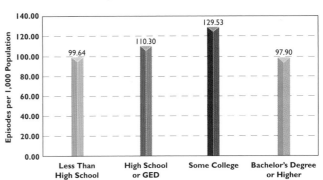

PERCENTAGES AND RATES OF MEDICALLY CONSULTED INJURIES BY FAMILY INCOME, UNITED STATES, 2004

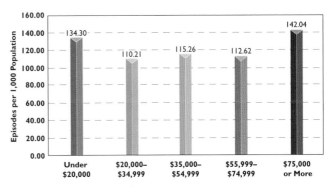

INJURY-RELATED HOSPITAL EMERGENCY DEPARTMENT VISITS, 2004

About 41.4 million visits to hospital emergency departments in 2004 were due to injuries.

About 38% of all hospital emergency department visits in the United States were injury related, according to information from the 2004 National Hospital Ambulatory Medical Care Survey conducted for the National Center for Health Statistics. There were approximately 110.2 million visits made to emergency departments, of which about 41.4 million were injury related. This resulted in an annual rate of about 38.2 emergency department visits per 100 persons, of which about 14.4 visits per 100 persons were injury related.

Males had a higher rate of injury-related visits than females. For males, about 15.4 visits per 100 males were recorded; for females the rate was 13.3 per 100 females. Those aged 15 to 24 had the highest rate of injury-related visits for males, while those aged 75 and over had the highest rate for females.

Falls and motor-vehicle accidents were the leading causes of injury-related emergency department visits,

accounting for over 20% and 11% of the total, respectively. In total, about 8.5 million visits to emergency departments were made in 2004 due to accidental falls, and about 4.7 million were made due to motor-vehicle accidents. The next leading types were struck against or struck accidentally by objects or persons with 3.5 million visits (over 8% of the total), and accidents caused by cutting or piercing instruments, which accounted for about 2.5 million visits (over 6% of the total).

Black or African American persons had higher rates of injury-related visits to emergency departments than did whites for every age group. The difference varied from a high of 9.9 injuries per 100 population in the 25- to 44-year-old age group to a low of 3.7 injuries per 100 population for those in the 65- to 74-year-old age group.

NUMBER AND PERCENT DISTRIBUTION OF EMERGENCY DEPARTMENT VISITS BY CAUSE OF INJURY, UNITED STATES, 2004

Cause of Injury and E-code[a]	Number of Visits (000)	Percent
All Injury-Related Visits	**41,390**	**100.0%**
Unintentional Injuries, E800–E869, E880–E929	**28,123**	**67.9**
Accidental Falls, E880.0–E886.9, E888	8,482	20.5
Total Motor-Vehicle Accidents, E810–E825	4,687	11.3
Motor-vehicle traffic, E810–E819	*4,336*	*10.5*
Motor-vehicle, nontraffic, E820–E825(.0–.5, .7–.9)	*351*	*0.8*
Striking Against or Struck Accidentally by Objects or Persons, E916–E917	3,472	8.4
Accidents Caused by Cutting or Piercing Instruments, E920	2,530	6.1
Accidents Due to Natural and Environmental Factors, E900–E909, E928.0–E928.2	2,018	4.9
Overexertion and Strenuous Movements, E927	1,773	4.3
Accidental Poisoning by Drugs, Medicinal Substances, Biologicals, Other Solid and Liquid Substances, Gases and Vapors, E850–E869	1,043	2.5
Foreign Body, E914–E915	899	2.2
Pedalcycle, Nontraffic, E800–E807(.3), E820–E825(.6), E826.1, E826.9	450	1.1
Accidents Caused by Fire and Flames, Hot Substances or Object, Caustic or Corrosive Material, and Steam, E890–E899, E924	438	1.1
Caught Accidentally In or Between Objects, E918	438	1.1
Machinery, E919	340	0.8
Other Transportation, E800–E807(.0–.2, .8–.9), E826(.0, .2–.8), E827–E829, E831, E833–E845	150	0.4

Cause of Injury and E-code[a]	Number of Visits (000)	Percent
Suffocation, E911–E913	99	0.2
Other Mechanism,[b] E830, E832, E846–E848, E910, E921–E923, E925–E926, E928.3, E928.8, E929.0–E929.5	1,168	2.8
Mechanism Unspecified, E887, E928.9, E929.8, E929.9	136	0.3
Intentional Injuries, E950–E959, E960–E969, E970–E978, E990–E999	**2,327**	**5.6**
Assault, E960–E969	1,774	4.3
Unarmed Fight or Brawl and Striking by Blunt or Thrown Object, E960.0, E968.2	949	2.3
Assault by Cutting and Piercing Instrument, E966	100	0.2
Assault by Other and Unspecified Mechanism,[d] E960.1, E962–E964, E965.5–E965.9, E967–E968.1, E968.3–E969	725	1.8
Self-inflicted Injury, E950–E959	535	1.3
Poisoning by Solid or Liquid Substances, Gases or Vapors, E950–E952	337	0.8
Other and Unspecified Mechanism,[d] E953–E959	199	0.5
Injuries of Undetermined Intent, E980–E989	**218**	**0.5**
Adverse Effects of Medical Treatment, E870–E879, E930–E949	**1,837**	**4.4**
Medical and Surgical Complications, E870–E879	1,094	2.6
Adverse Drug Effects, E930–E949	743	1.8
Alcohol and/or Drug Abuse[e]	**1,657**	**4.0**
Other and Unknown[f]	**7,228**	**17.5**

Source: McCaig, L.F. & Nawar, E.W. (2006). National Hospital Ambulatory Medical Care Survey: 2004 Emergency Department Summary (Advance Data, Number 372, June 23, 2006). Hyattsville, MD: National Center for Health Statistics.

Note: Sum of parts may not add to total due to rounding.

[a] *Based on the International Classification of Diseases, 9th Revision, Clinical Modification (ICD-9-CM).*
[b] *Includes drowning, firearms, and other mechanism.*
[c] *Includes assault by firearms and explosives, and other mechanism.*
[d] *Includes injury by cutting and piercing instrument, and other and unspecified mechanism.*
[e] *Allcohol and drug abuse are not contained in the "Supplementary Classification of External Causes of Injury and Poisoning," but are frequently recorded as a cause of injury or poisoning.*
[f] *Includes all other major E-code categories where the estimate was too low to be reliable and uncodable, illegible, and blank E-codes.*

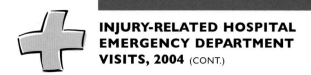
RATE[a] OF INJURY-RELATED VISITS TO EMERGENCY DEPARTMENTS BY PATIENT AGE AND SEX, 2004

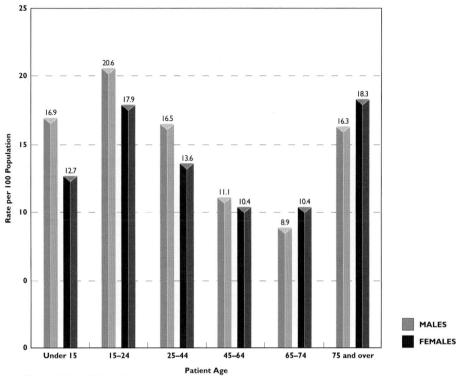

[a]Number of visits per 100 populations.

RATE[a] OF INJURY-RELATED VISITS TO EMERGENCY DEPARTMENTS BY PATIENT AGE AND RACE, 2004

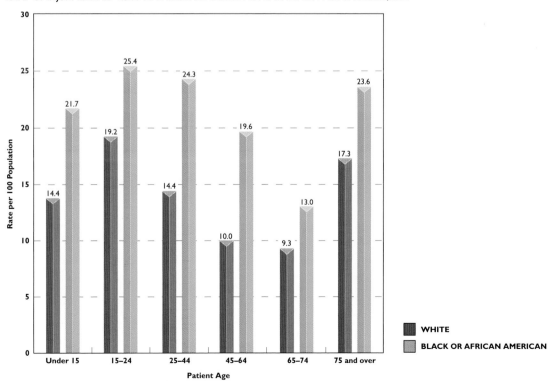

[a]Number of visits per 100 populations.

PRINCIPAL CLASSES BY STATE

The states listed below participate in the Injury Mortality Tabulations reporting system. Reports from these states are used to make current year estimates. See the Technical Appendix for more information.

The estimated total number of unintentional-injury deaths for 2005 increased 1% from 2004. The number of unintentional-injury deaths in the Home class was down 8%, while the number in the Work class decreased by 1%. The Total and Motor-Vehicle classes each showed increases of 1% and the Public Nonmotor-Vehicle class increased by 15%. The population death rate for the Home class decreased 1% and the rates for the Total and Work classes remained unchanged. The rates for the Motor-Vehicle and Public Nonmotor-Vehicle classes showed increases of 1% and 13%, respectively, from 2004 to 2005.

PRINCIPAL CLASSES OF UNINTENTIONAL-INJURY DEATHS BY STATE, 2005

State	Total[a]		Motor-Vehicle[b]		Work[c]		Home		Public Nonmotor-Vehicle	
	Deaths	Rate[d]	Deaths	Rate[d]	Deaths	Rate[d]	Deaths	Rate[d]	Deaths	Rate[d]
Total U.S.	**113,000**	**38.1**	**45,800**	**15.5**	**4,961**	**1.7**	**37,000**	**12.5**	**27,600**	**9.3**
Delaware	243	28.8	133	15.8	11	1.3	54	6.4	54	6.4
Florida	9,040	50.8	3,625	20.4	281	1.6	2,979	16.7	1,999	11.2
Idaho	656	45.9	317	22.2	32	2.2	156	10.9	162	11.3
Kansas	1,067	38.9	436	15.9	59	2.1	315	11.5	275	10.0
Kentucky	2,346	56.2	926	22.2	94	2.3	508	12.2	858	20.6
Missouri	2,628	45.3	1,112	19.2	104	1.8	588	10.1	438	7.6
Ohio	4,312	37.6	1,351	11.8	—	—	—	—	—	—
South Dakota	435	56.1	200	25.8	27	3.5	—	—	—	—
Virginia	2,316	30.6	819	10.8	107	1.4	740	9.8	283	3.7

Source: Provisional reports of vital statistics registrars; deaths are by place of occurrence. U.S. totals are National Safety Council estimates.
[a] The all-class total may not equal the sum of the separate class totals because Motor-Vehicle and other transportation deaths occurring to persons in the course of their employment are included in the Work death totals as well as the Motor-Vehicle and Public Nonmotor-Vehicle totals and also because unclassified deaths are included in the total.
[b] Differences between the figures given above and those on pages 162 and 163 are due in most cases to the inclusion of nontraffic deaths in this table.
[c] Work death totals may be too low where incomplete information on death certificates results in the deaths being included in the Public class. The Work totals may include some cases that are not compensable. For compensable cases only, see page 53.
[d] Deaths per 100,000 population.

RACE AND HISPANIC ORIGIN

The rank of unintentional-injuries as a cause of death varies with race and Hispanic origin. While ranking fifth overall (following heart disease, cancer, stroke, and chronic lower respiratory diseases), unintentional injuries rank third for Hispanics after heart disease and cancer.

By race, unintentional injuries rank fifth for whites and blacks, and fourth (after heart disease, cancer, and stroke) for Asians, Pacific Islanders, American Indians, and Alaskan Natives.

UNINTENTIONAL-INJURY DEATH RATES BY RACE, HISPANIC ORIGIN, AND SEX, UNITED STATES, 2003

| Race and Sex | Total | | | Hispanic Origin | | | | | |
| | | | | Non-Hispanic | | | Hispanic | | |
	Rank	Number	Rate	Rank	Number	Rate	Rank	Number	Rate
All Races	5	109,277	37.6	5	98,406	39.2	3	10,418	26.1
Males	3	70,532	49.3	3	62,290	50.9	3	7,899	38.3
Females	7	38,745	26.2	6	36,116	28.1	5	2,519	13.0
White	5	93,381	39.9	5	82,815	42.0	3	10,205	(b)
Males	3	59,912	51.7	4	51,888	53.6	3	7,754	(b)
Females	6	33,469	28.3	7	30,927	30.7	5	2,451	(b)
Black	5	12,351	33.3	5	12,154	34.2	3	115	(b)
Males	3	8,385	47.5	3	8,237	48.7	3	82	(b)
Females	6	3,966	20.4	6	3,917	21.0	5	33	(b)
Not White or Black[a]	4	3,545	18.2	4	3,437	19.1	3	98	(b)
Males	3	2,235	23.4	3	2,165	24.7	3	63	(b)
Females	4	1,310	13.1	4	1,272	13.8	4	35	(b)

Source: National Safety Council analysis of National Center for Health Statistics mortality data and Census Bureau population data.
Note: Rates are deaths per 100,000 population in each race/sex/Hispanic origin group. Total column includes 453 deaths for which Hispanic origin was not determined.
[a]Includes American Indian, Alaskan Native, Asian, Native Hawaiian and Pacific Islander.
[b]Race is not well reported for persons of Hispanic origin. Population death rates are unreliable.

LEADING CAUSES OF UNINTENTIONAL-INJURY DEATH BY RACE, HISPANIC ORIGIN, AND SEX, UNITED STATES, 2003

| Cause of Death | All Races | | | White | | | Black | | | Not White or Black[a] | | |
	Both	Male	Female	Both	Male	Female	Both	Male	Female	Both	Male	Female
Motor vehicle	44,757	30,655	14,102	37,424	25,660	11,764	5,431	3,834	1,597	1,902	1,161	741
Poisoning	19,457	13,176	6,281	16,690	11,333	5,357	2,396	1,609	787	371	234	137
Fall	17,229	8,910	8,319	15,855	8,099	7,756	920	537	383	454	274	180
Suffocation by inhalation or ingestion	4,272	2,222	2,050	3,685	1,908	1,777	486	259	227	101	55	46
Fires, flames, smoke	3,369	1,948	1,421	2,526	1,480	1,046	775	433	342	68	35	33
Drowning	3,306	2,632	674	2,622	2,067	555	480	407	73	204	158	46

| Cause of Death | Non-Hispanic | | | Hispanic | | | Unknown | | |
	Both	Male	Female	Both	Male	Female	Both	Male	Female
Motor Vehicle	38,849	26,202	12,647	5,753	4,340	1,413	155	113	42
Poisoning	17,537	11,655	5,882	1,802	1,428	374	118	93	25
Fall	16,337	8,320	8,017	840	557	283	52	33	19
Suffocation by inhalation or ingestion	4,085	2,112	1,973	174	102	72	13	8	5
Fires, flames, smoke	3,147	1,809	1,338	203	128	75	19	11	8
Drowning	2,816	2,202	614	458	399	59	32	31	1

Source: National Safety Council analysis of National Center for Health Statistics mortality data.
[a]Includes American Indian, Alaskan Native, Asian, Native Hawaiian and Pacific Islander.

DISASTER DEATHS, 2005

Disasters are front page news even though the lives lost in the United States are relatively few when compared to the day-to-day life losses from unintentional injuries (see "While You Speak! page 31). Listed below are the United States disasters that occurred in 2005 and took 5 or more lives of which the National Safety Council is aware.

In addition to the disasters listed in the table, there were 11 residential fires that claimed five or six lives each. There were also 46 motor-vehicle traffic crashes in 2005 that resulted in five to nine deaths each.

DISASTER DEATHS, UNITED STATES, 2005

Type and Location	No. of Deaths	Date of Disaster
Major Disasters (25 or more deaths)		
Hurricane Katrina, Florida, Louisiana, Mississippi	1,323	August 25, 29–30
Hurricane Rita, Louisiana, Texas	119	September 24–25
Hurricane Wilma, Florida	35	October 24
Other Disasters (5–24 deaths)		
Bus fire (during Hurricane Rita evacuation), Texas	23	September 23
Tornado, Indiana, Kentucky	23	November 6
Heat wave, Arizona	21	July
Snow storms, Eastern U.S.	20	January 22–23
Tour boat capsized, New York	20	October 2
Seaplane crash, Florida	20	December 19
Oil refinery explosion, Texas	14	March 23
Hurricane Dennis, Florida	12	July 10
Train crash, California	11	January 26
Residential fire, Louisiana	11	March
Rain and mudslide, California	10	January 10
Rains, flooding, Northeastern U.S.	10	October 7–14
Freight train collision with chlorine gas leak, South Carolina	9	January 6
Storms, flooding, landslides, avalanches, California	9	February 17–23
Residential fire, Ohio	9	May
Storms, Arizona	7	December 28–January 12
Storms, Ohio	5	January 8–9

Source: National Climatic Data Center, infoplease.com, National Fire Protection Association, National Highway Traffic Safety Administration, and Federal Railroad Administration.
Note: Some death totals are estimates and may differ among sources.

While you make a 10-minute safety speech, 2 persons will be killed and about 459 will suffer a disabling injury. Costs will amount to $11,900,000. On the average, there are 13 unintentional-injury deaths and about 2,750 disabling injuries every hour during the year.

Deaths and disabling injuries by class occurred in the nation at the following rates in 2005:

DEATHS AND DISABLING INJURIES BY CLASS, 2005

Class	Severity	One Every —	Number per . . .			2005 Total
			Hour	Day	Week	
All	**Deaths**	**5 minutes**	**13**	**310**	**2,170**	**113,000**
	Injuries	**1 seconds**	**2,750**	**66,000**	**463,500**	**24,100,000**
Motor-Vehicle	Deaths	11 minutes	5	125	880	45,800
	Injuries	13 seconds	270	6,600	46,200	2,400,000
Work	Deaths	106 minutes	1	14	100	4,961
	Injuries	9 seconds	420	10,100	71,200	3,700,000
Workers Off-the-Job	Deaths	11 minutes	6	135	950	49,300
	Injuries	4 seconds	940	22,500	157,700	8,200,000
Home	Deaths	14 minutes	4	101	710	37,000
	Injuries	4 seconds	1,020	24,400	171,200	8,900,000
Public Nonmotor-Vehicle	Deaths	19 minutes	3	76	530	27,600
	Injuries	3 seconds	1,050	25,200	176,900	9,200,000

Source: National Safety Council estimates.

DEATHS EVERY HOUR . . .

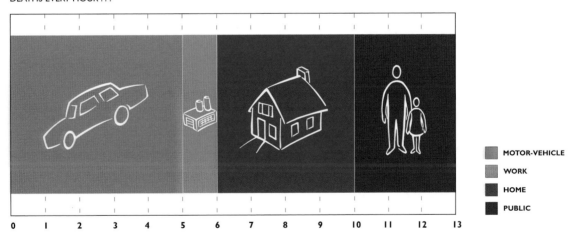

MOTOR-VEHICLE
WORK
HOME
PUBLIC

AN UNINTENTIONAL-INJURY DEATH EVERY FIVE MINUTES . . .

Five Minutes

CHILDREN AND YOUTHS

Motor-vehicle crashes are the leading cause of injury deaths among children.

In 2003, unintentional injuries caused over 12,000 deaths among American children and adolescents under the age of 19 years. Teenagers between the ages of 15 and 19 years accounted for more than half of the total. The injury mortality rate for older teenagers (15–19 years) was nearly 5 times that for younger teens (10–14 years) and 6 times that for children (5–9 years). Deaths due to motor-vehicle crashes and poisoning account for most of these differences. Among youth in general, the relationship between age and all-cause injury mortality expressed in terms of both rates as well as absolute numbers can be described as a J-shaped pattern, where 8-10-year-olds have the lowest risk.

For infants under 1 year of age, unintentional injuries are the sixth leading cause of death, following congenital anomalies; short gestation and low birth weight; sudden infant death syndrome; maternal complications of pregnancy; and complications involving the placenta, cord, and membranes (see page 10). Although unintentional injuries only account for about 3.4% of deaths for those under age 1, the number of unintentional-injury deaths for this age is greater than for any age from 1 to 15 years. Nearly 60% of infant deaths due to injuries are attributed to cases of mechanical suffocation.

UNINTENTIONAL-INJURY DEATHS BY EVENT, AGE 0–19, UNITED STATES, 2003

Age	Population (000)	Total	Rates[a]	Motor-vehicle	Falls	Poisoning	Drowning	Fires/Flames	Choking[b]	Mechanical Suffocation	Firearms	All Other
<1 year	4,031	945	23.4	145	14	20	58	30	61	558	0	59
1–19 years	77,197	11,090	14.4	7,532	189	630	1,004	514	132	159	151	779
1 year	3,990	526	13.2	172	21	18	159	45	43	35	0	33
2 years	4,040	491	12.2	148	21	13	153	67	22	19	1	47
3 years	3,882	392	10.1	166	6	9	89	57	14	6	2	43
4 years	3,836	308	8.0	135	6	9	55	55	9	11	4	24
5 years	3,846	264	6.9	143	1	3	41	41	2	6	0	27
6 years	3,874	209	5.4	128	7	5	23	20	3	3	1	19
7 years	3,958	209	5.3	116	1	4	30	29	2	2	7	18
8 years	4,024	206	5.1	125	3	2	20	24	3	6	2	21
9 years	4,059	208	5.1	134	2	4	12	23	5	5	3	20
10 years	4,144	211	5.1	133	5	5	21	14	1	4	4	24
11 years	4,216	230	5.5	146	5	6	23	18	0	7	4	21
12 years	4,284	294	6.9	181	2	14	28	25	2	11	3	28
13 years	4,361	336	7.7	223	10	9	30	11	1	8	8	36
14 years	4,196	451	10.7	313	9	9	40	10	4	6	17	43
15 years	4,128	589	14.3	447	7	26	35	15	0	4	18	37
16 years	4,080	1,109	27.2	889	15	51	46	14	3	7	16	68
17 years	4,100	1,436	35.0	1,166	16	80	67	16	4	11	12	64
18 years	4,124	1,802	43.7	1,404	29	150	70	16	10	5	25	93
19 years	4,055	1,819	44.9	1,363	23	213	62	14	4	3	24	113
0–4 years	19,779	2,662	13.5	766	68	69	514	254	149	629	7	206
5–9 years	19,761	1,096	5.5	646	14	18	126	137	15	22	13	105
10–14 years	21,201	1,522	7.2	996	31	43	142	78	8	36	36	152
15–19 years	20,487	6,755	33.0	5,269	90	520	280	75	21	30	95	375

Source: National Safety Council tabulations of National Center for Health Statistics mortality data.
Note: Data does not include "age unknown" cases, which totaled 76 in 2003.
[a] *Deaths per 100,000 population in each age group.*
[b] *Suffocation by inhalation or ingestion of food or other object.*

ADULTS

Injury mortality rate increases with age.

In the United States, 97,166 adults aged 20 years and older sustained fatal unintentional injuries in 2003. Motor-vehicle crashes (38.1%), poisoning (19.3%), and falls (17.5%) were the leading causes of injury death in this age group. The occurrence of injury-related deaths varies considerably with age. While the proportion of deaths due to motor-vehicle crashes decreases with age primarily as a result of driving cessation among older adults, the number of fall-related deaths increases. The proportion of poisoning-related deaths gradually increases from the age of 20 (17.4%) and peaks at around the age of 40–44 years (38.4%). Thereafter, it markedly decreases so that by the age of 75, fatal poisonings account for less than 3% of all injury-related deaths.

The differences across age groups can be also described in terms of injury mortality rates. As illustrated in the table below, the age-specific mortality rates appear to be relatively constant between the ages of 20 and 70 years and, then, sharply increase more than tenfold, likely reflecting the physical frailty of the oldest old and their increased risk of complications and poor functional recovery following an injury.

Clinical studies demonstrate that after a serious injury, elderly patients have higher in-hospital and long-term mortality than their younger counterparts even when other factors (e.g., injury severity, number of injuries, presence of other medical conditions, complications) are taken into account. At the same time, injury severity, number of injuries, and complications each independently correlates with increased injury mortality among the elderly.[a]

[a] Jacoby, S. F., Ackerson, T. H., & Richmond, T. S. (2006). Outcome from serious injury in older adults. Journal of Nursing Scholarship, 38 (2), 133–140.

UNINTENTIONAL-INJURY DEATHS BY EVENT, AGES 20 AND OLDER, UNITED STATES, 2003

Age	Population (000)	Total	Rates[a]	Motor-vehicle	Falls	Poisoning	Drowning	Fires/ Flames	Choking[b]	Mechanical Suffocation	Natural Heat/Cold	Firearms	All Other
20–24	20,768	8,517	41.0	5,703	140	1,479	287	124	35	48	20	105	576
25–29	19,133	6,284	32.8	3,644	139	1,517	191	118	41	58	29	74	473
30–34	20,726	6,257	30.2	3,189	146	1,918	165	134	48	48	36	46	527
35–39	21,413	7,495	35.0	3,289	255	2,674	217	167	74	79	44	57	639
40–44	22,991	9,271	40.3	3,672	381	3,556	245	228	114	73	64	61	877
45–49	21,765	8,865	40.7	3,286	508	3,351	211	270	155	55	67	48	914
50–54	19,041	6,972	36.6	2,788	535	2,083	186	256	165	55	70	44	790
55–59	15,723	5,186	33.0	2,232	579	957	153	204	182	35	71	36	737
60–64	12,111	3,984	32.9	1,726	641	413	112	188	204	24	54	26	596
65–69	9,745	3,711	38.1	1,444	787	229	102	198	233	15	42	23	638
70–74	8,606	4,370	50.8	1,523	1,261	174	100	221	335	25	61	16	654
75–79	7,468	5,875	78.7	1,680	2,136	146	94	226	494	16	62	16	1,005
80–84	5,417	7,233	133.5	1,530	3,113	138	68	234	706	22	83	21	1,318
85–89	3,025	6,839	226.1	961	3,220	105	58	157	659	21	70	3	1,585
90–94	1,285	4,352	338.7	343	2,221	47	20	67	425	11	39	3	1,176
95–99	349	1,620	464.2	53	806	10	5	24	167	4	16	0	535
100 and older	57	335	587.7	1	157	4	0	5	42	0	3	0	123
20 and older	**209,623**	**97,166**	**46.4**	**37,064**	**17,025**	**18,801**	**2,214**	**2,821**	**4,079**	**589**	**831**	**579**	**13,163**
25 and older	**188,855**	**88,649**	**46.9**	**31,361**	**16,885**	**17,322**	**1,927**	**2,697**	**4,044**	**541**	**811**	**474**	**12,587**
35 and older	**148,996**	**76,108**	**51.1**	**24,528**	**16,600**	**13,887**	**1,571**	**2,445**	**3,955**	**435**	**746**	**354**	**11,587**
45 and older	**104,592**	**59,342**	**56.7**	**17,567**	**15,964**	**7,657**	**1,109**	**2,050**	**3,767**	**283**	**638**	**236**	**10,071**
55 and older	**63,786**	**43,505**	**68.2**	**11,493**	**14,921**	**2,223**	**712**	**1,524**	**3,447**	**173**	**501**	**144**	**8,367**
65 and older	**35,952**	**34,335**	**95.5**	**7,535**	**13,701**	**853**	**447**	**1,132**	**3,061**	**114**	**376**	**82**	**7,034**
75 and older	**17,601**	**26,254**	**149.2**	**4,568**	**11,653**	**450**	**245**	**713**	**2,493**	**74**	**273**	**43**	**5,742**

Source: National Safety Council tabulations of National Center for Health Statistics mortality data.
Note: Data does not include "age unknown" cases, which totaled 76 in 2003.
[a] Deaths per 100,000 population in each age group.
[b] Suffocation by inhalation or ingestion of food or other object.

TRENDS IN UNINTENTIONAL-INJURY DEATH RATES

Age-adjusted rates, which eliminate the effect of shifts in the age distribution of the population, have decreased 58% from 1912 to 2005 — from 100.4 to 38.0. The adjusted rates, which are shown in the graph on the opposite page, are standardized to the year 2000 standard U.S. population. The break in the lines at 1948 shows the estimated effect of changes in the International Classification of Diseases (ICD). The break in the lines at 1992 resulted from the adoption of the Bureau of Labor Statistics Census of Fatal Occupational Injuries for work-related deaths. Another change in the ICD in 1999 also affects the trends. See the Technical Appendix for comparability.

The table below shows the change in the age distribution of the population since 1910.

The age-adjusted death rate for all unintentional-injuries increased and decreased significantly several times during the period from 1910 to 1940. Since 1940, there have been some setbacks, such as in the early 1960s, but the overall trend has been positive. The age-adjusted death rates for unintentional-injury deaths in the work and home classes have declined fairly steadily since they became available in the late 1920s, although the home class rates have increased since the early 1990s. The rates in the public class declined for three decades, rose in the 1960s and then continued declining. The age-adjusted motor-vehicle death rate rose steadily from 1910 to the late 1930s as the automobile became more widely used. A sharp drop in use occurred during World War II and a sharp rise in rates occurred in the 1960s, with death rates reflecting economic cycles and a long-term downward trend since then.

UNITED STATES POPULATION, SELECTED YEARS

Year	All Ages	0–14	15–24	25–44	45–64	65 & Older
Number (in thousands)						
1910	91,973[a]	29,499	18,121	26,810	13,424	3,950
2000[b]	274,634	58,964	38,077	81,892	60,991	34,710
2005	296,410	60,700	42,077	84,005	72,838	36,790
Percent						
1910	100.0%	32.1%	19.7%	29.2%	14.6%	4.3%
2000[b]	100.0%	21.5%	13.9%	29.8%	22.2%	12.6%
2005	100.0%	20.5%	14.2%	28.3%	24.6%	12.4%

Source: For 1910: U. S. Bureau of the Census. (1960). Historical Statistics of the United States, Colonial Times to 1957. Series A 71–85. Washington, DC: U.S. Government Printing Office. For 2000: Anderson, R.N., & Rosenberg, H.M. (1998). Age standardization of death rates: Implementation of the year 2000 standard. National Vital Statistics Reports, 47(3), 13. For 2005: U.S. Census Bureau, Monthly Postcensal Resident Population, by Single Year of Age, Sex, Race, and Hispanic Origin. Retrieved June 20, 2006 from: www.census.gov/popest/national/asrh/2005_nat_res.html.
[a] Includes 169,000 persons with age unknown.
[b] This is the population used for standardization (age-adjustment) and differs slightly from the actual 2000 population, which totaled 275,306,000.

AGE-ADJUSTED DEATH RATES BY CLASS OF INJURY, UNITED STATES, 1910–2005

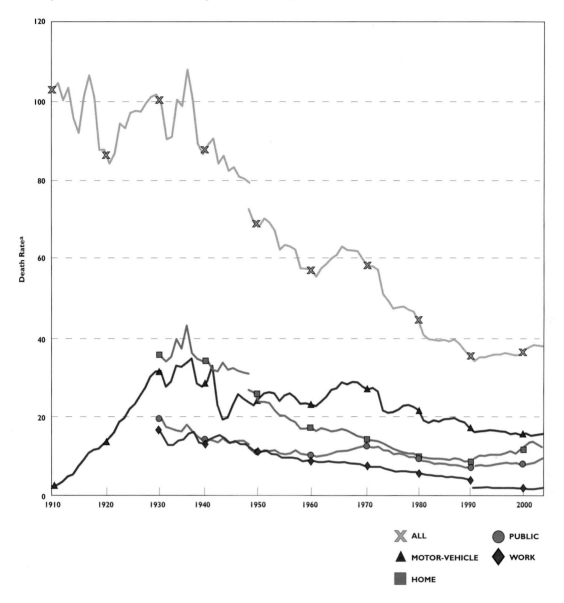

aDeaths per 100,000 population, adjusted to 2000 standard population. The break at 1948 shows the estimated effect of classification changes.
The break at 1992 is due to the adoption of the Bureau of Labor Statistics' Census of Fatal Occupational Injuries for work-related deaths.

PRINCIPAL CLASSES OF UNINTENTIONAL-INJURY DEATHS

PRINCIPAL CLASSES OF UNINTENTIONAL-INJURY DEATHS, UNITED STATES, 1903–2005

Year	Total[a] Deaths	Rate[b]	Motor-Vehicle Deaths	Rate[b]	Work Deaths	Rate[b]	Home Deaths	Rate[b]	Public Nonmotor-Vehicle Deaths	Rate[b]
1903	70,600	87.2	(c)	—	(c)	—	(c)	—	(c)	—
1904	71,500	86.6	(c)	—	(c)	—	(c)	—	(c)	—
1905	70,900	84.2	(c)	—	(c)	—	(c)	—	(c)	—
1906	80,000	93.2	400	0.5	(c)	—	(c)	—	(c)	—
1907	81,900	93.6	700	0.8	(c)	—	(c)	—	(c)	—
1908	72,300	81.2	800	0.9	(c)	—	(c)	—	(c)	—
1909	72,700	80.1	1,300	1.4	(c)	—	(c)	—	(c)	—
1910	77,900	84.4	1,900	2.0	(c)	—	(c)	—	(c)	—
1911	79,300	84.7	2,300	2.5	(c)	—	(c)	—	(c)	—
1912	78,400	82.5	3,100	3.3	(c)	—	(c)	—	(c)	—
1913	82,500	85.5	4,200	4.4	(c)	—	(c)	—	(c)	—
1914	77,000	78.6	4,700	4.8	(c)	—	(c)	—	(c)	—
1915	76,200	76.7	6,600	6.6	(c)	—	(c)	—	(c)	—
1916	84,800	84.1	8,200	8.1	(c)	—	(c)	—	(c)	—
1917	90,100	88.2	10,200	10.0	(c)	—	(c)	—	(c)	—
1918	85,100	82.1	10,700	10.3	(c)	—	(c)	—	(c)	—
1919	75,500	71.9	11,200	10.7	(c)	—	(c)	—	(c)	—
1920	75,900	71.2	12,500	11.7	(c)	—	(c)	—	(c)	—
1921	74,000	68.4	13,900	12.9	(c)	—	(c)	—	(c)	—
1922	76,300	69.4	15,300	13.9	(c)	—	(c)	—	(c)	—
1923	84,400	75.7	18,400	16.5	(c)	—	(c)	—	(c)	—
1924	85,600	75.6	19,400	17.1	(c)	—	(c)	—	(c)	—
1925	90,000	78.4	21,900	19.1	(c)	—	(c)	—	(c)	—
1926	91,700	78.7	23,400	20.1	(c)	—	(c)	—	(c)	—
1927	92,700	78.4	25,800	21.8	(c)	—	(c)	—	(c)	—
1928	95,000	79.3	28,000	23.4	19,000	15.8	30,000	24.9	21,000	17.4
1929	98,200	80.8	31,200	25.7	20,000	16.4	30,000	24.6	20,000	16.4
1930	99,100	80.5	32,900	26.7	19,000	15.4	30,000	24.4	20,000	16.3
1931	97,300	78.5	33,700	27.2	17,500	14.1	29,000	23.4	20,000	16.1
1932	89,000	71.3	29,500	23.6	15,000	12.0	29,000	23.2	18,000	14.4
1933	90,932	72.4	31,363	25.0	14,500	11.6	29,500	23.6	18,500	14.7
1934	100,977	79.9	36,101	28.6	16,000	12.7	34,000	26.9	18,000	14.2
1935	99,773	78.4	36,369	28.6	16,500	13.0	32,000	25.2	18,000	14.2
1936	110,052	85.9	38,089	29.7	18,500	14.5	37,000	28.9	19,500	15.2
1937	105,205	81.7	39,643	30.8	19,000	14.8	32,000	24.8	18,000	14.0
1938	93,805	72.3	32,582	25.1	16,000	12.3	31,000	23.9	17,000	13.1
1939	92,623	70.8	32,386	24.7	15,500	11.8	31,000	23.7	16,000	12.2
1940	96,885	73.4	34,501	26.1	17,000	12.9	31,500	23.9	16,500	12.5
1941	101,513	76.3	39,969	30.0	18,000	13.5	30,000	22.5	16,500	12.4
1942	95,889	71.6	28,309	21.1	18,000	13.4	30,500	22.8	16,000	12.0
1943	99,038	73.8	23,823	17.8	17,500	13.0	33,500	25.0	17,000	12.7
1944	95,237	71.7	24,282	18.3	16,000	12.0	32,500	24.5	16,000	12.0
1945	95,918	72.4	28,076	21.2	16,500	12.5	33,500	25.3	16,000	12.1
1946	98,033	70.0	33,411	23.9	16,500	11.8	33,000	23.6	17,500	12.5
1947	99,579	69.4	32,697	22.8	17,000	11.9	34,500	24.1	18,000	12.6
1948 (5th Rev.)[d]	98,001	67.1	32,259	22.1	16,000	11.0	35,000	24.0	17,000	11.6
1948 (6th Rev.)[d]	93,000	63.7	32,259	22.1	16,000	11.0	31,000	21.2	16,000	11.0
1949	90,106	60.6	31,701	21.3	15,000	10.1	31,000	20.9	15,000	10.1
1950	91,249	60.3	34,763	23.0	15,500	10.2	29,000	19.2	15,000	9.9
1951	95,871	62.5	36,996	24.1	16,000	10.4	30,000	19.6	16,000	10.4
1952	96,172	61.8	37,794	24.3	15,000	9.6	30,500	19.6	16,000	10.3
1953	95,032	60.1	37,955	24.0	15,000	9.5	29,000	18.3	16,500	10.4
1954	90,032	55.9	35,586	22.1	14,000	8.7	28,000	17.4	15,500	9.6
1955	93,443	56.9	38,426	23.4	14,200	8.6	28,500	17.3	15,500	9.4
1956	94,780	56.6	39,628	23.7	14,300	8.5	28,000	16.7	16,000	9.6
1957	95,307	55.9	38,702	22.7	14,200	8.3	28,000	16.4	17,500	10.3
1958	90,604	52.3	36,981	21.3	13,300	7.7	26,500	15.3	16,500	9.5
1959	92,080	52.2	37,910	21.5	13,800	7.8	27,000	15.3	16,500	9.3
1960	93,806	52.1	38,137	21.2	13,800	7.7	28,000	15.6	17,000	9.4
1961	92,249	50.4	38,091	20.8	13,500	7.4	27,000	14.8	16,500	9.0
1962	97,139	52.3	40,804	22.0	13,700	7.4	28,500	15.3	17,000	9.2
1963	100,669	53.4	43,564	23.1	14,200	7.5	28,500	15.1	17,500	9.3
1964	105,000	54.9	47,700	25.0	14,200	7.4	28,000	14.6	18,500	9.7
1965	108,004	55.8	49,163	25.4	14,100	7.3	28,500	14.7	19,500	10.1
1966	113,563	58.1	53,041	27.1	14,500	7.4	29,500	15.1	20,000	10.2
1967	113,169	57.3	52,924	26.8	14,200	7.2	29,000	14.7	20,500	10.4
1968	114,864	57.6	54,862	27.5	14,300	7.2	28,000	14.0	21,500	10.8
1969	116,385	57.8	55,791	27.7	14,300	7.1	27,500	13.7	22,500	11.2
1970	114,638	56.2	54,633	26.8	13,800	6.8	27,000	13.2	23,500	11.5
1971	113,439	54.8	54,381	26.3	13,700	6.6	26,500	12.8	23,500	11.4
1972	115,448	55.2	56,278	26.9	14,000	6.7	26,500	12.7	23,500	11.2
1973	115,821	54.8	55,511	26.3	14,300	6.8	26,500	12.5	24,500	11.6

See source and footnotes on page 37.

PRINCIPAL CLASSES OF UNINTENTIONAL-INJURY DEATHS, UNITED STATES, 1903–2005, Cont.

Year	Total[a] Deaths	Total[a] Rate[b]	Motor-Vehicle Deaths	Motor-Vehicle Rate[b]	Work Deaths	Work Rate[b]	Home Deaths	Home Rate[b]	Public Nonmotor-Vehicle Deaths	Public Nonmotor-Vehicle Rate[b]
1974	104,622	49.0	46,402	21.8	13,500	6.3	26,000	12.2	23,000	10.8
1975	103,030	47.8	45,853	21.3	13,000	6.0	25,000	11.6	23,000	10.6
1976	100,761	46.3	47,038	21.6	12,500	5.7	24,000	11.0	21,500	10.0
1977	103,202	47.0	49,510	22.5	12,900	5.9	23,200	10.6	22,200	10.1
1978	105,561	47.5	52,411	23.6	13,100	5.9	22,800	10.3	22,000	9.9
1979	105,312	46.9	53,524	23.8	13,000	5.8	22,500	10.0	21,000	9.4
1980	105,718	46.5	53,172	23.4	13,200	5.8	22,800	10.0	21,300	9.4
1981	100,704	43.9	51,385	22.4	12,500	5.4	21,700	9.5	19,800	8.6
1982	94,082	40.6	45,779	19.8	11,900	5.1	21,200	9.2	19,500	8.4
1983	92,488	39.6	44,452	19.0	11,700	5.0	21,200	9.1	19,400	8.3
1984	92,911	39.4	46,263	19.6	11,500	4.9	21,200	9.0	18,300	7.8
1985	93,457	39.3	45,901	19.3	11,500	4.8	21,600	9.1	18,800	7.9
1986	95,277	39.7	47,865	19.9	11,100	4.6	21,700	9.0	18,700	7.8
1987	95,020	39.2	48,290	19.9	11,300	4.7	21,400	8.8	18,400	7.6
1988	97,100	39.7	49,078	20.1	11,000	4.5	22,700	9.3	18,400	7.5
1989	95,028	38.5	47,575	19.3	10,900	4.4	22,500	9.1	18,200	7.4
1990	91,983	36.9	46,814	18.8	10,100	4.0	21,500	8.6	17,400	7.0
1991	89,347	35.4	43,536	17.3	9,800	3.9	22,100	8.8	17,600	7.0
1992	86,777	34.0	40,982	16.1	4,968[e]	1.9[e]	24,000[e]	9.4[e]	19,000[e]	7.4[e]
1993	90,523	35.1	41,893	16.3	5,035	2.0	26,100	10.1	19,700	7.6
1994	91,437	35.1	42,524	16.3	5,338	2.1	26,300	10.1	19,600	7.5
1995	93,320	35.5	43,363	16.5	5,018	1.9	27,200	10.3	20,100	7.6
1996	94,948	35.8	43,649	16.5	5,058	1.9	27,500	10.4	21,000	7.9
1997	95,644	35.7	43,458	16.2	5,162	1.9	27,700	10.3	21,700	8.1
1998	97,835	36.2	43,501	16.1	5,120	1.9	29,000	10.7	22,600	8.4
1999[f]	97,860	35.9	42,401	15.5	5,185	1.9	30,500	11.2	22,200	8.1
2000	97,900	35.6	43,354	15.7	5,022	1.8	29,200	10.6	22,700	8.2
2001	101,537	35.6	43,788	15.4	5,042	1.8	33,200	11.6	21,800	7.6
2002	106,742	37.1	45,380	15.8	4,726	1.6	36,400	12.6	22,500	7.8
2003[g]	109,277	37.6	44,757	15.4	4,725	1.6	38,800	13.3	23,200	8.0
2004[g]	112,000	38.1	45,300	15.4	4,999	1.7	40,000	13.6	24,000	8.2
2005[h]	113,000	38.1	45,800	15.5	4,961	1.7	37,000	12.5	27,600	9.3
Changes										
1995 to 2005	+21%	+7%	+6%	–6%	–1%	–11%	+36%	+21%	+37%	+22%
2004 to 2005	+1%	0%	+1%	+1%	–1%	0%	–8%	–8%	+15%	+13%

Source: Total and motor-vehicle deaths, 1903–1932 based on National Center for Health Statistics death registration states; 1933-1948 (5th Rev.), 1949–1963, 1965–2003 are NCHS totals for the U.S. Work deaths for 1992–2005 are from the Bureau of Labor Statistics, Census of Fatal Occupational Injuries. All other figures are National Safety Council estimates.
[a] Duplications between Motor-Vehicle, Work, and Home are eliminated in the Total column.
[b] Rates are deaths per 100,000 population.
[c] Data insufficient to estimate yearly totals.
[d] In 1948 a revision was made in the International Classification of Diseases. The first figures for 1948 are comparable with those for earlier years, the second with those for later years.
[e] Adoption of the Census of Fatal Occupational Injuries figure for the Work class necessitated adjustments to the Home and Public classes. See the Technical Appendix for details.
[f] In 1999 a revision was made in the International Classification of Diseases. See the Technical Appendix for comparability with earlier years.
[g] Revised.
[h] Preliminary.

UNINTENTIONAL-INJURY DEATHS BY AGE

UNINTENTIONAL-INJURY DEATHS BY AGE, UNITED STATES, 1903–2005

Year	All Ages	Under 5 Years	5–14 Years	15–24 Years	25–44 Years	45–64 Years	65–74 Years	75 Years & Over[a]
1903	70,600	9,400	8,200	10,300	20,100	12,600	10,000	
1904	71,500	9,700	9,000	10,500	19,900	12,500	9,900	
1905	70,900	9,800	8,400	10,600	19,600	12,600	9,900	
1906	80,000	10,000	8,400	13,000	24,000	13,600	11,000	
1907	81,900	10,500	8,300	13,400	24,900	14,700	10,100	
1908	72,300	10,100	7,600	11,300	20,500	13,100	9,700	
1909	72,700	9,900	7,400	10,700	21,000	13,300	10,400	
1910	77,900	9,900	7,400	11,900	23,600	14,100	11,000	
1911	79,300	11,000	7,500	11,400	22,400	15,100	11,900	
1912	78,400	10,600	7,900	11,500	22,200	14,700	11,500	
1913	82,500	9,800	7,400	12,200	24,500	16,500	12,100	
1914	77,000	10,600	7,900	11,000	21,400	14,300	11,800	
1915	76,200	10,300	8,200	10,800	20,500	14,300	12,100	
1916	84,800	11,600	9,100	7,700	24,900	17,800	13,700	
1917	90,100	11,600	9,700	11,700	24,400	18,500	14,200	
1918	85,100	10,600	10,100	10,600	21,900	17,700	14,200	
1919	75,500	10,100	10,000	10,200	18,600	13,800	12,800	
1920	75,900	10,200	9,900	10,400	18,100	13,900	13,400	
1921	74,000	9,600	9,500	9,800	18,000	13,900	13,200	
1922	76,300	9,700	9,500	10,000	18,700	14,500	13,900	
1923	84,400	9,900	9,800	11,000	21,500	16,900	15,300	
1924	85,600	10,200	9,900	11,900	20,900	16,800	15,900	
1925	90,000	9,700	10,000	12,400	22,200	18,700	17,000	
1926	91,700	9,500	9,900	12,600	22,700	19,200	17,800	
1927	92,700	9,200	9,900	12,900	22,900	19,700	18,100	
1928	95,000	8,900	9,800	13,100	23,300	20,600	19,300	
1929	98,200	8,600	9,800	14,000	24,300	21,500	20,000	
1930	99,100	8,200	9,100	14,000	24,300	22,200	21,300	
1931	97,300	7,800	8,700	13,500	23,100	22,500	21,700	
1932	89,000	7,100	8,100	12,000	20,500	20,100	21,200	
1933	90,932	6,948	8,195	12,225	21,005	20,819	21,740	
1934	100,977	7,034	8,272	13,274	23,288	24,197	24,912	
1935	99,773	6,971	7,808	13,168	23,411	23,457	24,958	
1936	110,052	7,471	7,866	13,701	24,990	26,535	29,489	
1937	105,205	6,969	7,704	14,302	23,955	24,743	27,532	
1938	93,805	6,646	6,593	12,129	20,464	21,689	26,284	
1939	92,628	6,668	6,378	12,066	20,164	20,842	26,505	
1940	96,885	6,851	6,466	12,763	21,166	21,840	27,799	
1941	101,513	7,052	6,702	14,346	22,983	22,509	27,921	
1942	95,889	7,220	6,340	13,732	21,141	20,764	26,692	
1943	99,038	8,039	6,636	15,278	20,212	20,109	28,764	
1944	95,237	7,912	6,704	14,750	19,115	19,097	27,659	
1945	95,918	7,741	6,836	12,446	19,393	20,097	29,405	
1946	98,033	7,949	6,545	13,366	20,705	20,249	29,219	
1947	99,579	8,219	6,069	13,166	21,155	20,513	30,457	
1948 (5th Rev.)[b]	98,001	8,387	5,859	12,595	20,274	19,809	31,077	
1948 (6th Rev.)[b]	93,000	8,350	5,850	12,600	20,300	19,300	9,800	16,800
1949	90,106	8,469	5,539	11,522	19,432	18,302	9,924	16,918
1950	91,249	8,389	5,519	12,119	20,663	18,665	9,750	16,144
1951	95,871	8,769	5,892	12,366	22,363	19,610	10,218	16,653
1952	96,172	8,871	5,980	12,787	21,950	19,892	10,026	16,667
1953	95,032	8,678	6,136	12,837	21,422	19,479	9,927	16,553
1954	90,032	8,380	5,939	11,801	20,023	18,299	9,652	15,938
1955	93,443	8,099	6,099	12,742	29,911	19,199	9,929	16,464
1956	94,780	8,173	6,319	13,545	20,986	19,207	10,160	16,393
1957	95,307	8,423	6,454	12,973	20,949	19,495	10,076	16,937
1958	90,604	8,789	6,514	12,744	19,658	18,095	9,431	15,373
1959	92,080	8,748	6,511	13,269	19,666	18,937	9,475	15,474
1960	93,806	8,950	6,836	13,457	19,600	19,385	9,689	15,829
1961	92,249	8,622	6,717	13,431	19,273	19,134	9,452	15,620
1962	97,139	8,705	6,751	14,557	19,955	20,335	10,149	16,687
1963	100,669	8,688	6,962	15,889	20,529	21,262	10,194	17,145
1964	100,500	8,670	7,400	17,420	22,080	22,100	10,400	16,930
1965	108,004	8,586	7,391	18,688	22,228	22,900	10,430	17,781
1966	113,563	8,507	7,958	21,030	23,134	24,022	10,706	18,206
1967	113,169	7,825	7,874	21,645	23,255	23,826	10,645	18,099
1968	114,864	7,263	8,369	23,012	23,684	23,896	10,961	17,679
1969	116,385	6,973	8,186	24,668	24,410	24,192	10,643	17,313
1970	114,638	6,594	8,203	24,336	23,979	24,164	10,644	16,718
1971	113,439	6,496	8,143	24,733	23,535	23,240	10,494	16,798
1972	115,448	6,142	8,242	25,762	23,852	23,658	10,446	17,346
1973	115,821	6,037	8,102	26,550	24,750	23,059	10,243	17,080

See source and footnotes on page 39.

UNINTENTIONAL-INJURY DEATHS BY AGE, UNITED STATES, 1903–2005, Cont.

Year	All Ages	Under 5 Years	5–14 Years	15–24 Years	25–44 Years	45–64 Years	65–74 Years	75 Years & Over[a]
1974	104,622	5,335	7,037	24,200	22,547	20,334	9,323	15,846
1975	103,030	4,948	6,818	24,121	22,877	19,643	9,220	15,403
1976	100,761	4,692	6,308	24,316	22,399	19,000	8,823	15,223
1977	103,202	4,470	6,305	25,619	23,460	19,167	9,006	15,175
1978	105,561	4,766	6,118	26,622	25,024	18,774	9,072	15,185
1979	105,312	4,429	5,689	26,574	26,097	18,346	9,013	15,164
1980	105,718	4,479	5,224	26,206	26,722	18,140	8,997	15,950
1981	100,704	4,130	4,866	23,582	26,928	17,339	8,639	15,220
1982	94,082	4,108	4,504	21,306	25,135	15,907	8,224	14,898
1983	92,488	3,999	4,321	19,756	24,996	15,444	8,336	15,636
1984	92,911	3,652	4,198	19,801	25,498	15,273	8,424	16,065
1985	93,457	3,746	4,252	19,161	25,940	15,251	8,583	16,524
1986	95,277	3,843	4,226	19,975	27,201	14,733	8,499	16,800
1987	95,020	3,871	4,198	18,695	27,484	14,807	8,686	17,279
1988	97,100	3,794	4,215	18,507	28,279	15,177	8,971	18,157
1989	95,028	3,770	4,090	16,738	28,429	15,046	8,812	18,143
1990	91,983	3,496	3,650	16,241	27,663	14,607	8,405	17,921
1991	89,347	3,626	3,660	15,278	26,526	13,693	8,137	18,427
1992	86,777	3,286	3,388	13,662	25,808	13,882	8,165	18,586
1993	90,523	3,488	3,466	13,966	27,277	14,434	8,125	19,767
1994	91,437	3,406	3,508	13,898	27,012	15,200	8,279	20,134
1995	93,320	3,067	3,544	13,842	27,660	16,004	8,400	20,803
1996	94,948	2,951	3,433	13,809	27,092	16,717	8,780	22,166
1997	94,644	2,770	3,371	13,367	27,129	17,521	8,578	22,908
1998	97,835	2,689	3,254	13,349	27,172	18,286	8,892	24,193
1999[c]	97,860	2,743	3,091	13,656	27,121	18,924	8,208	24,117
2000	97,900	2,707	2,979	14,113	27,182	19,783	7,698	23,438
2001	101,537	2,690	2,836	14,411	27,784	21,002	7,835	24,979
2002	106,742	2,587	2,718	15,412	29,279	23,020	8,086	25,640
2003[d]	109,277	2,662	2,618	15,272	29,307	25,007	8,081	26,330
2004[d]	112,000	2,600	2,700	15,300	29,500	25,800	8,200	27,900
2005[e]	113,000	2,400	2,500	15,200	30,200	26,800	8,200	27,700
Changes								
1995 to 2005	+21%	−22%	−29%	+10%	+9%	+67%	−2%	+33%
2004 to 2005	+1%	−8%	−7%	−1%	+2%	+4%	0%	−1%

Source: 1903 to 1932 based on National Center for Health Statistics data for registration states; 1933–1948 (5th Rev.), 1949–1963, 1965–2003 are NCHS totals. All other figures are National Safety Council estimates. See Technical Appendix for comparability.
[a] *Includes age unknown. In 2003, these deaths numbered 76.*
[b] *In 1948, a revision was made in the International Classification of Diseases. The first figures for 1948 are comparable with those for earlier years, the second with those for later years.*
[c] *In 1999, a revision was made in the International Classification of Diseases. See the Technical Appendix for comparability with earlier years.*
[d] *Revised.*
[e] *Preliminary.*

UNINTENTIONAL-INJURY DEATH RATES BY AGE

UNINTENTIONAL-INJURY DEATH RATES[a] BY AGE, UNITED STATES, 1903–2005

Year	Standardized Rate[b]	All Ages	Under 5 Years	5–14 Years	15–24 Years	25–44 Years	45–64 Years	65–74 Years	75 Years & Over[c]
1903	99.4	87.2	98.7	46.8	65.0	87.4	111.7	299.8	
1904	103.4	86.6	99.1	50.9	64.9	84.6	108.1	290.0	
1905	98.4	84.2	98.6	47.0	64.1	81.4	106.2	282.5	
1906	114.2	93.2	99.1	46.5	77.1	97.3	111.7	306.0	
1907	112.4	93.6	102.7	45.5	78.0	98.8	117.8	274.2	
1908	99.7	81.2	97.5	41.2	64.4	79.5	102.2	256.7	
1909	97.4	80.1	94.2	39.6	59.9	79.6	101.0	268.2	
1910	103.0	84.4	92.8	39.1	65.3	87.3	104.0	276.0	
1911	104.7	84.7	101.9	39.3	62.1	81.4	108.7	292.1	
1912	100.4	82.5	97.1	40.5	62.3	79.2	103.2	275.8	
1913	103.5	85.5	88.4	37.4	65.2	85.6	112.5	281.7	
1914	95.9	78.6	94.3	38.9	58.5	73.2	94.6	268.1	
1915	92.1	76.7	90.8	39.7	57.3	69.0	92.1	268.8	
1916	101.4	84.1	101.4	43.3	40.8	82.5	112.1	297.6	
1917	106.7	88.2	108.4	45.3	62.1	79.8	113.8	301.2	
1918	101.2	82.1	91.0	46.5	58.7	72.2	106.3	294.2	
1919	87.7	71.9	87.2	45.9	55.3	60.1	81.8	262.0	
1920	87.8	71.2	87.4	44.9	55.5	56.9	85.6	289.5	
1921	84.3	68.4	80.8	42.4	51.4	55.5	79.4	259.8	
1922	86.9	69.4	80.6	41.5	51.4	57.1	81.4	265.1	
1923	94.5	75.7	82.0	42.4	55.6	64.5	92.6	282.8	
1924	93.3	75.6	82.9	42.4	58.6	61.7	90.2	283.5	
1925	97.2	78.4	78.6	42.3	59.7	64.7	97.8	293.9	
1926	97.7	78.7	77.9	41.4	59.9	65.4	98.2	298.7	
1927	97.5	78.4	75.9	41.0	60.2	65.2	98.0	295.4	
1928	99.6	79.3	74.4	40.4	59.9	65.6	99.9	306.2	
1929	101.2	80.8	73.3	40.0	63.1	67.7	102.1	308.9	
1930	101.8	80.5	71.8	36.9	62.3	67.0	102.9	317.9	
1931	99.2	78.5	69.9	35.2	59.7	63.0	102.1	313.3	
1932	90.5	71.3	65.1	32.8	52.7	55.6	89.3	296.9	
1933	91.1	72.4	65.5	33.4	53.6	56.3	90.8	295.3	
1934	100.5	79.9	68.1	33.9	57.8	61.8	103.3	328.5	
1935	97.9	78.4	68.5	32.2	56.9	61.6	98.0	319.8	
1936	108.1	85.9	74.4	32.9	58.8	65.3	108.6	367.4	
1937	100.7	81.7	69.6	32.7	60.9	62.1	99.3	333.4	
1938	89.4	72.3	65.3	28.5	51.3	52.5	85.4	308.9	
1939	86.7	70.8	62.9	28.2	50.7	51.2	81.0	300.0	
1940	89.1	73.4	64.8	28.8	53.5	53.2	83.4	305.7	
1941	90.7	76.3	65.0	29.7	60.9	57.2	84.8	297.4	
1942	84.3	71.6	63.9	27.9	59.8	52.4	77.1	275.5	
1943	86.3	73.8	66.9	29.0	69.7	50.3	73.6	287.8	
1944	82.5	71.7	63.2	29.1	72.9	48.9	68.9	268.6	
1945	83.4	72.4	59.8	29.5	64.5	50.5	71.6	277.6	
1946	81.0	70.0	60.2	28.1	61.7	48.8	70.9	267.9	
1947	80.5	69.4	57.4	25.8	59.6	49.0	70.6	270.7	
1948 (5th Rev.)[d]	79.5	67.1	56.3	24.6	56.8	46.2	66.8	267.4	
1948 (6th Rev.)[d]	72.5	63.7	56.0	24.5	56.8	46.2	65.1	122.4	464.3
1949	69.0	60.6	54.4	23.0	52.2	43.5	60.6	120.4	450.7
1950	68.1	60.3	51.4	22.6	55.0	45.6	60.5	115.8	414.7
1951	70.1	62.5	50.8	23.6	57.7	49.0	62.7	117.1	413.6
1952	69.0	61.8	51.5	22.5	60.9	47.7	62.7	111.1	399.8
1953	67.0	60.1	49.5	22.1	61.4	46.4	60.5	106.7	383.6
1954	62.2	55.9	46.7	20.5	56.4	43.0	55.9	100.7	354.4
1955	63.4	56.9	43.9	20.7	60.1	44.7	57.7	100.8	350.2
1956	63.0	56.6	43.3	20.2	63.3	44.7	56.7	100.6	335.6
1957	62.2	55.9	43.5	19.9	59.5	44.6	56.6	97.5	333.3
1958	57.5	52.3	44.5	19.6	56.2	42.0	51.7	89.3	292.6
1959	57.4	52.2	43.6	18.9	56.5	42.1	53.2	87.7	284.7
1960	57.3	52.1	44.0	19.1	55.6	42.0	53.6	87.6	281.4
1961	55.4	50.4	42.0	18.1	54.0	41.2	52.1	83.8	267.9
1962	57.5	52.3	42.6	18.0	55.0	42.7	54.6	88.5	277.7
1963	58.6	53.4	42.8	18.2	57.2	44.0	56.3	87.9	277.0
1964	60.0	54.9	43.1	19.1	59.9	47.3	57.6	88.9	263.9
1965	61.9	55.8	43.4	18.7	61.6	47.7	58.8	88.5	268.7
1966	63.0	58.1	44.4	19.9	66.9	49.6	60.7	89.8	267.4
1967	62.1	57.3	42.2	19.4	66.9	49.7	59.2	88.5	257.4
1968	62.0	57.6	40.6	20.5	69.2	50.1	58.5	90.2	244.0
1969	61.8	57.8	40.2	20.0	71.8	51.2	58.4	86.6	232.0
1970	59.8	56.2	38.4	20.1	68.0	49.8	57.6	85.2	219.6
1971	58.1	54.8	37.7	20.1	66.1	48.4	54.7	82.7	213.2
1972	58.0	55.2	35.9	20.6	67.6	47.5	55.2	80.8	214.2
1973	57.1	54.8	35.8	20.6	68.2	48.0	53.3	77.3	206.3

See source and footnotes on page 41.

ALL UNINTENTIONAL INJURIES

UNINTENTIONAL-INJURY DEATHS BY AGE, UNITED STATES, 1903–2005, Cont.

Year	Standardized Rate[b]	All Ages	Under 5 Years	5–14 Years	15–24 Years	25–44 Years	45–64 Years	65–74 Years	75 Years & Over[c]
1974	50.9	49.0	32.4	18.2	60.9	42.7	46.7	68.7	186.7
1975	49.3	47.8	30.7	17.8	59.5	42.3	44.9	66.2	175.5
1976	47.3	46.3	30.0	16.7	58.9	40.3	43.2	62.0	168.4
1977	47.6	47.0	28.7	17.0	61.3	40.9	43.4	61.5	164.0
1978	47.8	47.5	30.3	16.9	63.1	42.3	42.4	60.5	159.7
1979	47.0	46.9	27.6	16.1	62.6	42.7	41.3	58.8	154.8
1980	46.5	46.5	27.2	15.0	61.7	42.3	40.8	57.5	158.6
1981	44.0	43.9	24.4	14.2	55.9	41.2	39.0	54.4	147.4
1982	40.6	40.6	23.8	13.2	51.2	37.3	35.8	50.9	140.0
1983	39.6	39.6	22.8	12.7	48.2	36.0	34.7	50.8	142.8
1984	39.4	39.4	20.6	12.4	48.9	35.7	34.3	50.7	142.8
1985	39.2	39.3	21.0	12.6	47.9	35.3	34.2	50.9	143.0
1986	39.4	39.7	21.4	12.6	50.5	36.1	33.0	49.6	141.5
1987	39.0	39.2	21.4	12.4	48.1	35.7	33.0	49.8	141.6
1988	39.5	39.7	20.9	12.3	48.5	36.1	33.4	50.9	145.3
1989	38.4	38.5	20.4	11.8	44.8	35.7	32.8	49.3	141.5
1990	36.7	36.9	18.5	10.4	44.0	34.2	31.6	46.4	136.5
1991	35.3	35.4	18.9	10.2	42.0	32.3	29.3	44.5	136.7
1992	34.0	34.0	16.8	9.3	37.8	31.3	28.7	44.2	134.5
1993	35.0	35.1	17.7	9.4	38.8	33.0	29.1	43.6	139.9
1994	35.0	35.1	17.3	9.4	38.4	32.5	29.9	44.3	139.2
1995	35.4	35.5	15.7	9.3	38.2	33.2	30.6	44.8	140.6
1996	35.7	35.8	15.3	8.9	38.1	32.3	31.1	47.0	145.9
1997	35.7	35.7	14.5	8.7	36.5	32.5	31.6	46.3	146.2
1998	36.1	36.2	14.2	8.3	35.9	32.6	31.9	48.3	151.1
1999[e]	35.8	35.9	14.5	7.8	36.1	32.7	32.0	45.0	147.7
2000	35.5	35.6	14.3	7.5	36.7	33.0	32.3	42.3	140.8
2001	35.7	35.6	13.9	6.9	36.1	32.7	32.6	42.8	146.8
2002	37.1	37.1	13.2	6.6	37.9	34.7	34.6	44.2	148.2
2003[f]	37.6	37.6	13.5	6.4	37.0	34.8	36.4	44.0	149.6
2004[f]	38.1	38.1	13.0	6.6	36.7	35.1	36.5	44.7	156.3
2005[g]	37.9	38.1	11.8	6.2	36.1	36.0	36.8	44.0	152.6

Changes									
1995 to 2005		+7%	−25%	−33%	−5%	+8%	+20%	−2%	+9%
2004 to 2005		0%	−9%	−6%	−2%	+3%	+1%	−2%	−2%

2005 Population (Millions)									
Total[h]		296.410	20.304	40.397	42.077	84.005	72.838	18.640	18.150
Male		146.000	10.381	20.675	21.647	42.361	35.522	8.529	6.883
Female		150.410	9.922	19.721	20.430	41.644	37.316	10.110	11.267

Source: All figures are National Safety Council estimates. See Technical Appendix for comparability.
[a] *Rates are deaths per 100,000 resident population in each age group.*
[b] *Adjusted to the year 2000 standard population to remove the influence of changes in age distribution between 1903 and 2001.*
[c] *Includes age unknown.*
[d] *In 1948, a revision was made in the* International Classification of Diseases. *The first figures for 1948 are comparable with those for earlier years, the second with those for later years.*
[e] *In 1999, a revision was made in the* International Classification of Diseases. *See the Technical Appendix for comparability.*
[f] *Revised.*
[g] *Preliminary.*
[h] *Sum of parts may not equal total due to rounding.*

PRINCIPAL TYPES OF UNINTENTIONAL-INJURY DEATHS

PRINCIPAL TYPES OF UNINTENTIONAL-INJURY DEATHS, UNITED STATES, 1903–1998

Year	Total	Motor-Vehicle	Falls	Drowning[a]	Fires/Burns[b]	Ingest. of Food/Object	Firearms	Poison (Solid, Liquid)	Poison (Gas, Vapor)	All Other
1903	70,600	(c)	(c)	9,200	(c)	(c)	2,500	(c)	(c)	58,900
1904	71,500	(c)	(c)	9,300	(c)	(c)	2,800	(c)	(c)	59,400
1905	70,900	(c)	(c)	9,300	(c)	(c)	2,000	(c)	(c)	59,600
1906	80,000	400	(c)	9,400	(c)	(c)	2,100	(c)	(c)	68,100
1907	81,900	700	(c)	9,000	(c)	(c)	1,700	(c)	(c)	70,500
1908	72,300	800	(c)	9,300	(c)	(c)	1,900	(c)	(c)	60,300
1909	72,700	1,300	(c)	8,500	(c)	(c)	1,600	(c)	(c)	61,300
1910	77,900	1,900	(c)	8,700	(c)	(c)	1,900	(c)	(c)	65,400
1911	79,300	2,300	(c)	9,000	(c)	(c)	2,100	(c)	(c)	65,900
1912	78,400	3,100	(c)	8,600	(c)	(c)	2,100	(c)	(c)	64,600
1913	82,500	4,200	15,100	10,300	8,900	(c)	2,400	3,200	(c)	38,400
1914	77,000	4,700	15,000	8,700	9,100	(c)	2,300	3,300	(c)	33,900
1915	76,200	6,600	15,000	8,600	8,400	(c)	2,100	2,800	(c)	32,700
1916	84,800	8,200	15,200	8,900	9,500	(c)	2,200	2,900	(c)	37,900
1917	90,100	10,200	15,200	7,600	10,800	(c)	2,300	2,800	(c)	41,200
1918	85,100	10,700	13,200	7,000	10,200	(c)	2,500	2,700	(c)	38,800
1919	75,500	11,200	11,900	9,100	9,100	(c)	2,800	3,100	(c)	28,300
1920	75,900	12,500	12,600	6,100	9,300	(c)	2,700	3,300	(c)	29,400
1921	74,000	13,900	12,300	7,800	7,500	(c)	2,800	2,900	(c)	26,800
1922	76,300	15,300	13,200	7,000	8,300	(c)	2,900	2,800	(c)	26,800
1923	84,400	18,400	14,100	6,800	9,100	(c)	2,900	2,800	2,700	27,600
1924	85,600	19,400	14,700	7,400	7,400	(c)	2,900	2,700	2,900	28,200
1925	90,000	21,900	15,500	7,300	8,600	(c)	2,800	2,700	2,800	28,400
1926	91,700	23,400	16,300	7,500	8,800	(c)	2,800	2,600	3,200	27,100
1927	92,700	25,800	16,500	8,100	8,200	(c)	3,000	2,600	2,700	25,800
1928	95,000	28,000	17,000	8,600	8,400	(c)	2,900	2,800	2,800	24,500
1929	98,200	31,200	17,700	7,600	8,200	(c)	3,200	2,600	2,800	24,900
1930	99,100	32,900	18,100	7,500	8,100	(c)	3,200	2,600	2,500	24,200
1931	97,300	33,700	18,100	7,600	7,100	(c)	3,100	2,600	2,100	23,000
1932	89,000	29,500	18,600	7,500	7,100	(c)	3,000	2,200	2,100	19,000
1933	90,932	31,363	18,962	7,158	6,781	(c)	3,014	2,135	1,633	19,886
1934	100,977	36,101	20,725	7,077	7,456	(c)	3,033	2,148	1,643	22,794
1935	99,773	36,369	21,378	6,744	7,253	(c)	2,799	2,163	1,654	21,413
1936	110,052	38,089	23,562	6,659	7,939	(c)	2,817	2,177	1,665	27,144
1937	105,205	39,643	22,544	7,085	7,214	(c)	2,576	2,190	1,675	22,278
1938	93,805	32,582	23,239	6,881	6,491	(c)	2,726	2,077	1,428	18,381
1939	92,623	32,386	23,427	6,413	6,675	(c)	2,618	1,963	1,440	17,701
1940	96,885	34,501	23,356	6,202	7,521	(c)	2,375	1,847	1,583	19,500
1941	101,513	39,969	22,764	6,389	6,922	(c)	2,396	1,731	1,464	19,878
1942	95,889	28,309	22,632	6,696	7,901	(c)	2,678	1,607	1,741	24,325
1943	99,038	23,823	24,701	7,115	8,726	921	2,282	1,745	2,014	27,711
1944	95,237	24,282	22,989	6,511	8,372	896	2,392	1,993	1,860	25,942
1945	95,918	28,076	23,847	6,624	7,949	897	2,385	1,987	2,120	22,033
1946	98,033	33,411	23,109	6,442	7,843	1,076	2,801	1,961	1,821	19,569
1947	99,579	32,697	24,529	6,885	8,033	1,206	2,439	1,865	1,865	14,060
1948 (5th Rev.)[d]	98,001	32,259	24,836	6,428	7,743	1,315	2,191	1,753	2,045	19,611
1948 (6th Rev.)[d]	93,000	32,259	22,000	6,500	6,800	1,299	2,330	1,600	2,020	17,192
1949	90,106	31,701	22,308	6,684	5,982	1,341	2,326	1,634	1,617	16,513
1950	91,249	34,763	20,783	6,131	6,405	1,350	2,174	1,584	1,769	16,290
1951	95,871	36,996	21,376	6,489	6,788	1,456	2,247	1,497	1,627	17,395
1952	96,172	37,794	20,945	6,601	6,922	1,434	2,210	1,440	1,397	17,429
1953	95,032	37,955	20,631	6,770	6,579	1,603	2,277	1,391	1,223	16,603
1954	90,032	35,586	19,771	6,334	6,083	1,627	2,271	1,339	1,223	15,798
1955	93,443	38,426	20,192	6,344	6,352	1,608	2,120	1,431	1,163	15,807
1956	94,780	39,628	20,282	6,263	6,405	1,760	2,202	1,422	1,213	15,605
1957	95,307	38,702	20,545	6,613	6,269	2,043	2,369	1,390	1,143	16,233
1958	90,604	36,981	18,248	6,582[e]	7,291[e]	2,191[e]	2,172	1,429	1,187	14,523
1959	92,080	37,910	18,774	6,434	6,898	2,189	2,258	1,661	1,141	14,815
1960	93,806	38,137	19,023	6,529	7,645	2,397	2,334	1,679	1,253	14,809
1961	92,249	38,091	18,691	6,525	7,102	2,499	2,204	1,804	1,192	14,141
1962	97,139	40,804	19,589	6,439	7,534	1,813	2,092	1,833	1,376	15,659
1963	100,669	43,564	19,335	6,347	8,172	1,949	2,263	2,061	1,489	15,489
1964	105,000	47,700	18,941	6,709	7,379	1,865	2,275	2,100	1,360	16,571
1965	108,004	49,163	19,984	6,799	7,347	1,836	2,344	2,110	1,526	16,895
1966	113,563	53,041	20,066	7,084	8,084	1,831	2,558	2,283	1,648	16,968
1967	113,169	52,924	20,120	7,076	7,423	1,980	2,896	2,506	1,574	16,670
1968	114,864	54,862	18,651	7,372[e]	7,335	3,100[e]	2,394[e]	2,583	1,526	17,041
1969	116,385	55,791	17,827	7,699	7,163	3,712	2,309	2,967	1,549	16,368
1970	114,638	54,633	16,926	7,860	6,718	2,753	2,406	3,679	1,620	18,043
1971	113,439	54,381	16,755	7,396	6,776	2,877	2,360	3,710	1,646	17,538
1972	115,448	56,278	16,744	7,586	6,714	2,830	2,442	3,728	1,690	17,436
1973	115,821	55,511	16,506	8,725	6,503	3,013	2,618	3,683	1,652	17,610

See source and footnotes on page 43.

PRINCIPAL TYPES OF UNINTENTIONAL-INJURY DEATHS, UNITED STATES, 1903–1998, Cont.

Year	Total	Motor-Vehicle	Falls	Drowninga	Fires/Burnsb	Ingest. of Food/Object	Firearms	Poison (Solid, Liquid)	Poison (Gas, Vapor)	All Other
1974	104,622	46,402	16,339	7,876	6,236	2,991	2,513	4,016	1,518	16,731
1975	103,030	45,853	14,896	8,000	6,071	3,106	2,380	4,694	1,577	16,453
1976	100,761	47,038	14,136	6,827	6,338	3,033	2,059	4,161	1,569	15,600
1977	103,202	49,510	13,773	7,126	6,357	3,037	1,982	3,374	1,596	16,447
1978	105,561	52,411	13,690	7,026	6,163	3,063	1,806	3,035	1,737	16,630
1979	105,312	53,524	13,216	6,872	5,991	3,243	2,004	3,165	1,472	15,825
1980	105,718	53,172	13,294	7,257	5,822	3,249	1,955	3,089	1,242	16,638
1981	100,704	51,385	12,628	6,277	5,697	3,331	1,871	3,243	1,280	14,992
1982	94,082	45,779	12,077	6,351	5,210	3,254	1,756	3,474	1,259	14,922
1983	92,488	44,452	12,024	6,353	5,028	3,387	1,695	3,382	1,251	14,916
1984	92,911	46,263	11,937	5,388	5,010	3,541	1,668	3,808	1,103	14,193
1985	93,457	45,901	12,001	5,316	4,938	3,551	1,649	4,091	1,079	14,931
1986	95,277	47,865	11,444	5,700	4,835	3,692	1,452	4,731	1,009	14,549
1987	95,020	48,290	11,733	5,100	4,710	3,688	1,440	4,415	900	14,744
1988	97,100	49,078	12,096	4,966	4,965	3,805	1,501	5,353	873	14,463
1989	95,028	47,575	12,151	4,015	4,716	3,578	1,489	5,603	921	14,980
1990	91,983	46,814	12,313	4,685	4,175	3,303	1,416	5,055	748	13,474
1991	89,347	43,536	12,662	4,818	4,120	3,240	1,441	5,698	736	13,096
1992	86,777	40,982	12,646	3,542	3,958	3,182	1,409	6,449	633	13,976
1993	90,523	41,893	13,141	3,807	3,900	3,160	1,521	7,877	660	14,564
1994	91,437	42,524	13,450	3,942	3,986	3,065	1,356	8,309	685	14,120
1995	93,320	43,363	13,986	4,350	3,761	3,185	1,225	8,461	611	14,378
1996	94,948	43,649	14,986	3,959	3,741	3,206	1,134	8,872	638	14,763
1997	95,644	43,458	15,447	4,051	3,490	3,275	981	9,587	576	14,779
1998	97,835	43,501	16,274	4,406	3,255	3,515	866	10,255	546	15,217

PRINCIPAL TYPES OF UNINTENTIONAL-INJURY DEATHS, UNITED STATES, 1999–2005

Year	Total	Motor-Vehicle	Falls	Poisoning	Ingest. of Food/Object	Drowningf	Fires, Flames, Smokeb	Mechanical Suffocation	Firearms	All Other
1999g	97,860	42,401	13,162	12,186	3,885	3,529	3,348	1,618	824	16,907
2000	97,900	43,354	13,322	12,757	4,313	3,482	3,377	1,335	776	15,184
2001	101,537	43,788	15,019	14,078	4,185	3,281	3,309	1,370	802	15,705
2002	106,742	45,380	16,257	17,550	4,128	3,447	3,159	1,389	762	13,670
2003h	109,277	44,757	17,229	19,457	4,272	3,306	3,369	1,309	730	14,850
2004h	112,000	45,300	17,500	20,000	4,500	3,600	3,600	1,400	750	15,350
2005i	113,000	45,800	17,700	20,900	4,600	3,600	3,100	1,400	730	15,170

Changes										
1995 to 2005	+20%	+6%	(j)	(j)	+44%	(j)	−18%	(j)	−40%	(j)
2004 to 2005	+1%	+1%	+1%	+5%	+2%	0%	−14%	0%	−3%	−1%

Source: National Center for Health Statistics and National Safety Council. See Technical Appendix for comparability.
a Includes drowning in water transport accidents.
b Includes burns by fire, and deaths resulting from conflagration regardless of nature of injury.
c Comparable data not available.
d In 1948, a revision was made in the International Classification of Diseases. The first figures for 1948 are comparable with those for earlier years, the second with those for later years.
e Data are not comparable to previous years shown due to classification changes in 1958 and 1968.
f Excludes water transport drownings.
g In 1999, a revision was made in the International Classification of Diseases. See the Technical Appendix for comparability.
h Revised.
i Preliminary.
j Comparison not valid because of change in classifications (see footnote "g").

UNINTENTIONAL-INJURY DEATH RATES[a] FOR PRINCIPAL TYPES, UNITED STATES, 1903–1998

Year	Total	Motor-Vehicle	Falls	Drowning[b]	Fires/Burns[c]	Ingest. of Food/Object	Firearms	Poison (Solid, Liquid)	Poison (Gas, Vapor)	All Other
1903	87.2	(d)	(d)	11.4	(d)	(d)	3.1	(d)	(d)	72.7
1904	86.6	(d)	(d)	11.3	(d)	(d)	3.4	(d)	(d)	71.9
1905	84.2	(d)	(d)	11.1	(d)	(d)	2.4	(d)	(d)	70.7
1906	93.2	0.5	(d)	11.0	(d)	(d)	2.4	(d)	(d)	79.3
1907	93.6	0.8	(d)	10.4	(d)	(d)	2.0	(d)	(d)	80.4
1908	81.2	0.9	(d)	10.5	(d)	(d)	2.1	(d)	(d)	67.7
1909	80.1	1.4	(d)	9.4	(d)	(d)	1.8	(d)	(d)	67.5
1910	84.4	2.0	(d)	9.4	(d)	(d)	2.1	(d)	(d)	70.9
1911	84.7	2.5	(d)	9.6	(d)	(d)	2.2	(d)	(d)	70.4
1912	82.5	3.3	(d)	9.0	(d)	(d)	2.2	(d)	(d)	68.0
1913	85.5	4.4	15.5	10.6	9.1	(d)	2.5	3.3	(d)	40.1
1914	78.6	4.8	15.1	8.8	9.1	(d)	2.3	3.3	(d)	35.2
1915	76.7	6.6	14.9	8.6	8.4	(d)	2.1	2.8	(d)	33.3
1916	84.1	8.1	14.9	8.7	9.3	(d)	2.2	2.8	(d)	38.1
1917	88.2	10.0	14.7	7.4	10.5	(d)	2.2	2.7	(d)	40.7
1918	82.1	10.3	12.8	6.8	9.9	(d)	2.4	2.6	(d)	37.3
1919	71.9	10.7	11.4	6.9	8.7	(d)	2.7	3.0	(d)	28.5
1920	71.2	11.7	11.8	5.7	8.7	(d)	2.5	3.1	(d)	27.7
1921	68.4	12.9	11.3	7.2	6.9	(d)	2.6	2.7	(d)	24.8
1922	69.4	13.9	12.0	6.4	7.5	(d)	2.6	2.5	(d)	24.5
1923	75.7	16.5	12.6	6.1	8.1	(d)	2.6	2.5	2.4	24.9
1924	75.6	17.1	12.9	6.5	8.4	(d)	2.5	2.4	2.5	23.3
1925	78.4	19.1	13.4	6.3	7.4	(d)	2.4	2.3	2.4	25.1
1926	78.7	20.1	13.9	6.4	7.5	(d)	2.4	2.2	2.7	23.5
1927	78.4	21.8	13.9	6.8	6.9	(d)	2.5	2.2	2.3	22.0
1928	79.3	23.4	14.1	7.1	7.0	(d)	2.4	2.3	2.3	20.7
1929	80.8	25.7	14.5	6.2	6.7	(d)	2.6	2.1	2.3	20.7
1930	80.5	26.7	14.7	6.1	6.6	(d)	2.6	2.1	2.0	19.7
1931	78.5	27.2	14.6	6.1	5.7	(d)	2.5	2.1	1.7	18.6
1932	71.3	23.6	14.9	6.0	5.7	(d)	2.4	1.8	1.7	15.2
1933	72.4	25.0	15.1	5.7	5.4	(d)	2.4	1.7	1.3	15.8
1934	79.9	28.6	16.4	5.6	5.9	(d)	2.4	1.7	1.3	18.0
1935	78.4	28.6	16.8	5.3	5.7	(d)	2.2	1.7	1.3	16.8
1936	85.9	29.7	18.4	5.2	6.2	(d)	2.2	1.7	1.3	21.2
1937	81.7	30.8	17.5	5.5	5.6	(d)	2.0	1.7	1.3	17.3
1938	72.3	25.1	17.9	5.3	5.0	(d)	2.1	1.6	1.1	14.2
1939	70.8	24.7	17.9	4.9	5.1	(d)	2.0	1.5	1.1	13.6
1940	73.4	26.1	17.7	4.7	5.7	(d)	1.8	1.4	1.2	14.8
1941	76.3	30.0	17.1	4.8	5.2	(d)	1.8	1.3	1.1	15.0
1942	71.6	21.1	16.9	5.0	5.9	(d)	2.0	1.2	1.3	18.2
1943	73.8	17.8	18.4	5.3	6.5	0.7	1.7	1.3	1.5	20.6
1944	71.7	18.3	17.3	4.9	6.3	0.7	1.8	1.5	1.4	19.5
1945	72.4	21.2	18.0	5.0	6.0	0.7	1.8	1.5	1.6	16.6
1946	70.0	23.9	16.5	4.6	5.6	0.8	2.0	1.4	1.3	13.9
1947	69.4	22.8	17.1	4.8	5.6	0.8	1.7	1.3	1.3	14.0
1948 (5th Rev.)[e]	67.1	22.1	17.0	4.4	5.3	0.9	1.5	1.2	1.4	13.3
1948 (6th Rev.)[e]	63.7	22.1	15.1	4.5	4.7	0.9	1.6	1.1	1.4	12.3
1949	60.6	21.3	15.0	4.5	4.0	0.9	1.6	1.1	1.1	11.1
1950	60.3	23.0	13.7	4.1	4.2	0.9	1.4	1.1	1.2	10.7
1951	62.5	24.1	13.9	4.2	4.4	1.0	1.5	1.0	1.1	11.3
1952	61.8	24.3	13.5	4.2	4.5	0.9	1.4	0.9	0.9	11.2
1953	60.1	24.0	13.0	4.3	4.2	1.0	1.4	0.9	0.8	10.2
1954	55.9	22.1	12.3	3.9	3.8	1.0	1.4	0.8	0.8	9.8
1955	56.9	23.4	12.3	3.9	3.9	1.0	1.3	0.9	0.7	9.5
1956	56.6	23.7	12.1	3.7	3.8	1.1	1.3	0.8	0.7	9.4
1957	55.9	22.7	12.1	3.9	3.7	1.2	1.4	0.8	0.7	9.4
1958	52.3	21.3	10.5	3.8[f]	4.2[f]	1.3[f]	1.3	0.8	0.7	8.4
1959	52.2	21.5	10.6	3.7	3.9	1.2	1.3	0.9	0.7	8.4
1960	52.1	21.2	10.6	3.6	4.3	1.3	1.3	0.9	0.7	8.2
1961	50.4	20.8	10.2	3.6	3.9	1.4	1.2	1.0	0.7	7.6
1962	52.3	22.0	10.5	3.5	4.1	1.0	1.1	1.0	0.7	8.4
1963	53.4	23.1	10.3	3.4	4.3	1.0	1.2	1.1	0.8	8.2
1964	54.9	25.0	9.9	3.5	3.9	1.0	1.2	1.1	0.7	8.4
1965	55.8	25.4	10.3	3.5	3.8	1.0	1.2	1.1	0.8	8.7
1966	58.1	27.1	10.3	3.6	4.8	0.9	1.3	1.2	0.8	8.1
1967	57.3	26.8	10.2	3.6	3.8	1.0	1.5	1.3	0.8	8.3
1968	57.6	27.5	9.4	3.7[f]	3.7[f]	1.6[f]	1.2[f]	1.3	0.8	8.4
1969	57.8	27.7	8.9	3.8	3.6	1.8	1.2	1.5	0.8	8.5
1970	56.2	26.8	8.3	3.9	3.3	1.4	1.2	1.8	0.8	8.7
1971	54.8	26.3	8.1	3.6	3.3	1.4	1.1	1.8	0.8	8.4
1972	55.2	26.9	8.0	3.6	3.2	1.4	1.2	1.8	0.8	8.3
1973	54.8	26.3	7.8	4.1	3.1	1.4	1.2	1.7	0.8	8.4

See source and footnotes on page 45.

UNINTENTIONAL-INJURY DEATH RATES[a] FOR PRINCIPAL TYPES, UNITED STATES, 1903–1998, Cont.

Year	Total	Motor-Vehicle	Falls	Drowning[b]	Fires/Burns[c]	Ingest. of Food/Object	Firearms	Poison (Solid, Liquid)	Poison (Gas, Vapor)	All Other
1974	49.0	21.8	7.7	3.7	2.9	1.4	1.2	1.8	0.7	7.8
1975	47.8	21.3	6.9	3.7	2.8	1.4	1.1	2.2	0.7	7.7
1976	46.3	21.6	6.5	3.1	2.9	1.4	0.9	1.9	0.7	7.3
1977	47.0	22.5	6.3	3.2	2.9	1.4	0.9	1.5	0.7	7.6
1978	47.5	23.6	6.2	3.2	2.8	1.4	0.8	1.4	0.8	7.3
1979	46.9	23.8	5.9	3.1	2.7	1.4	0.9	1.4	0.7	7.0
1980	46.5	23.4	5.9	3.2	2.6	1.4	0.9	1.4	0.5	7.2
1981	43.9	22.4	5.5	2.7	2.5	1.5	0.8	1.4	0.6	6.5
1982	40.6	19.8	5.2	2.7	2.2	1.4	0.8	1.5	0.5	6.5
1983	39.6	19.0	5.1	2.7	2.2	1.4	0.7	1.4	0.5	6.6
1984	39.4	19.6	5.1	2.3	2.1	1.5	0.7	1.6	0.5	6.0
1985	39.3	19.3	5.0	2.2	2.1	1.5	0.7	1.7	0.5	6.3
1986	39.7	19.9	4.8	2.4	2.0	1.5	0.6	2.0	0.4	6.1
1987	39.2	19.9	4.8	2.1	1.9	1.5	0.6	1.8	0.4	6.2
1988	39.7	20.1	4.9	2.0	2.0	1.6	0.6	2.2	0.4	5.9
1989	38.5	19.3	4.9	1.9	1.9	1.4	0.6	2.3	0.4	5.8
1990	36.9	18.8	4.9	1.9	1.7	1.3	0.6	2.0	0.3	5.4
1991	35.4	17.3	5.0	1.8	1.6	1.3	0.6	2.3	0.3	5.2
1992	34.0	16.1	5.0	1.4	1.6	1.2	0.6	2.5	0.2	5.4
1993	35.1	16.3	5.1	1.5	1.5	1.2	0.6	3.1	0.3	5.5
1994	35.1	16.3	5.2	1.5	1.5	1.2	0.5	3.2	0.3	5.4
1995	35.5	16.5	5.3	1.7	1.4	1.2	0.5	3.2	0.2	5.5
1996	35.8	16.5	5.6	1.5	1.4	1.2	0.4	3.3	0.2	5.7
1997	35.7	16.2	5.8	1.5	1.3	1.2	0.4	3.6	0.2	5.5
1998	36.2	16.1	6.0	1.6	1.2	1.3	0.3	3.8	0.2	5.7

UNINTENTIONAL-INJURY DEATH RATES[a] FOR PRINCIPAL TYPES, UNITED STATES, 1999–2005

Year	Total	Motor-Vehicle	Falls	Poisoning	Ingest. of Food/Object	Drowning[g]	Fires, Flames Smoke[c]	Mechanical Suffocation	Firearms	All Other
1999[h]	35.9	15.5	4.8	4.5	1.4	1.3	1.2	0.6	0.3	6.3
2000	35.6	15.7	4.8	4.6	1.6	1.3	1.2	0.5	0.3	5.5
2001	35.6	15.4	5.3	4.9	1.5	1.2	1.2	0.5	0.3	5.5
2002	37.1	15.8	5.6	6.4	1.4	1.2	1.1	0.5	0.3	4.7
2003[i]	37.6	15.4	5.9	6.7	1.5	1.1	1.2	0.4	0.3	5.1
2004[i]	38.1	15.4	6.0	6.8	1.5	1.2	1.2	0.5	0.3	5.2
2005[j]	38.1	15.5	6.0	7.1	1.6	1.2	1.0	0.5	0.2	5.1
Changes										
1995 to 2005	+7%	−6%	(k)	(k)	+33%	(k)	−29%	(k)	−60%	(k)
2004 to 2005	0%	+1%	0%	+4%	+7%	0%	−17%	0%	−33%	−2%

Source: National Safety Council estimates. See Technical Appendix for comparability.
[a] Deaths per 100,000 population.
[b] Includes drowning in water transport accidents.
[c] Includes burns by fire, and deaths resulting from conflagration regardless of nature of injury.
[d] Comparable data not available.
[e] In 1948, a revision was made in the International Classification of Diseases. The first figures for 1948 are comparable with those for earlier years, the second with those for later years.
[f] Data are not comparable to previous years shown due to classification changes in 1958 and 1968.
[g] Excludes water transport drownings.
[h] In 1999, a revision was made in the International Classification of Diseases. See the Technical Appendix for comparability.
[i] Revised.
[j] Preliminary.
[k] Comparison not valid because of change in classifications (see footnote "h").

OCCUPATIONAL

INJURY FACTS®

NATIONAL SAFETY COUNCIL

Between 1912 and 2005, unintentional work deaths per 100,000 population were reduced 92% , from 21 to 1.7. In 1912, an estimated 18,000 to 21,000 workers' lives were lost. In 2005, in a work force nearly quadrupled in size and producing 10 times the goods and services, there were only 4,961 accidental work deaths.

In addition to unintentional (accidental) fatal work injuries, 741 homicides and suicides occurred in the workplace in 2005. These intentional injuries are not included in the unintentional-injury data shown here.

The State Data section, which begins on page 150, shows fatal occupational injuries and nonfatal injury and illness incidence rates by state.

Unintentional-Injury Deaths **4,961**
Unintentional-Injury Deaths per 100,000 Workers **3.5**
Disabling Unintentional Injuries **3,700,000**
Workers **142,946,000**
Costs . . . . **$160.4 billion**

UNINTENTIONAL INJURIES AT WORK BY INDUSTRY, UNITED STATES, 2005

Industry Division	Workers[a] (000)	Deaths[a]		Deaths per 100,000 Workers[a]		Disabling Injuries
		2005	Change from 2004	2005	Change from 2004	
All Industries[b]	**142,946**	**4,961**	**−1%**	**3.5**	**−2%**	**3,700,000**
Agriculture[c]	2,141	696	+7%	31.6	+6%	80,000
Mining[c]	620	154	+1%	24.8	−12%	20,000
Construction	10,740	1,155	−4%	10.8	−8%	480,000
Manufacturing	16,173	358	−15%	2.2	−14%	450,000
Wholesale trade	4,570	192	+3%	4.2	+3%	130,000
Retail trade	16,733	197	+4%	1.2	+1%	470,000
Transportation & warehousing	4,989	827	+6%	16.6	−1%	270,000
Utilities	834	29	−43%	3.5	−43%	20,000
Information	3,209	57	+16%	1.8	+19%	40,000
Financial activities	9,975	65	−4%	0.7	−6%	90,000
Professional & business services	13,891	441	+10%	3.2	+9%	180,000
Educational & health services	18,834	119	−3%	0.6	−5%	530,000
Leisure & hospitality	11,618	112	−22%	1.0	−24%	240,000
Other services[c]	6,990	148	+3%	2.1	+1%	140,000
Government	21,629	404	−7%	1.9	−8%	560,000

Source: Deaths from Bureau of Labor Statistics, Census of Fatal Occupational Injuries. All other figures are National Safety Council estimates based on data from the Bureau of Labor Statistics.
Note: The National Safety Council adopted the Bureau of Labor Statistics' Census of Fatal Occupational Injuries (CFOI), beginning with the 1992 data year, as the authoritative count of work-related deaths. See the Technical Appendix for additional information.
[a] Deaths include persons of all ages. Workers and death rates include persons 16 years and older.
[b] All Industries includes 7 deaths for which industry could not be determined.
[c] Agriculture includes forestry, fishing, and hunting. Mining includes oil and gas extraction. Other services excludes public administration.

UNINTENTIONAL WORK-INJURY DEATHS AND DEATH RATES, UNITED STATES, 1992–2005

Year	Deaths	Workers (in thousands)	Death per 100,000 workers
1992	4,965	119,168	4.2
1993	5,034	120,778	4.2
1994	5,338	124,470	4.3
1995	5,015	126,248	4.0
1996	5,069	127,997	4.0
1997	5,160	130,810	3.9
1998	5,117	132,772	3.9
1999	5,184	134,688	3.8
2000	5,022	136,402	3.7
2001	5,042	136,246	3.7
2002	4,726	137,731	3.4
2003[a]	4,725	138,988	3.4
2004[a]	4,999	140,504	3.6
2005[b]	4,961	142,946	3.5

Source: Deaths are from the Bureau of Labor Statistics, Census of Fatal Occupational Injuries. Employment is from the Bureau of Labor Statistics and is based on the Current Population Survey. All other data are National Safety Council estimates.
Note: Deaths include persons of all ages. Workers and death rates include persons 16 years and older. Workers are persons ages 16 and older gainfully employed, including owners, managers, other paid employees, the self-employed, unpaid family workers, and active-duty resident military personnel. Because of adoption of the Census of Fatal Occupational Injuries, deaths and rates from 1992 to the present are not comparable to prior years. See the Technical Appendix for additional information.
[a] Revised.
[b] Preliminary.

WORKERS, UNINTENTIONAL-INJURY DEATHS, AND DEATH RATES, UNITED STATES, 1992–2005

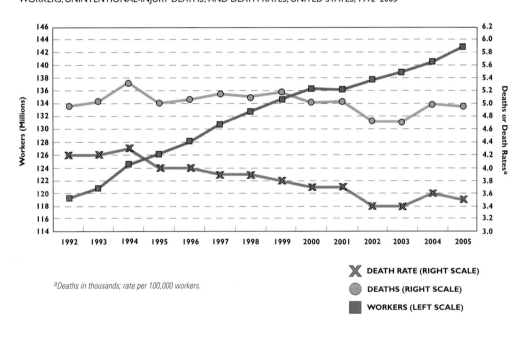

[a]Deaths in thousands; rate per 100,000 workers.

✕ DEATH RATE (RIGHT SCALE)
● DEATHS (RIGHT SCALE)
■ WORKERS (LEFT SCALE)

50

OCCUPATIONAL-INJURY DEATHS AND DEATH RATES, UNITED STATES, 1992–2002

Year	Total	Homicide & Suicide	Unintentional								
			All Industries[a]	Agri-culture[b]	Mining, Quarrying[c]	Construc-tion	Manufac-turing	Transpor-tation & Public Utilities	Trade[d]	Services[e]	Govern-ment
Deaths											
1992	6,217	1,252	4,965	779	175	889	707	767	415	601	586
1993	6,331	1,297	5,034	842	169	895	698	753	450	631	527
1994	6,632	1,294	5,338	814	177	1,000	734	819	492	676	534
1995	6,275	1,260	5,015	769	155	1,021	640	784	461	608	528
1996	6,202	1,133	5,069	762	151	1,025	660	883	451	615	321
1997	6,238	1,078	5,160	799	156	1,075	678	882	451	593	504
1998	6,055	938	5,117	808	143	1,136	631	830	443	634	465
1999	6,054	870	5,184	776	122	1,168	671	918	425	623	451
2000	5,920	898	5,022	693	153	1,114	624	872	447	643	460
2001	5,915	873[f]	5,042	714	169	1,183	546	844	431	636	507
2002	5,534	808	4,726	758	120	1,092	523	843	381	569	437
Deaths per 100,000 Workers											
1992	5.2	1.0	4.2	23.1	26.4	13.7	3.6	11.5	1.7	1.6	3.0
1993	5.2	1.0	4.2	26.0	25.3	13.3	3.6	11.0	1.8	1.6	2.6
1994	5.3	1.0	4.3	22.8	26.5	14.4	3.7	11.6	1.9	1.7	2.7
1995	4.9	1.0	4.0	21.4	24.8	14.3	3.1	11.0	1.8	1.5	2.7
1996	4.8	0.9	4.0	21.2	26.6	13.7	3.2	12.2	1.7	1.4	1.6
1997	4.8	0.8	3.9	22.5	24.7	13.7	3.3	11.6	1.7	1.3	2.6
1998	4.5	0.7	3.9	22.7	23.1	14.1	3.1	10.8	1.6	1.4	2.4
1999	4.5	0.6	3.8	22.6	21.7	13.8	3.4	11.5	1.5	1.3	2.2
2000	4.3	0.7	3.7	20.1	29.4	12.4	3.1	10.8	1.6	1.4	2.3
2001	4.3	0.6[f]	3.7	22.0	29.9	13.0	2.9	10.4	1.6	1.3	2.5
2002	4.0	0.6	3.4	21.8	23.3	11.9	2.9	10.5	1.4	1.1	2.1

Source: Deaths are from Bureau of Labor Statistics, Census of Fatal Occupational Injuries. Rates are National Safety Council estimates based on Bureau of Labor Statistics employment data. Deaths include persons of all ages. Death rates include persons 16 years and older. Industry divisions based on the Standard Industrial Classification Manual.
[a] Includes deaths with industry unknown.
[b] Agriculture includes forestry, fishing, and agricultural services.
[c] Mining includes oil and gas extraction.
[d] Trade includes wholesale and retail trade.
[e] Services includes finance, insurance, and real estate.
[f] Excludes 2,886 homicides of workers on September 11, 2001.

OCCUPATIONAL-INJURY DEATHS AND DEATH RATES, UNITED STATES, 2003–2005

Year	Total	Homicide & Suicide	Unintentional															
			All Industries[a]	Agriculture, Forestry, Fishing & Hunting	Mining	Construction	Manufacturing	Wholesale Trade	Retail Trade	Transportation & Warehousing	Utilities	Information	Financial Activities	Professional & Business Services	Educational & Health Services	Leisure & Hospitality	Other Services	Government
Deaths																		
2003	5,575	850	4,725	676	141	1,094	379	169	148	735	29	57	82	396	116	142	123	434
2004[b]	5,764	765	4,999	652	152	1,203	422	187	189	779	51	49	68	401	123	144	144	434
2005[c]	5,702	741	4,961	696	154	1,155	358	192	197	827	29	57	65	441	119	112	148	404
Deaths per 100,000 Workers																		
2003	4.0	0.6	3.4	30.0	26.9	11.4	2.3	3.8	0.9	16.0	3.3	1.6	0.9	2.9	0.6	1.3	1.8	2.1
2004[b]	4.1	0.5	3.6	29.7	28.3	11.7	2.6	4.1	1.2	16.7	6.1	1.5	0.7	2.9	0.7	1.3	2.1	2.0
2005[c]	4.0	0.5	3.5	31.6	24.8	10.8	2.2	4.2	1.2	16.6	3.5	1.8	0.7	3.2	0.6	1.0	2.1	1.9

Source: Deaths are from Bureau of Labor Statistics, Census of Fatal Occupational Injuries. Rates are National Safety Council estimates based on Bureau of Labor Statistics employment data. Deaths include persons of all ages. Death rates include persons 16 years and older. Industry divisions based on the North American Industry Classification System.
[a] Includes deaths with industry unknown.
[b] Revised.
[c] Preliminary.

The true cost to the nation, to employers, and to individuals of work-related deaths and injuries is much greater than the cost of workers' compensation insurance alone. The figures presented below show the National Safety Council's estimates of the total economic costs of occupational deaths and injuries. Cost estimating procedures were revised for the 1993 edition of *Accident Facts*® and additional revisions were made for the 2005–2006 edition. For this reason, costs should not be compared to prior years.

TOTAL COST IN 2005................. **$160.4 billion**

Includes wage and productivity losses of $80.0 billion, medical costs of $31.3 billion, and administrative expenses of $34.4 billion. Includes employers' uninsured costs of $10.7 billion such as the money value of time lost by workers other than those with disabling injuries, who are directly or indirectly involved in injuries, and the cost of time required to investigate injuries, write up injury reports, etc. Also includes damage to motor vehicles in work injuries of $1.7 billion and fire losses of $2.3 billion.

Cost per Worker **$1,100**
This figure indicates the value of goods or services each worker must produce to offset the cost of work injuries. It is *not* the average cost of a work injury.

Cost per Death **$1,190,000**
Cost per Disabling Injury **$38,000**

These figures include estimates of wage losses, medical expenses, administrative expenses, and employer costs, and exclude property damage costs except to motor-vehicles.

TIME LOST BECAUSE OF WORK INJURIES

DAYS LOST
TOTAL TIME LOST IN 2005 .... **120,000,000**
Due to Injuries in 2005 .... **80,000,000**
Includes primarily the actual time lost during the year from disabling injuries, except that it does not include time lost on the day of the injury or time required for further medical treatment or check-up following the injured person's return to work.

Fatalities are included at an average loss of 150 days per case, and permanent impairments are included at actual days lost plus an allowance for lost efficiency resulting from the impairment.

Not included is time lost by persons with nondisabling injuries or other persons directly or indirectly involved in the incidents.

DAYS LOST
Due to Injuries in Prior Years **40,000,000**
This is an indicator of the productive time lost in 2005 due to permanently disabling injuries that occurred in prior years.

DAYS LOST
TIME LOSS IN FUTURE YEARS
FROM 2005 INJURIES **65,000,000**
Includes time lost in future years due to on-the-job deaths and permanently disabling injuries that occurred in 2005.

WORKER DEATHS AND INJURIES ON AND OFF THE JOB

52

Nine out of 10 deaths and more than two thirds of the disabling injuries suffered by workers in 2005 occurred off the job. The ratios of off-the-job deaths and injuries to on-the-job were 9.9 to 1 and 2.2 to 1, respectively.

Production time lost due to off-the-job injuries totaled about 195,000,000 days in 2005, compared with 80,000,000 days lost by workers injured on the job.

Production time lost in future years due to off-the-job injuries in 2005 will total an estimated 470,000,000 days, more than seven times the 65,000,000 days lost in future years from 2005's on-the-job injuries.

Off-the-job injuries to workers cost the nation at least $223.7 billion in 2005 compared to $160.4 billion for on-the-job injuries.

WORKERS' ON- AND OFF-THE-JOB INJURIES, UNITED STATES, 2005

Place	Deaths		Disabling Injuries	
	Number	Rate[a]	Number	Rate[a]
On- and off-the-job	54,261	0.013	11,900,000	2.8
On-the-job	4,961	0.003	3,700,000	2.4
Off-the-job	49,300	0.018	8,200,000	3.0
Motor-vehicle	24,100	0.084	1,300,000	4.5
Public nonmotor-vehicle	10,000	0.023	3,300,000	7.4
Home	15,200	0.008	3,600,000	1.8

Source: National Safety Council estimates. Procedures for allocating time spent on and off the job were revised for the 1990 edition. Rate basis changed to 200,000 hours for the 1998 edition. Death and injury rates are not comparable to rate estimates prior to the 1998 edition.
[a] *Per 200,000 hours exposure by place.*

WORKERS' ON- AND OFF-THE-JOB INJURIES, 2005

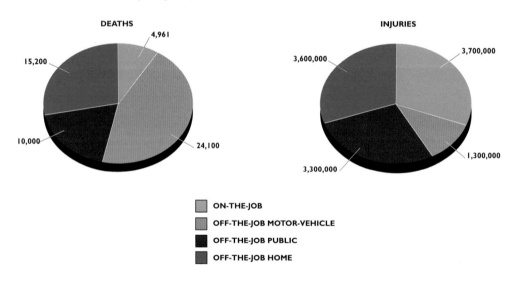

DEATHS

INJURIES

ON-THE-JOB
OFF-THE-JOB MOTOR-VEHICLE
OFF-THE-JOB PUBLIC
OFF-THE-JOB HOME

According to the National Academy of Social Insurance, an estimated $56.0 billion, including benefits under deductible provisions, was paid out under workers' compensation in 2004 (the latest year for which data were available), an increase of about 2.4% from 2003. Of this total, $29.9 billion was for income benefits and $26.1 billion was for medical and hospitalization costs. Private carriers paid about $28.3 billion of the total workers' compensation benefits in 2004. In 2004, approximately 125.9 million workers were covered by workers' compensation — an increase of 0.9% from the 124.7 million in 2003.

The table below shows the trend in the number of compensated or reported cases in each reporting state. Due to the differences in population, industries, and coverage of compensation laws, comparison among states should not be made.

WORKERS' COMPENSATION CASES, 2003–2005

State	Deaths[a]			Cases[a]			2004 Compensation Paid ($000)
	2005	2004	2003	2005	2004	2003	
Alabama[b]	86	66	83	18,848	19,201	19,739	575,697
Arkansas[b]	91	74	78	13,793	13,449	13,786	225,689
Colorado	—	113[c]	93[c]	—	29,231[c]	28,752[c]	834,594
Connecticut	66	70	59	53,786	56,362	56,524	684,930
District of Columbia	17	7	9	10,165	10,128	10,139	98,443
Florida[b]	253[c]	283[c]	301	66,891[c]	75,128[c]	78,636	2,759,712
Hawaii	—	32	26	—	26,321	28,668	271,290
Indiana	118	93	88	65,410	68,224	70,303	608,717
Iowa[b]	50	48	50	18,775	19,626	21,723	445,832
Louisiana[f]	66	61	54	13,047	17,859	10,419	589,209
Michigan	—	81	88	—	37,022	39,768	1,517,386
Minnesota[f]	42	52	48	—	123,960	127,610	933,975
Mississippi[b]	83	73	86	12,536	13,197	13,413	305,516
Missouri	89[c]	159	157	145,467	141,378	143,275	1,119,871
Montana	30	21	23	32,164	32,443	33,321	211,059
Nevada[f]	71	55	37	82,864	86,653	72,570	357,937
New Hampshire	24	23	20	47,711	50,334	52,366	213,964
New Mexico	—	33	22	—	37,874	37,408	196,123
North Carolina	138	157	186	64,975	65,881	60,050	1,159,117
North Dakota[d]	13	18	15	19,887	19,184	18,753	83,237
Ohio[f]	223	297	257	178,015	189,046	208,301	2,442,137
Oregon[f, g]	31	46	41	22,114	22,325	21,832	506,813
Pennsylvania[b]	122	130	140	102,259	93,566	99,161	2,594,238
Rhode Island[b]	4	2	12	6,971	7,226	7,391	142,268
Vermont	10	10	18	20,950	20,812	20,872	128,076
Washington	—	77	70	—	194,563	193,707	1,836,097

Source: Deaths and Cases—State workers' compensation authorities for calendar or fiscal year. States not listed did not respond to the survey. Compensation Paid — Sengupta, I., Reno, V., P., & Burton, J. F., Jr., (July, 2006). Workers' compensation: benefits, coverage, and costs, 2004. Washington DC: National Academy of Social Insurance.

Note: Dash (—) indicates data not available.

Definitions:
  Reported case—a reported case may or may not be work-related and may not receive compensation.
  Compensated case—a case determined to be work-related and for which compensation was paid.

[a]Reported cases involving medical and indemnity benefits, unless otherwise noted.
[b]Reported cases involving indemnity benefits only.
[c]Preliminary.
[d]Reported and closed or compensated cases.
[e]Closed or compensated cases involving indemnity benefits only.
[f]Closed or compensated cases only.
[g]Accepted disabling claims, including lost-time claims in which the worker misses 3 or more days of work, has a validated hospital admittance, or a fatal injury.
[h]First reported and compensated cases involving indemnity benefits only.

WORKERS' COMPENSATION CLAIMS COSTS, 2003–2004

Head injuries are the most costly workers' compensation claims.

The data in the graphs on this and the next page are from the National Council on Compensation Insurance's (NCCI) Detailed Claim Information (DCI) file, a stratified random sample of lost-time claims in 41 states. Total incurred costs consist of medical and indemnity payments plus case reserves on open claims, and are calculated as of the second report (18 months after the initial report of injury). Injuries that result in medical payments only, without lost time, are not included. For open claims, costs include all payments as of the second report plus case reserves for future payments. Because the estimates are based on a sample, they can be volatile from year to year due to the influence of a small but variable number of large claims.

The average cost for all claims combined in 2003–2004 was $19,382, up 9% from the 2002–2003 average of $17,787.

Cause of Injury. The most costly lost-time workers' compensation claims by cause of injury, according to the NCCI data, are for those resulting from motor-vehicle crashes. These injuries averaged $35,873 per workers' compensation claim filed in 2003 and 2004. The other causes with above average costs were those involving a fall or slip ($22,802).

Nature of Injury. The most costly lost-time workers' compensation claims by the nature of the injury are for those resulting from amputation. These injuries averaged $36,993 per workers' compensation claim filed in 2003 and 2004. The next highest costs were for injuries resulting in fracture ($25,711), and other trauma ($24,685).

Part of Body. The most costly lost-time workers' compensation claims are for those involving the head or central nervous system. These injuries averaged $42,110 per workers' compensation claim filed in 2003 and 2004. The next highest costs were for injuries involving multiple body parts ($32,637), and the neck ($28,239). Injuries to the arm/shoulder; hip, thigh, and pelvis; leg; and lower back also had above average costs.

AVERAGE TOTAL INCURRED COSTS PER CLAIM BY CAUSE OF INJURY, 2003–2004

AVERAGE TOTAL INCURRED COSTS PER CLAIM BY NATURE OF INJURY, 2003–2004

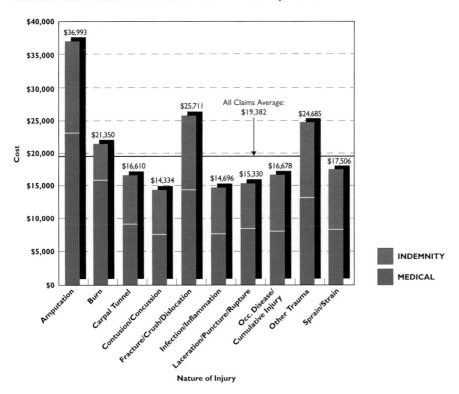

AVERAGE TOTAL INCURRED COSTS PER CLAIM BY PART OF BODY, 2003–2004

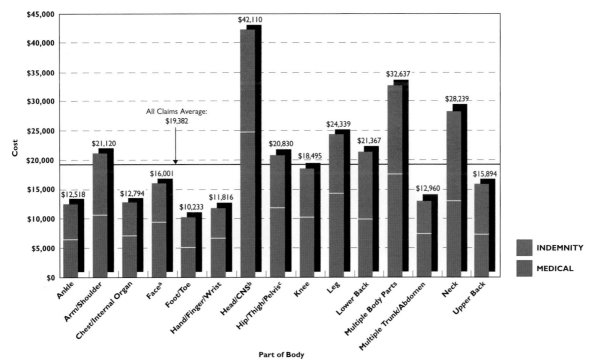

[a]Includes teeth, mouth, and eyes.
[b]Central nervous system.
[c]Includes sacrum and coccyx.
Please note that these are estimates based on a sample of claims reported to NCCI and can be volatile from year to year due to the influence of a small but variable number of large claims.

CAUSES OF WORK-RELATED DEATHS AND INJURIES

Incidents involving motor-vehicles are the leading cause of work-related deaths followed by contacts with objects or equipment and falls. For nonfatal cases with days away from work, contacts with objects or equipment is the leading cause followed by overexertion and falls

WORK-RELATED DEATHS AND INJURIES BY EVENT OR EXPOSURE, UNITED STATES, 2004

Event or Exposure	Deaths[s]
Total, all events or exposures	**5,764**
Contact with object or equipment	1,009
Struck against object	*17*
Struck by object	*602*
Caught in objects or equipment	*269*
Caught in collapsing materials	*117*
Fall	822
Fall to lower level	*738*
Fall on same level	*61*
Bodily reaction and exertion	8
Exposure to harmful substance	464
Contact with electric current	*254*
Contact with temperature extremes	*27*
Exposure to caustic or noxious substances	*116*
Oxygen deficiency	*65*
Drowning	51
In confined space	9
Transportation accidents	2,490
Motor-vehicle accidents	*2,114*
Highway accident	1,398
Nonhighway accident except rail, air, water	338
Pedestrian struck by vehicle, mobile equipment	378
Railway accident	*50*
Water vehicle accident	*91*
Aircraft accident	*231*
Fires, explosions	159
Fires	*84*
Explosions	*75*
Assaults and violent acts	809
By person	*559*
Self-inflicted	*206*
By animals	*40*
Other and nonclassifiable	3

Event or Exposure	Cases With Days Away From Work[b]
Total, all events or exposures	**1,259,320**
Contact with object or equipment	335,160
Struck against object	*83,330*
Struck by object	*170,080*
Caught in object or equipment	*55,160*
Caught in collapsing material	*350*
Fall	255,600
Fall to lower level	*79,800*
Fall on same level	*167,010*
Bodily reaction and exertion	511,750
Bodily reaction	*135,720*
Bending, climbing, crawling, reaching, twisting	54,130
Slips, trips, loss of balance—without fall	37,500
Overexertion	*316,670*
Overexertion in lifting	173,400
Repetitive motion	48,710
Exposure to harmful substance	52,830
Contact with electric current	*2,650*
Contact with temperature extremes	*18,960*
Exposure to caustic or noxious substances	*27,020*
Transportation accidents	62,860
Highway accident	*38,950*
Nonhighway accident except rail, air, water	*10,190*
Pedestrian struck by vehicle, mobile equipment	*10,760*
Railway accident	*270*
Water vehicle accident	*350*
Aircraft accident	*780*
Fires, explosions	2,420
Fires	*1,390*
Explosions	*1,030*
Assaults and violent acts	24,880
By person	*17,670*
By animals	*7,090*
Other and nonclassifiable	13,810

Source: Bureau of Labor Statistics.
[a]*Includes deaths among all workers.*
[b]*Includes cases with days away from work among private sector wage and salary workers. Excludes government employees, the self employed, and unpaid family workers.*

DEATHS[a] BY EVENT OR EXPOSURE, UNITED STATES, 2004

CASES WITH DAYS AWAY FROM WORK[b] BY EVENT OR EXPOSURE, UNITED STATES, 2004

- ■ BODILY REACTION AND EXERTION
- ■ FALL
- ■ CONTACT WITH OBJECT OR EQUIPMENT
- ■ OTHER AND NONCLASSIFIABLE
- ■ ASSAULTS AND VIOLENT ACTS
- ■ FIRES, EXPLOSIONS
- ■ TRANSPORTATION ACCIDENTS
- ■ EXPOSURE TO HARMFUL SUBSTANCE

[a]*Includes deaths among all workers.*
[b]*Includes cases with days away from work among private sector wage and salary workers. Excludes government employees, the self employed, and unpaid family workers.*

According to the Bureau of Labor Statistics, sprains and strains were the most common type of injury involving days away from work in 2004, accounting for 42% of the total 1,259,320 injuries in private industry. Bruises and contusions were the second most common, followed by cuts, lacerations, and punctures. Overall, the manufacturing, education and health services, and retail trade industry sectors had the highest number of injuries, combining to make up over 47% of the total.

NUMBER OF NONFATAL OCCUPATIONAL INJURIES AND ILLNESSES INVOLVING DAYS AWAY FROM WORK[a] BY NATURE OF INJURY AND INDUSTRY SECTOR, PRIVATE INDUSTRY, UNITED STATES, 2004

Nature of Injury	Private Sector[b,c]	Industry Sector								
		Manufac-turing	Education and Health Services	Retail Trade	Construc-tion	Trans. & Ware-housing[d]	Leisure and Hospitality	Prof. and Business Services	Wholesale Trade	All Other Sectors[b,e]
Total[c]	1,259,320	226,090	189,980	178,760	153,200	120,010	95,380	90,500	81,140	124,270
Sprains, strains	525,390	80,800	99,790	79,700	57,310	57,850	32,720	33,180	35,700	48,340
Fractures	94,040	18,470	10,210	11,830	15,790	7,440	5,920	6,550	6,310	11,530
Cuts, lacerations, punctures	114,140	25,600	5,290	17,640	22,040	5,020	14,200	7,980	6,320	10,050
Bruises, contusions	114,680	18,840	17,200	17,940	10,410	13,540	9,420	9,470	7,100	10,780
Heat burns	18,520	3,850	1,990	1,700	1,700	510	6,490	490	490	1,300
Chemical burns	7,360	2,060	1,150	1,120	810	360	430	570	310	540
Amputations	8,160	3,640	50	1,000	1,530	140	210	240	470	890
Carpal tunnel syndrome	18,710	6,470	2,150	2,110	1,090	870	770	1,810	800	2,640
Tendonitis	6,930	2,440	830	930	430	590	150	440	360	760
Multiple injuries	50,350	7,720	6,890	6,250	6,340	5,140	3,680	4,530	2,950	6,840
With fractures	9,960	2,200	1,050	880	1,880	680	260	910	490	1,600
With sprains	19,720	2,180	3,990	3,030	1,880	1,880	1,770	1,370	890	2,720
Soreness, Pain	104,560	15,200	19,230	14,510	10,720	11,520	7,960	7,620	8,100	9,710
Back pain	37,930	4,710	7,970	4,950	4,110	3,530	2,850	2,830	3,300	3,680
All other natures	196,480	40,990	25,200	24,030	25,040	17,010	13,440	17,620	12,240	20,910

Source: Bureau of Labor Statistics Occupational Injuries and Illnesses Profiles Data, accessed July 14, 2006 from http://data.bls.gov/GQT/servlet/StartProfile?data_tool=Profile.

[a]Days-away-from-work cases include those that result in days away from work with or without job transfer or restriction.
[b]Excludes farms with less than 11 employees.
[c]Data may not sum to row and column totals because of rounding and exclusion of nonclassifiable responses.
[d]Data for transportation do not reflect the changes OSHA made to its recordkeeping requirements effective January 1, 2002; therefore, estimates for these industries are not comparable with estimates for other industries.
[e]Includes Agriculture, Forestry, Fishing and Hunting; Financial Activities; Information; Mining (including oil and gas extraction); Other Services; and Utilities. Data for mining do not reflect the changes OSHA made to its recordkeeping requirements effective January 1, 2002; therefore, estimates for these industries are not comparable with estimates for other industries.

BENCHMARKING INCIDENCE RATES

Safety professionals in business and industry often want to compare, or benchmark, the occupational injury and illness incidence rates of their establishments with the national average rates compiled by the U.S. Bureau of Labor Statistics (BLS) through its annual Survey of Occupational Injuries and Illnesses.[a] The incidence rates published on the following pages are for 2005 and were compiled under the revised OSHA record-keeping requirements that became effective in 2002.

Step 1.

The first step in benchmarking is to calculate the incidence rates for the establishment. The basic formula for computing incidence rates is $(N \times 200,000)/EH$, or, the number of cases (N) multiplied by $200,000$ then divided by the number of hours worked (EH) by all employees during the time period, where $200,000$ is the base for 100 full-time workers (working 40 hours per week, 50 weeks per year). Because the BLS rates are based on reports from entire establishments, both the OSHA 300 Log and the number of hours worked should cover the whole establishment being benchmarked. The hours worked and the log also should cover the same time period, (e.g., a month, quarter, or full year). The following rates may be calculated.

Total Cases — the incidence rate of total OSHA-recordable cases per 200,000 hours worked. For this rate, N is the total number of cases on the OSHA 300 Log.

Cases With Days Away From Work or Job Transfer or Restriction — the incidence rate of cases with days away from work, or job transfer, or restriction. N is the count of cases with a check in column H or column I of the OSHA 300 Log.

Cases With Days Away From Work — the incidence rate of cases with days away from work. N is the count of cases with a check in column H of the OSHA 300 Log.

Cases With Job Transfer or Restriction — the incidence rate of cases with job transfer or restriction, but no days away from work. N is the count of cases with a check in column I of the OSHA 300 Log.

Other Recordable Cases — the incidence rate of recordable cases without days away from work or job transfer or restriction. N is the count of cases with a check in column J of the OSHA 300 Log.

In the flow chart on the opposite page, post the number of cases to each box in the top row and the number of employee hours worked in its box. Then use the formula to calculate the rates and write them in the last row of boxes in Step 1.

Step 2.

After computing one or more of the rates, the next step is to determine the North American Industry Classification System (NAICS) code for the establishment.[b] (NAICS replaced the Standard Industrial Classification [SIC] code beginning in 2003.) This code is used to find the appropriate BLS rate for comparison. NAICS codes may be found on the Internet at www.census.gov/naics. The site also contains a crosswalk between NAICS and SIC codes. Otherwise, call a regional BLS office for assistance.

Write the establishment's NAICS code in the box in Step 2 of the flow chart.

Step 3.

Once the NAICS code is known, the national average incidence rates may be found by (a) consulting the table of rates on pages 62–64, (b) visiting the BLS Internet site (www.bls.gov/iif), or (c) by calling a regional BLS office. Note that some tables on the Internet site provide incidence rates by size of establishment and rate quartiles within each NAICS code. These rates may be useful for a more precise comparison. Note that the incidence rates for 2001 and earlier years were compiled under the old OSHA record-keeping requirements in effect at that time. Caution must be used in comparing rates computed for 2002 and later years with earlier years — keeping in mind the differences in record-keeping requirements.

In the flow chart on the opposite page, post the rates from the BLS survey to the boxes in Step 3. Now compare these with the rates calculated in Step 1.

An alternative way of benchmarking is to compare the current incidence rates for an establishment to its own prior historical rates to determine if the rates are improving and if progress is satisfactory (using criteria set by the organization).

[a]Bureau of Labor Statistics. (1997). BLS Handbook of Methods. *Washington, DC: U.S. Government Printing Office (or on the Internet at http://www.bls.gov/opub/hom/home.htm).*
[b]Executive Office of the President, Office of Management and Budget. (2002). North American Industry Classification System, United States 2002. *Springfield, VA: National Technical Information Service.*

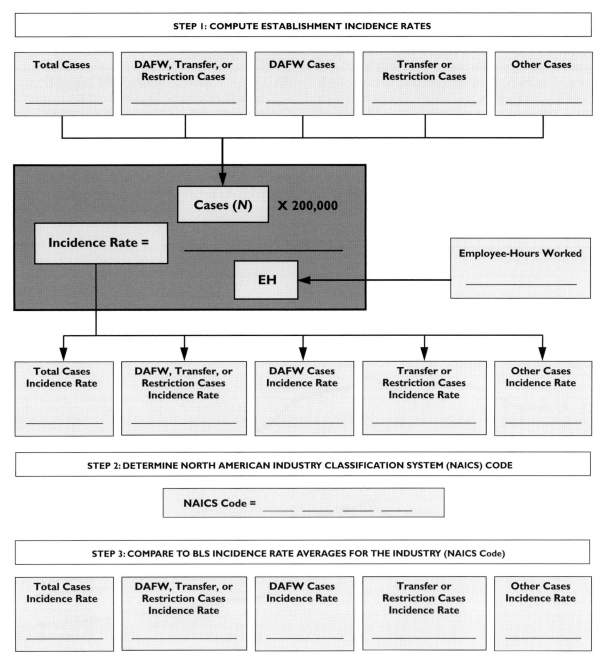

STEP 1: COMPUTE ESTABLISHMENT INCIDENCE RATES

Total Cases	DAFW, Transfer, or Restriction Cases	DAFW Cases	Transfer or Restriction Cases	Other Cases

Cases (N) X 200,000

Incidence Rate =

EH

Employee-Hours Worked

Total Cases Incidence Rate	DAFW, Transfer, or Restriction Cases Incidence Rate	DAFW Cases Incidence Rate	Transfer or Restriction Cases Incidence Rate	Other Cases Incidence Rate

STEP 2: DETERMINE NORTH AMERICAN INDUSTRY CLASSIFICATION SYSTEM (NAICS) CODE

NAICS Code = _____ _____ _____ _____

STEP 3: COMPARE TO BLS INCIDENCE RATE AVERAGES FOR THE INDUSTRY (NAICS Code)

Total Cases Incidence Rate	DAFW, Transfer, or Restriction Cases Incidence Rate	DAFW Cases Incidence Rate	Transfer or Restriction Cases Incidence Rate	Other Cases Incidence Rate

See page 58 for detailed instructions.
DAFW = Days Away From Work

TRENDS IN OCCUPATIONAL INCIDENCE RATES

Incidence rates continue recent downward trend.

Four of the five occupational injury and illness incidence rates published by the Bureau of Labor Statistics for 2005 decreased from 2005. The incidence rate for total recordable cases was 4.6 per 100 full-time workers in 2005, down 4% from the 2004 rate of 4.8. The incidence rate for total cases with days away from work, job transfer, or restriction was 2.4, a decrease of 4%. The incidence rate for cases with days away from work was 1.4 in 2005, unchanged from 2004. The incidence rate for cases with job transfer or restriction was 1.0 in 2004, down 9% from 1.1 in 2004. The incidence rate for other recordable cases was 2.2, down 4% from the 2004 rate of 2.3.

There have been several changes that affect comparability of incidence rates from year to year. The North American Industry Classification System (NAICS) replaced the Standard Industrial Classification (SIC) system beginning with the 2003 survey of occupational injuries and illnesses. Revisions to the Occupational Safety and Health Administration's (OSHA) occupational injury and illness recordkeeping requirements became effective in 2002. Beginning with 1992, the Bureau of Labor Statistics revised its annual survey to include only nonfatal cases and stopped publishing the incidence rate of lost workdays.

OCCUPATIONAL INJURY AND ILLNESS INCIDENCE RATES, BUREAU OF LABOR STATISTICS, UNITED STATES, 1985–2005

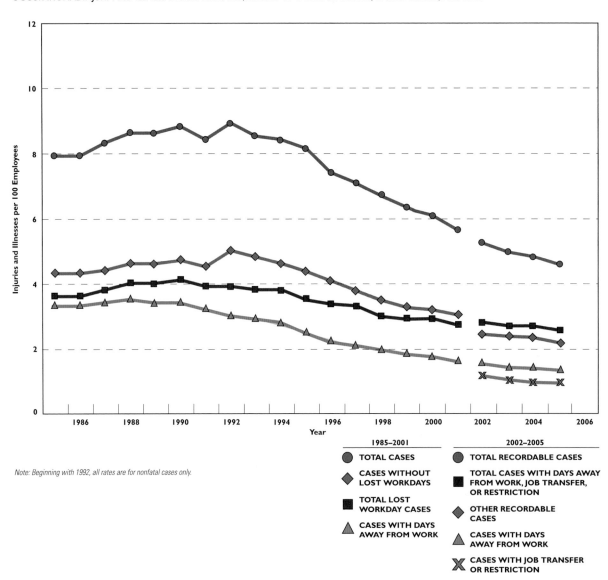

Note: Beginning with 1992, all rates are for nonfatal cases only.

OCCUPATIONAL INJURIES AND ILLNESSES

The tables below and on pages 62-64 present the results of the 2005 Survey of Occupational Injuries and Illnesses conducted by the Bureau of Labor Statistics (BLS), U.S. Department of Labor. The survey collects data on injuries and illnesses (from the OSHA 300 Log) and employee-hours worked from a nationwide sample of about 182,400 establishments representing the private sector of the economy. The survey excludes public employees, private households, the self-employed, and farms with fewer than 11 employees. The incidence rates give the number of cases per 100 full-time workers per year using 200,000 employee-hours as the equivalent. Definitions of the terms are given in the Glossary on page 183.

Beginning with 1992 data, the BLS revised its annual survey to include only nonfatal cases and stopped publishing incidence rates of lost workdays. Beginning with 2003 data, the BLS adopted the North American Industry Classification System for publication of the incidence rates by industry.

BLS ESTIMATES OF NONFATAL OCCUPATIONAL INJURY AND ILLNESS INCIDENCE RATES AND NUMBER OF INJURIES AND ILLNESSES BY INDUSTRY SECTOR, 2005

Industry Sector	Total Recordable Cases	Cases With Days Away From Work, Job Transfer, or Restriction			Other Recordable Cases
		Total	Cases With Days Away From Work	Cases With Job Transfer or Restriction	
Incidence Rate per 100 Full-Time Workers[c]					
Private Sector[d]	**4.6**	**2.4**	**1.4**	**1.0**	**2.2**
Goods Producing[d]	6.2	3.4	1.8	1.6	2.8
Natural Resources and Mining[d]	5.1	2.9	1.8	1.0	2.2
Agriculture, forestry, fishing & hunting[d]	6.1	3.3	2.1	1.2	2.8
Mining	3.6	2.2	1.5	0.8	1.4
Construction	6.3	3.4	2.4	1.0	2.9
Manufacturing	6.3	3.5	1.5	2.0	2.8
Service Providing	4.1	2.1	1.2	0.9	2.0
Trade, Transportation, and Utilities	5.2	3.0	1.7	1.3	2.2
Wholesale trade	4.5	2.7	1.5	1.2	1.8
Retail trade	5.0	2.6	1.5	1.2	2.4
Transportation and warehousing	7.0	4.6	2.9	1.7	2.4
Utilities	4.6	2.4	1.3	1.0	2.3
Information	2.1	1.1	0.7	0.4	1.0
Financial Activities	1.7	0.8	0.5	0.2	0.9
Professional and Business Services	2.4	1.2	0.7	0.5	1.2
Education and Health Services	5.5	2.6	1.5	1.1	2.9
Leisure and Hospitality	4.7	1.8	1.1	0.7	2.9
Other Services	3.2	1.5	1.0	0.5	1.7
Number of Injuries and Illnesses (in thousands)					
Private Sector[d]	**4,214.2**	**2,184.8**	**1,234.7**	**950.1**	**2,029.4**
Goods Producing[d]	1,387.6	756.4	394.1	362.3	631.2
Natural Resources and Mining[d]	76.9	43.2	27.9	15.3	33.7
Agriculture, forestry, fishing & hunting[d]	54.6	29.5	18.9	10.6	25.1
Mining	22.2	13.7	9.0	4.6	8.6
Construction	414.9	222.5	157.1	65.4	192.4
Manufacturing	895.9	490.8	209.1	281.7	405.0
Service Providing	2,826.6	1,428.4	840.6	587.8	1,398.3
Trade, Transportation, and Utilities	1,155.5	659.5	380.7	278.8	496.0
Wholesale trade	246.6	146.8	80.2	66.6	99.9
Retail trade	603.1	314.2	175.9	138.4	288.9
Transportation and warehousing	280.5	185.6	117.4	68.2	94.9
Utilities	25.3	12.9	7.2	5.7	12.4
Information	58.9	30.9	20.7	10.2	27.9
Financial Activities	120.6	56.2	38.2	18.0	64.4
Professional and Business Services	292.5	148.8	91.8	56.9	143.7
Education and Health Services	705.9	333.2	186.4	146.8	372.7
Leisure and Hospitality	398.5	154.9	93.9	61.0	243.6
Other Services	94.8	44.8	28.8	16.0	49.9

Source: Bureau of Labor Statistics.
[a] Industry Sector and 2 and 3 digit NAICS code totals on pages 62–64 include data for industries not shown separately.
[b] North American Industry Classification System, 2002 Edition, for industries shown on pages 62–64.
[c] Incidence Rate = $\dfrac{\text{Number of injuries \& illnesses} \times 200{,}000}{\text{Total hours worked by all employees during period covered}}$
  where 200,000 is the base for 100 full-time workers (working 40 hours per week, 50 weeks per year). The "Total Recordable Cases" rate is based on the number of cases with check marks in columns (G), (H), (I), and (J) of the OSHA 300 Log. The "Cases With Days Away From Work, Job Transfer, or Restriction — Total" rate is based on columns (H) and (I). The "Cases With Days Away From Work" rate is based on column (H). The "Cases With Job Transfer or Restriction" rate is based on column (I). The "Other Recordable Cases" rate is based on column (J).
[d] Excludes farms with less than 11 employees.
[e] Fewer than 15 cases.
[f] Data not available.
[g] Rate less than 0.05.

BLS ESTIMATES OF NONFATAL OCCUPATIONAL INJURY AND ILLNESS INCIDENCE RATES FOR SELECTED INDUSTRIES, 2005

Industry[a]	NAICS Code[b]	Total Recordable Cases	Cases With Days Away From Work, Job Transfer, or Restriction — Total	Cases With Days Away From Work	Cases With Job Transfer or Restriction	Other Recordable Cases
PRIVATE SECTOR[d]		**4.6**	**2.4**	**1.4**	**1.0**	**2.2**
Goods Producing[d]		**6.2**	**3.4**	**1.8**	**1.6**	**2.8**
Natural Resources and Mining[d]		**5.1**	**2.9**	**1.8**	**1.0**	**2.2**
Agriculture, forestry, fishing and hunting[d]	11	6.1	3.3	2.1	1.2	2.8
Crop production	111	5.7	3.1	1.9	1.2	2.7
Animal production	112	8.2	4.4	2.7	1.7	3.8
Forestry and logging	113	6.4	3.3	2.8	0.5	3.1
Fishing, hunting, and trapping	114	4.2	2.6	2.3	0.3	1.6
Support activities for agriculture and forestry	115	5.4	3.0	1.9	1.1	2.4
Mining	21	3.6	2.2	1.5	0.8	1.4
Oil and gas extraction	211	2.1	1.2	0.9	0.3	0.9
Mining (except oil and gas)	212	4.1	2.7	2.0	0.7	1.4
Coal mining	2121	5.1	3.5	3.2	0.3	1.6
Metal ore mining	2122	3.5	2.1	1.1	1.0	1.4
Nonmetallic mineral mining and quarrying	2123	3.5	2.4	1.4	1.0	1.2
Support activities for mining	213	3.9	2.2	1.2	1.0	1.7
Construction		**6.3**	**3.4**	**2.4**	**1.0**	**2.9**
Construction of buildings	236	5.3	2.8	2.0	0.8	2.5
Residential building construction	2361	5.3	3.1	2.4	0.7	2.2
Nonresidential building construction	2362	5.4	2.6	1.7	0.9	2.9
Heavy and civil engineering construction	237	5.6	3.1	2.1	1.1	2.5
Utility system construction	2371	5.6	3.2	2.3	0.9	2.4
Land subdivision	2372	3.5	1.5	1.0	0.5	2.1
Highway, street, and bridge construction	2373	6.3	3.5	2.1	1.5	2.8
Other heavy and civil engineering construction	2379	5.0	3.0	2.2	0.8	2.1
Specialty trade contractors	238	6.8	3.6	2.6	1.1	3.2
Foundation, structure, and building exterior contractors	2381	8.5	5.0	3.4	1.6	3.5
Building equipment contractors	2382	6.7	3.1	2.3	0.8	3.6
Building finishing contractors	2383	6.2	3.6	2.5	1.1	2.6
Other specialty trade contractors	2389	5.7	3.3	2.4	0.9	2.4
Manufacturing		**6.3**	**3.5**	**1.5**	**2.0**	**2.8**
Food manufacturing	311	7.7	4.9	1.6	3.4	2.8
Animal food manufacturing	3111	7.2	3.7	1.8	1.9	3.5
Grain and oilseed milling	3112	5.3	3.1	1.2	1.9	2.2
Sugar and confectionery product manufacturing	3113	7.8	4.7	1.5	3.2	3.1
Fruit and vegetable preserving and specialty food mfg.	3114	7.4	4.4	1.6	2.8	3.0
Dairy product manufacturing	3115	9.3	6.1	2.6	3.5	3.2
Animal slaughtering and processing	3116	9.1	6.1	1.3	4.8	3.0
Seafood product preparation and packaging	3117	6.7	3.6	2.5	1.0	3.1
Bakeries and tortilla manufacturing	3118	6.3	4.3	1.7	2.6	2.0
Other food manufacturing	3119	5.8	3.6	1.4	2.2	2.2
Beverage and tobacco product manufacturing	312	8.1	5.4	2.5	2.9	2.7
Beverage manufacturing	3121	8.6	5.8	2.6	3.2	2.8
Tobacco manufacturing	3122	4.7	2.5	1.7	0.8	2.2
Textile mills	313	4.4	2.3	0.8	1.4	2.1
Fiber, yarn, and thread mills	3131	4.9	2.4	0.5	1.9	2.5
Fabric mills	3132	4.3	2.3	0.8	1.4	2.0
Textile and fabric finishing and fabric coating mills	3133	4.0	2.1	1.0	1.1	1.9
Textile product mills	314	4.9	2.8	0.9	1.9	2.0
Textile furnishings mills	3141	4.7	2.7	0.7	2.0	2.0
Other textile product mills	3149	5.1	3.0	1.3	1.7	2.1
Apparel manufacturing	315	3.3	1.5	0.8	0.7	1.8
Apparel knitting mills	3151	4.6	2.1	1.0	1.2	2.5
Cut and sew apparel manufacturing	3152	2.9	1.3	0.8	0.6	1.5
Apparel accessories and other apparel mfg.	3159	5.1	2.4	0.9	1.5	2.7
Leather and allied product manufacturing	316	6.6	3.8	1.7	2.2	2.8
Footwear manufacturing	3162	7.1	3.6	1.5	2.1	3.6
Other leather and allied product manufacturing	3169	4.6	2.6	1.2	1.3	2.0
Wood product manufacturing	321	9.4	5.2	2.5	2.7	4.2
Sawmills and wood preservation	3211	9.4	5.0	2.8	2.2	4.4
Veneer, plywood, and engineered wood product mfg.	3212	8.2	4.7	2.0	2.7	3.4
Other wood product manufacturing	3219	9.8	5.4	2.5	2.9	4.4
Paper manufacturing	322	4.4	2.5	1.2	1.3	1.9
Pulp, paper, and paperboard mills	3221	3.4	1.6	1.1	0.5	1.8
Converted paper product manufacturing	3222	4.8	2.9	1.3	1.7	1.9
Printing and related support activities	323	4.1	2.3	1.1	1.2	1.8
Petroleum and coal products manufacturing	324	3.0	1.8	1.0	0.8	1.2
Chemical manufacturing	325	3.2	1.8	0.8	1.0	1.4
Basic chemical manufacturing	3251	2.4	1.3	0.7	0.6	1.0
Resin, synthetic rubber, and artificial and synthetic fibers and filaments manufacturing	3252	3.3	2.1	0.9	1.2	1.2
Pesticide, fertilizer, and other agricultural chemical mfg.	3253	3.7	1.9	0.8	1.1	1.8
Pharmaceutical and medicine manufacturing	3254	2.7	1.5	0.7	0.8	1.2
Paint, coating, and adhesive manufacturing	3255	4.1	1.9	0.8	1.1	2.2
Soap, cleaning compound, and toilet preparation mfg.	3256	3.7	2.2	0.8	1.4	1.5
Other chemical product and preparation mfg.	3259	4.3	2.6	1.3	1.3	1.7

See source and footnotes on page 61.

OCCUPATIONAL INJURIES
AND ILLNESSES (CONT.)

BLS ESTIMATES OF NONFATAL OCCUPATIONAL INJURY AND ILLNESS INCIDENCE RATES FOR SELECTED INDUSTRIES, 2005, Cont.

Industry[a]	NAICS Code[b]	Total Recordable Cases	Incidence Rates[c] Cases With Days Away From Work, Job Transfer, or Restriction — Total	Cases With Days Away From Work	Cases With Job Transfer or Restriction	Other Recordable Cases
Plastics and rubber products manufacturing	326	7.1	4.1	1.7	2.4	3.0
Plastics product manufacturing	3261	7.1	4.0	1.7	2.3	3.1
Rubber product manufacturing	3262	7.3	4.5	1.7	2.8	2.7
Nonmetallic mineral product manufacturing	327	8.0	4.9	2.5	2.3	3.2
Clay product and refractory manufacturing	3271	8.1	5.2	2.5	2.6	2.9
Glass and glass product manufacturing	3272	8.8	5.0	1.8	3.2	3.8
Cement and concrete product manufacturing	3273	8.2	5.2	3.0	2.2	3.0
Lime and gypsum product manufacturing	3274	3.9	1.5	0.4	1.1	2.5
Other nonmetallic mineral product manufacturing	3279	7.6	4.4	2.6	1.8	3.2
Primary metal manufacturing	331	9.1	4.7	2.2	2.6	4.4
Iron and steel mills and ferroalloy manufacturing	3311	5.4	2.8	1.4	1.4	2.6
Steel product manufacturing from purchased steel	3312	9.4	4.7	2.3	2.4	4.6
Alumina and aluminum production and processing	3313	6.9	4.1	1.7	2.4	2.8
Nonferrous metal (except aluminum) production and processing	3314	6.5	3.6	1.9	1.8	2.8
Foundries	3315	13.5	6.6	2.9	3.7	6.9
Fabricated metal product manufacturing	332	8.0	3.8	1.9	1.9	4.2
Forging and stamping	3321	9.7	4.8	1.9	2.9	4.8
Cutlery and handtool manufacturing	3322	8.0	3.4	1.6	1.8	4.6
Architectural and structural metals manufacturing	3323	9.4	4.6	2.4	2.2	4.8
Boiler, tank, and shipping container manufacturing	3324	7.8	3.8	1.8	1.9	4.0
Hardware manufacturing	3325	6.9	3.1	1.3	1.8	3.9
Spring and wire product manufacturing	3326	8.3	4.6	2.3	2.3	3.8
Machine shops; turned product; and screw, nut, and bolt manufacturing	3327	7.3	3.0	1.8	1.2	4.3
Coating, engraving, heat treating, and allied activities	3328	7.2	3.8	2.0	1.9	3.4
Other fabricated metal product manufacturing	3329	6.9	3.5	1.5	2.0	3.5
Machinery manufacturing	333	6.5	3.0	1.4	1.6	3.5
Agriculture, construction, and mining machinery mfg.	3331	7.6	3.5	1.6	1.9	4.1
Industrial machinery manufacturing	3332	5.9	2.4	1.3	1.1	3.4
Commercial and service machinery manufacturing	3333	4.8	2.3	0.8	1.5	2.5
Ventilation, heating, air-conditioning, and commercial refrigeration equipment manufacturing	3334	6.9	3.3	1.4	1.9	3.6
Metalworking machinery manufacturing	3335	6.9	2.9	1.5	1.4	4.0
Engine, turbine, and power transmission equipment mfg.	3336	5.4	2.6	1.2	1.3	2.8
Other general purpose machinery manufacturing	3339	6.4	3.2	1.5	1.7	3.2
Computer and electronic product manufacturing	334	2.0	1.0	0.5	0.6	1.0
Computer and peripheral equipment manufacturing	3341	1.0	0.5	0.2	0.2	0.5
Communications equipment manufacturing	3342	2.0	1.0	0.5	0.5	1.0
Audio and video equipment manufacturing	3343	3.6	2.2	0.8	1.4	1.4
Semiconductor and other electronic component mfg.	3344	2.2	1.1	0.5	0.5	1.2
Navigational, measuring, electromedical, and control instruments manufacturing	3345	2.2	1.2	0.5	0.6	1.0
Manufacturing and reproducing magnetic and optical media	3346	2.3	1.2	0.4	0.8	1.1
Electrical equipment, appliance, and component mfg.	335	5.2	2.8	1.1	1.7	2.5
Electric lighting equipment manufacturing	3351	5.1	2.9	1.2	1.7	2.2
Household appliance manufacturing	3352	5.4	2.6	0.9	1.8	2.7
Electrical equipment manufacturing	3353	5.2	2.7	1.1	1.6	2.5
Other electrical equipment and component mfg.	3359	5.2	2.9	1.1	1.7	2.4
Transportation equipment manufacturing	336	8.3	4.6	1.7	2.9	3.7
Motor vehicle manufacturing	3361	12.9	7.7	2.2	5.5	5.3
Motor vehicle body and trailer manufacturing	3362	11.8	5.4	2.3	3.1	6.5
Motor vehicle parts manufacturing	3363	7.8	4.4	1.5	2.9	3.4
Aerospace product and parts manufacturing	3364	4.3	2.4	1.0	1.4	1.9
Railroad rolling stock manufacturing	3365	5.2	2.1	1.2	0.9	3.1
Ship and boat building	3366	11.4	6.2	3.0	3.2	5.1
Other transportation equipment manufacturing	3369	7.3	3.8	1.8	2.0	3.5
Furniture and related product manufacturing	337	7.3	4.0	1.7	2.3	3.3
Household and institutional furniture and kitchen cabinet manufacturing	3371	7.5	4.2	1.8	2.4	3.2
Office furniture (including fixtures) manufacturing	3372	7.8	3.6	1.6	2.0	4.2
Other furniture related product manufacturing	3379	5.2	3.4	1.0	2.3	1.8
Miscellaneous manufacturing	339	4.4	2.4	1.0	1.4	2.0
Medical equipment and supplies manufacturing	3391	3.0	1.6	0.7	0.9	1.4
Other miscellaneous manufacturing	3399	5.6	3.1	1.3	1.8	2.5
Service Providing		**4.1**	**2.1**	**1.2**	**0.9**	**2.0**
Trade, Transportation, and Utilities		**5.2**	**3.0**	**1.7**	**1.3**	**2.2**
Wholesale trade	42	4.5	2.7	1.5	1.2	1.8
Merchant wholesalers, durable goods	423	4.1	2.2	1.3	0.9	1.9
Merchant wholesalers, nondurable goods	424	5.7	3.8	1.9	1.9	1.9

See source and footnotes on page 61.

NATIONAL SAFETY COUNCIL® INJURY FACTS® 2007 EDITION

BLS ESTIMATES OF NONFATAL OCCUPATIONAL INJURY AND ILLNESS INCIDENCE RATES FOR SELECTED INDUSTRIES, 2005, Cont.

Industry[a]	NAICS Code[b]	Total Recordable Cases	Incidence Rates[c] Cases With Days Away From Work, Job Transfer, or Restriction — Total	Cases With Days Away From Work	Cases With Job Transfer or Restriction	Other Recordable Cases
Wholesale electronic markets and agents and brokers	425	2.5	1.5	0.8	0.6	1.1
Retail trade	44–45	5.0	2.6	1.5	1.2	2.4
Motor vehicle and parts dealers	441	4.8	2.1	1.4	0.7	2.7
Furniture and home furnishings stores	442	5.0	2.8	1.8	1.0	2.2
Electronics and appliance stores	443	2.4	1.3	0.7	0.7	1.1
Building material & garden equipment and supplies dealers	444	7.5	3.9	2.1	1.8	3.6
Food and beverage stores	445	6.0	3.2	1.9	1.3	2.8
Health and personal care stores	446	2.4	1.2	0.8	0.4	1.2
Gasoline stations	447	3.5	1.7	1.2	0.5	1.8
Clothing and clothing accessories stores	448	2.7	1.0	0.6	0.4	1.6
Sporting goods, hobby, book, and music stores	451	3.3	1.3	0.8	0.5	2.0
General merchandise stores	452	6.7	3.9	1.7	2.2	2.9
Miscellaneous store retailers	453	3.6	2.0	1.2	0.9	1.6
Nonstore retailers	454	4.6	2.7	1.3	1.3	1.9
Transportation and warehousing	48–49	7.0	4.6	2.9	1.7	2.4
Air transportation	481	9.9	7.5	5.3	2.2	2.4
Rail transportation	482	2.5	1.9	1.6	0.2	0.6
Water transportation	483	3.9	2.4	1.8	0.6	1.5
Truck transportation	484	6.1	3.9	2.9	1.0	2.2
Transit and ground passenger transportation	485	6.2	3.5	2.3	1.2	2.7
Pipeline transportation	486	2.1	0.9	0.6	0.3	1.2
Scenic and sightseeing transportation	487	5.3	2.4	2.1	0.3	2.9
Support activities for transportation	488	5.5	3.4	2.3	1.1	2.2
Couriers and messengers	492	11.6	8.0	4.0	4.0	3.6
Warehousing and storage	493	8.2	5.4	2.2	3.2	2.8
Utilities	22	4.6	2.4	1.3	1.0	2.3
Electric power generation, transmission and distribution	2211	4.0	2.0	1.2	0.9	2.0
Natural gas distribution	2212	5.9	3.2	1.6	1.6	2.7
Water, sewage and other systems	2213	7.6	3.4	2.3	1.1	4.2
Information		**2.1**	**1.1**	**0.7**	**0.4**	**1.0**
Publishing industries (except Internet)	511	2.2	1.1	0.7	0.4	1.1
Broadcasting (except Internet)	515	2.0	1.0	0.6	0.4	1.0
Internet publishing and broadcasting	516	0.2	(e)	(f)	(f)	0.1
Telecommunications	517	2.6	1.5	1.1	0.4	1.1
Internet service providers, web search portals, and data processing services	518	1.1	0.5	0.3	0.2	0.6
Other information services	519	1.2	0.5	0.3	0.2	0.7
Financial Activities		**1.7**	**0.8**	**0.5**	**0.2**	**0.9**
Finance and insurance	52	1.0	0.4	0.3	0.1	0.6
Monetary authorities	521	1.8	0.9	0.5	0.4	0.9
Credit intermediation and related activities	522	1.0	0.4	0.3	0.1	0.7
Securities, commodity contracts, and other financial investments and related activities	523	0.3	0.1	0.1	(g)	0.2
Insurance carriers and related activities	524	1.2	0.4	0.3	0.1	0.8
Funds, trusts, and other financial activities	525	1.1	0.4	0.2	0.2	0.8
Real estate and rental and leasing	53	3.7	2.1	1.3	0.7	1.6
Real estate	531	3.3	1.8	1.3	0.5	1.5
Rental and leasing services	532	4.6	2.7	1.5	1.2	1.9
Lessors of nonfinancial intangible assets (except copyrighted works)	533	0.9	0.5	0.5	(e)	0.4
Professional and Business Services		**2.4**	**1.2**	**0.7**	**0.5**	**1.2**
Professional, scientific, and technical services	54	1.4	0.6	0.4	0.2	0.8
Management of companies and enterprises	55	2.4	1.3	0.6	0.7	1.1
Administrative and support and waste management and remediation services	56	3.7	2.0	1.3	0.7	1.7
Administrative and support services	561	3.4	1.8	1.2	0.6	1.6
Waste management and remediation services	562	7.1	4.7	2.7	2.0	2.4
Education and Health Services		**5.5**	**2.6**	**1.5**	**1.1**	**2.9**
Educational services	61	2.4	1.0	0.7	0.3	1.5
Health care and social assistance	62	5.9	2.8	1.6	1.3	3.1
Ambulatory health care services	621	2.8	1.0	0.6	0.3	1.8
Hospitals	622	8.1	3.3	1.8	1.5	4.8
Nursing and residential care facilities	623	9.1	5.7	2.9	2.8	3.5
Social assistance	624	4.3	2.2	1.3	0.9	2.1
Leisure and Hospitality		**4.7**	**1.8**	**1.1**	**0.7**	**2.9**
Arts, entertainment, and recreation	71	6.1	2.9	1.6	1.4	3.2
Accommodation and food services	72	4.5	1.7	1.0	0.6	2.8
Accommodation	721	6.1	3.3	1.7	1.6	2.8
Food services and drinking places	722	4.1	1.3	0.9	0.4	2.8
Other Services, Except Public Administration		**3.2**	**1.5**	**1.0**	**0.5**	**1.7**
Repair and maintenance	811	4.0	1.8	1.3	0.6	2.1
Personal and laundry services	812	2.7	1.6	0.8	0.7	1.2
Religious, grantmaking, civic, professional, and similar organizations	813	2.7	1.1	0.7	0.3	1.7

See source and footnotes on page 61.

BLS ESTIMATES OF NONFATAL OCCUPATIONAL INJURY AND ILLNESS INCIDENCE RATES FOR SELECTED INDUSTRIES, 2005

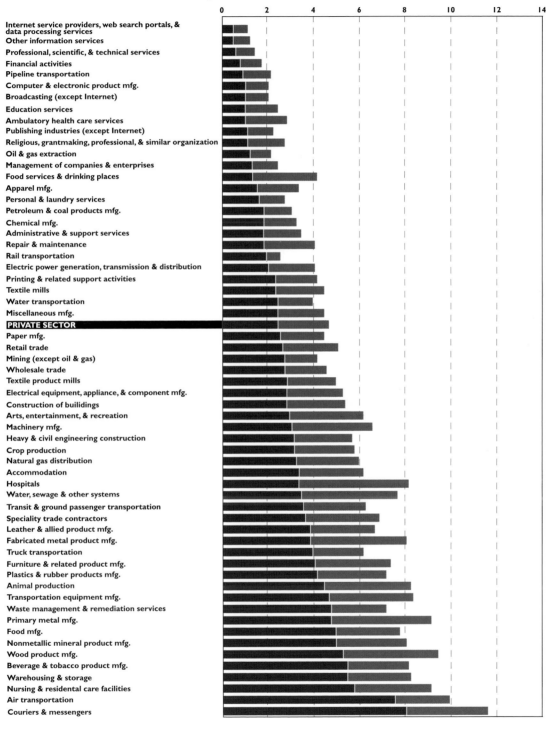

Internet service providers, web search portals, & data processing services
Other information services
Professional, scientific, & technical services
Financial activities
Pipeline transportation
Computer & electronic product mfg.
Broadcasting (except Internet)
Education services
Ambulatory health care services
Publishing industries (except Internet)
Religious, grantmaking, professional, & similar organization
Oil & gas extraction
Management of companies & enterprises
Food services & drinking places
Apparel mfg.
Personal & laundry services
Petroleum & coal products mfg.
Chemical mfg.
Administrative & support services
Repair & maintenance
Rail transportation
Electric power generation, transmission & distribution
Printing & related support activities
Textile mills
Water transportation
Miscellaneous mfg.
PRIVATE SECTOR
Paper mfg.
Retail trade
Mining (except oil & gas)
Wholesale trade
Textile product mills
Electrical equipment, appliance, & component mfg.
Construction of buildings
Arts, entertainment, & recreation
Machinery mfg.
Heavy & civil engineering construction
Crop production
Natural gas distribution
Accommodation
Hospitals
Water, sewage & other systems
Transit & ground passenger transportation
Speciality trade contractors
Leather & allied product mfg.
Fabricated metal product mfg.
Truck transportation
Furniture & related product mfg.
Plastics & rubber products mfg.
Animal production
Transportation equipment mfg.
Waste management & remediation services
Primary metal mfg.
Food mfg.
Nonmetallic mineral product mfg.
Wood product mfg.
Beverage & tobacco product mfg.
Warehousing & storage
Nursing & residental care facilities
Air transportation
Couriers & messengers

Note: Industries are shown at the 2-, 3-, or 4-digit NAICS level.
Total Cases with Days Away from Work, Job Transfer, or Restriction plus Other Recordable
Cases equals Total Recordable Cases.

■ **TOTAL CASES WITH DAYS AWAY FROM WORK, JOB TRANSFER, OR RESTRICTION**

■ **OTHER RECORDABLE CASES**

The tables on pages 67 through 82 present data on the characteristics of injured and ill workers and the injuries and illnesses that affected them. These data indicate how many workers died from on-the-job injuries and how many were affected by nonfatal injuries and illnesses. The data may be used to help set priorities for occupational safety and health programs and for benchmarking.

The fatality information covers only deaths due to injuries and comes from the Bureau of Labor Statistics (BLS) Census of Fatal Occupational Injuries. The data are for the calendar year 2004 and include wage and salary workers, the self-employed, and unpaid family workers in all types of businesses and industries.

The data on nonfatal cases cover both occupational injuries and illnesses and come from the BLS Survey of Occupational Injuries and Illnesses for 2004. The survey also is used to produce the incidence rates shown on the preceding pages. The estimates on the following pages are the number of cases involving days away from work (with or without days of restricted work activity). The survey does not cover the self-employed or unpaid family workers or federal, state, or local government employees.

Data are presented for the sex, age, occupation, and race or ethnic origin of the worker and for the nature of injury/illness, the part of body affected, the source of injury/illness, and the event or exposure that produced the injury/illness.

The text at the top of each page describes the kind of establishments that are included in the industry sector and gives the total number of workers in the industry in 2004 and the number working in the private sector.

How to Benchmark

Incidence rates, percent distributions, or ranks may be used for benchmarking purposes. The results of the calculations described here may be compared to similar rates, percent distributions, and rankings based on data for a company.

For nonfatal cases incidence rates, multiply the number of cases by 1,000 and then divide by the *private-sector* employment given in the text at the top of the page. This will give the number of cases with days away from work per 1,000 employees per year. For fatality rates, multiply the number of fatalities by 100,000 then divide by the *total* employment given at the top of the page. This will give the number of deaths per 100,000 employees per year.

To compute percent distributions, divide the number of cases for each characteristic by the total number of cases found on the first line of the table. Multiply the quotient by 100 and round to one decimal place. Percent distributions may not add to 100.0% because of unclassifiable cases not shown.

Ranks are determined by arranging the characteristics from largest to smallest within each group and then numbering consecutively starting with 1 for the largest.

Industry Sectors

Page 67 shows nonfatal injury/illness data for the private sector of the economy (excluding government entities) and fatal injury data for all industries (including government). Pages 68 through 81 present the data for industry sectors based on the North American Industry Classification System (NAICS). Page 82 presents the fatal injury data for government (the BLS Survey does not cover government entities nationwide, so no nonfatal case data are available).

The nonfatal occupational injury and illness data cover only private sector employees and exclude employees in federal, state, and local government entities and the self-employed. The fatal injury data cover all workers in both the private sector and government.

There were 140,504,000 people employed in 2004, of which 108,655,000 worked in the private sector.

NUMBER OF NONFATAL OCCUPATIONAL INJURIES AND ILLNESSES INVOLVING DAYS AWAY FROM WORKᵃ AND FATAL OCCUPATIONAL INJURIES BY SELECTED WORKER AND CASE CHARACTERISTICS, UNITED STATES, 2004

Characteristic	Private Industryᵇ,ᶜ Nonfatal Cases	All Industries Fatalities
Total	**1,259,320**	**5,764**
Sex		
Men	829,300	5,349
Women	425,470	415
Age		
Under 16	200	13
16 to 19	38,230	128
20 to 24	141,730	421
25 to 34	303,880	996
35 to 44	331,610	1,342
45 to 54	272,250	1,384
55 to 64	128,810	907
65 and over	23,950	569
Occupation		
Management, business, and financial	29,410	664
Professional and related	85,660	101
Service	257,580	867
Sales and related	82,000	355
Office and administrative support	89,540	91
Farming, fishing, and forestry	17,510	285
Construction and extractive	144,050	1,138
Installation, maintenance, and repair	107,940	384
Production	186,600	290
Transportation and material moving	257,210	1,511
Military occupations	—	71
Race or ethnic originᵈ		
White, non-Hispanic	591,570	4,061
Black, non-Hispanic	103,820	545
Hispanic	164,390	902
Other, multiple, and not reported	399,540	256
Nature of injury, illness		
Sprains, strains	525,390	13
Fractures	94,040	39
Cuts, lacerations, punctures	114,140	653
Bruises, contusions	114,680	—
Heat burns	18,510	143
Chemical burns	7,360	—
Amputations	8,160	20
Carpal tunnel syndrome	18,710	—
Tendonitis	6,930	—
Multiple injuries	50,350	2,005
Soreness, Pain	104,560	—
Back pain	37,930	—
All other	196,480	2,886

Characteristic	Private Industryᵇ,ᶜ Nonfatal Cases	All Industries Fatalities
Part of body affected		
Head	81,530	1,350
Eye	36,680	—
Neck	21,130	131
Trunk	447,140	972
Back	282,240	49
Shoulder	82,220	—
Upper extremities	290,460	12
Finger	107,860	—
Hand, except finger	50,190	—
Wrist	58,510	—
Lower extremities	269,490	65
Knee	99,720	10
Foot, toe	57,940	6
Body systems	14,300	910
Multiple	126,530	2,299
All other	8,750	25
Source of injury, illness		
Chemicals, chemical products	17,880	129
Containers	161,370	80
Furniture, fixtures	44,790	16
Machinery	82,160	475
Parts and materials	127,790	397
Worker motion or position	182,820	5
Floor, ground surfaces	234,010	786
Handtools	58,410	110
Vehicles	111,270	2,583
Health care patient	57,230	—
All other	181,590	1,183
Event or exposure		
Contact with object, equipment	335,160	1,009
Struck by object	170,080	602
Struck against object	83,330	17
Caught in object, equipment, material	55,510	386
Fall to lower level	79,800	738
Fall on same level	167,010	61
Slips, trips	37,500	—
Overexertion	316,670	—
Overexertion in lifting	173,400	—
Repetitive motion	48,710	—
Exposed to harmful substance	52,830	464
Transportation accidents	62,860	2,490
Highway accident	38,950	1,398
Nonhighway accident, except air, rail, water	10,190	338
Pedestrian, nonpassenger struck by vehicle, mobile equipment	10,760	378
Fires, explosions	2,420	159
Assault, violent act	24,880	809
By person	17,670	559
By other	7,220	250
All other	131,480	31

Source: National Safety Council tabulations of Bureau of Labor Statistics data.
Note: Because of rounding and data exclusion of nonclassifiable responses, data may not sum to the totals. Dashes (—) indicate data that do not meet publication guidelines.
ᵃDays away from work include those that result in days away from work with or without restricted work activity or job transfer.
ᵇExcludes farms with fewer than 11 employees.

ᶜData for mining operators in coal, metal, and nonmetal mining and for employees in railroad transportation are provided to BLS by the Mine Safety and Health Administration, U.S. Department of Labor; and the Federal Railroad Administration, U.S. Department of Transportation. Independent mining contractors are excluded from the coal, metal, and nonmetal mining industries. MSHA and FRA data do not reflect the changes in OSHA record-keeping requirements in 2002.
ᵈIn the fatalities column, non-Hispanic categories include cases with Hispanic origin not reported.

AGRICULTURE, FORESTRY, FISHING, HUNTING

The Agriculture, Forestry, Fishing and Hunting industry sector includes growing crops, raising animals, harvesting timber, and harvesting fish and other animals from a farm, ranch, or their natural habitats, and agricultural support services.

Employment in Agriculture, Forestry, Fishing, and Hunting totaled 2,232,000 in 2004 of which 1,175,000 were private sector employees.

NUMBER OF NONFATAL OCCUPATIONAL INJURIES AND ILLNESSES INVOLVING DAYS AWAY FROM WORK[a] AND FATAL OCCUPATIONAL INJURIES BY SELECTED WORKER AND CASE CHARACTERISTICS, UNITED STATES, AGRICULTURE, FORESTRY, FISHING, AND HUNTING, 2004

Characteristic	Nonfatal Cases[b]	Fatalities
Total	**19,750**	**669**
Sex		
Men	16,200	651
Women	3,550	18
Age		
Under 16	—	8
16 to 19	710	21
20 to 24	3,050	40
25 to 34	4,840	58
35 to 44	4,560	108
45 to 54	4,030	130
55 to 64	1,860	114
65 and over	350	190
Occupation		
Management, business, and financial	470	329
Professional and related	370	—
Service	670	9
Sales and related	160	—
Office and administrative support	70	—
Farming, fishing, and forestry	14,460	272
Construction and extractive	110	—
Installation, maintenance, and repair	900	6
Production	1,040	—
Transportation and material moving	1,490	44
Military occupations	—	—
Race or ethnic origin[c]		
White, non-Hispanic	6,850	528
Black, non-Hispanic	490	21
Hispanic	9,120	101
Other, multiple, and not reported	3,270	19
Nature of injury, illness		
Sprains, strains	6,060	—
Fractures	2,280	—
Cuts, lacerations, punctures	2,570	15
Bruises, contusions	2,050	—
Heat burns	60	8
Chemical burns	100	—
Amputations	190	6
Carpal tunnel syndrome	330	—
Tendonitis	120	—
Multiple injuries	1,490	203
Soreness, Pain	980	—
Back pain	*410*	—
All other	3,530	434

Characteristic	Nonfatal Cases[b]	Fatalities
Part of body affected		
Head	1,900	141
Eye	*1,000*	—
Neck	130	19
Trunk	6,050	149
Back	*3,520*	—
Shoulder	*1,020*	—
Upper extremities	4,600	—
Finger	*1,790*	—
Hand, except finger	*1,220*	—
Wrist	*650*	—
Lower extremities	4,540	—
Knee	*1,520*	—
Foot, toe	*960*	—
Body systems	180	138
Multiple	2,090	215
All other	270	—
Source of injury, illness		
Chemicals, chemical products	230	9
Containers	1,630	13
Furniture, fixtures	140	—
Machinery	1,580	76
Parts and materials	1,350	22
Worker motion or position	2,540	—
Floor, ground surfaces	3,780	28
Handtools	1,080	7
Vehicles	1,450	359
Health care patient	—	—
All other	5,960	155
Event or exposure		
Contact with object, equipment	7,080	203
Struck by object	*3,940*	*141*
Struck against object	*1,550*	—
Caught in object, equipment, material	*1,110*	*61*
Fall to lower level	2,070	24
Fall on same level	2,210	6
Slips, trips	490	—
Overexertion	2,580	—
Overexertion in lifting	*1,450*	—
Repetitive motion	510	—
Exposed to harmful substance	650	35
Transportation accidents	890	338
Highway accident	*330*	*101*
Nonhighway accident, except air, rail, water	*340*	*165*
Pedestrian, nonpassenger struck by vehicle, mobile equipment	*180*	*27*
Fires, explosions	60	13
Assault, violent act	960	47
By person	*140*	*7*
By other	*820*	*40*
All other	2,240	—

Source: National Safety Council tabulations of Bureau of Labor Statistics data.
Note: Because of rounding and data exclusion of nonclassifiable responses, data may not sum to the totals. Dashes (—) indicate data that do not meet publication guidelines.
[a]Days away from work include those that result in days away from work with or without restricted work activity or job transfer.

[b]Excludes farms with fewer than 11 employees.
[c]In the fatalities column, non-Hispanic categories include cases with Hispanic origin not reported.

The Mining industry sector includes extraction of naturally occurring mineral solids, such as coal and ores; liquid minerals, such as crude petroleum; and gases, such as natural gas. It also includes quarrying, well operations, beneficiating, other preparation customarily performed at the site, and mining support activities.

Mining employment in 2004 amounted to 539,000 workers of which 524,000 were private sector employees.

NUMBER OF NONFATAL OCCUPATIONAL INJURIES AND ILLNESSES INVOLVING DAYS AWAY FROM WORK[a] AND FATAL OCCUPATIONAL INJURIES BY SELECTED WORKER AND CASE CHARACTERISTICS, UNITED STATES, MINING, 2004

Characteristic	Nonfatal Cases[b]	Fatalities
Total	**9,350**	**152**
Sex		
Men	9,200	152
Women	150	—
Age		
Under 16	—	—
16 to 19	110	—
20 to 24	840	13
25 to 34	2,490	33
35 to 44	2,440	37
45 to 54	2,420	39
55 to 64	890	23
65 and over	80	6
Occupation		
Management, business, and financial	30	6
Professional and related	90	6
Service	20	—
Sales and related	—	—
Office and administrative support	30	—
Farming, fishing, and forestry	—	—
Construction and extractive	4,980	90
Installation, maintenance, and repair	1,770	16
Production	740	8
Transportation and material moving	1,630	25
Military occupations	—	—
Race or ethnic origin[c]		
White, non-Hispanic	2,970	132
Black, non-Hispanic	90	5
Hispanic	440	14
Other, multiple, and not reported	5,860	—
Nature of injury, illness		
Sprains, strains	3,450	—
Fractures	2,060	—
Cuts, lacerations, punctures	700	—
Bruises, contusions	770	—
Heat burns	130	6
Chemical burns	60	—
Amputations	90	—
Carpal tunnel syndrome	—	—
Tendonitis	—	—
Multiple injuries	350	68
Soreness, Pain	340	—
Back pain	100	—
All other	1,390	76

Characteristic	Nonfatal Cases[b]	Fatalities
Part of body affected		
Head	630	28
Eye	240	—
Neck	240	—
Trunk	3,250	28
Back	1,760	
Shoulder	540	—
Upper extremities	1,930	—
Finger	790	—
Hand, except finger	350	—
Wrist	250	—
Lower extremities	2,450	—
Knee	810	—
Foot, toe	460	—
Body systems	40	19
Multiple	790	73
All other	30	—
Source of injury, illness		
Chemicals, chemical products	500	—
Containers	570	—
Furniture, fixtures	40	—
Machinery	980	25
Parts and materials	1,480	21
Worker motion or position	520	—
Floor, ground surfaces	1,890	13
Handtools	630	—
Vehicles	720	62
Health care patient	—	—
All other	2,040	25
Event or exposure		
Contact with object, equipment	3,700	56
Struck by object	1,890	25
Struck against object	870	—
Caught in object, equipment, material	810	31
Fall to lower level	650	13
Fall on same level	1,290	—
Slips, trips	90	—
Overexertion	2,380	—
Overexertion in lifting	710	—
Repetitive motion	60	—
Exposed to harmful substance	300	9
Transportation accidents	250	61
Highway accident	60	36
Nonhighway accident, except air, rail, water	40	10
Pedestrian, nonpassenger struck by vehicle, mobile equipment	60	—
Fires, explosions	40	12
Assault, violent act	—	—
By person	—	—
By other	—	—
All other	580	—

Source: National Safety Council tabulations of Bureau of Labor Statistics data.
Note: Because of rounding and data exclusion of nonclassifiable responses, data may not sum to the totals. Dashes (—) indicate data that do not meet publication guidelines.
[a] Days away from work include those that result in days away from work with or without restricted work activity or job transfer.

[b] Data for mining operators in coal, metal, and nonmetal mining are provided to BLS by the Mine Safety and Health Administration, U.S. Department of Labor. Independent mining contractors are excluded from the coal, metal, and nonmetal mining industries. MSHA data do not reflect the changes in OSHA record-keeping requirements in 2002.
[c] In the fatalities column, non-Hispanic categories include cases with Hispanic origin not reported.

CONSTRUCTION

The Construction industry sector includes establishments engaged in construction of buildings, heavy construction other than buildings, and specialty trade contractors such as plumbing, electrical, carpentry, etc.

In 2004, employment in the Construction industry totaled 10,768,000 workers of which 8,409,000 were private sector employees.

NUMBER OF NONFATAL OCCUPATIONAL INJURIES AND ILLNESSES INVOLVING DAYS AWAY FROM WORK[a] AND FATAL OCCUPATIONAL INJURIES BY SELECTED WORKER AND CASE CHARACTERISTICS, UNITED STATES, CONSTRUCTION, 2004

Characteristic	Nonfatal Cases	Fatalities
Total	**153,200**	**1,234**
Sex		
Men	149,430	1,218
Women	3,670	16
Age		
Under 16	—	—
16 to 19	3,720	29
20 to 24	21,530	114
25 to 34	45,700	262
35 to 44	44,030	318
45 to 54	26,010	289
55 to 64	9,250	154
65 and over	840	65
Occupation		
Management, business, and financial	2,890	98
Professional and related	550	8
Service	760	8
Sales and related	400	—
Office and administrative support	1,350	—
Farming, fishing, and forestry	—	—
Construction and extractive	118,140	932
Installation, maintenance, and repair	17,000	73
Production	5,890	20
Transportation and material moving	6,080	87
Military occupations	—	—
Race or ethnic origin[b]		
White, non-Hispanic	90,020	799
Black, non-Hispanic	7,160	93
Hispanic	27,990	312
Other, multiple, and not reported	27,980	30
Nature of injury, illness		
Sprains, strains	57,310	—
Fractures	15,790	—
Cuts, lacerations, punctures	22,040	37
Bruises, contusions	10,410	—
Heat burns	1,700	24
Chemical burns	810	—
Amputations	1,530	—
Carpal tunnel syndrome	1,090	—
Tendonitis	430	—
Multiple injuries	6,340	413
Soreness, Pain	10,720	—
Back pain	*4,110*	—
All other	25,040	753

Characteristic	Nonfatal Cases	Fatalities
Part of body affected		
Head	11,570	347
Eye	*6,650*	—
Neck	2,190	29
Trunk	49,970	159
Back	*32,180*	*8*
Shoulder	*8,180*	—
Upper extremities	37,150	—
Finger	*14,770*	—
Hand, except finger	*7,210*	—
Wrist	*5,540*	—
Lower extremities	37,310	10
Knee	*13,430*	—
Foot, toe	*6,880*	—
Body systems	1,080	236
Multiple	12,530	448
All other	1,400	—
Source of injury, illness		
Chemicals, chemical products	1,660	26
Containers	6,750	10
Furniture, fixtures	1,940	5
Machinery	10,290	150
Parts and materials	32,670	152
Worker motion or position	20,630	—
Floor, ground surfaces	31,890	431
Handtools	14,530	18
Vehicles	8,220	257
Health care patient	—	—
All other	24,630	185
Event or exposure		
Contact with object, equipment	51,830	267
Struck by object	*27,950*	*150*
Struck against object	*12,720*	*6*
Caught in object, equipment, material	*5,380*	*109*
Fall to lower level	20,950	437
Fall on same level	12,700	—
Slips, trips	4,490	—
Overexertion	30,460	—
Overexertion in lifting	*16,860*	—
Repetitive motion	3,240	—
Exposed to harmful substance	5,220	170
Transportation accidents	5,670	287
Highway accident	*3,360*	*148*
Nonhighway accident, except air, rail, water	*1,040*	*45*
Pedestrian, nonpassenger struck by vehicle, mobile equipment	*1,120*	*78*
Fires, explosions	470	34
Assault, violent act	500	31
By person	*240*	*19*
By other	*260*	*12*
All other	17,670	5

Source: National Safety Council tabulations of Bureau of Labor Statistics data.
Note: Because of rounding and data exclusion of nonclassifiable responses, data may not sum to the totals. Dashes (—) indicate data that do not meet publication guidelines.

[a] Days away from work include those that result in days away from work with or without restricted work activity or job transfer.
[b] In the fatalities column, non-Hispanic categories include cases with Hispanic origin not reported.

MANUFACTURING

The Manufacturing industry sector includes establishments engaged in the mechanical or chemical transformation of materials, substances, or components into new products. It includes durable and nondurable goods such as food, textiles, apparel, lumber, wood products, paper and paper products, printing, chemicals and pharmaceuticals, petroleum and coal products, rubber and plastics products, metals and metal products, machinery, electrical equipment, and transportation equipment.

Manufacturing employment in 2004 was 16,484,000 workers of which 16,102,000 were private sector employees.

NUMBER OF NONFATAL OCCUPATIONAL INJURIES AND ILLNESSES INVOLVING DAYS AWAY FROM WORK[a] AND FATAL OCCUPATIONAL INJURIES BY SELECTED WORKER AND CASE CHARACTERISTICS, UNITED STATES, MANUFACTURING, 2004

Characteristic	Nonfatal Cases	Fatalities
Total	**226,090**	**463**
Sex		
Men	173,380	435
Women	52,660	28
Age		
Under 16	—	—
16 to 19	5,000	11
20 to 24	21,530	33
25 to 34	48,710	75
35 to 44	63,660	121
45 to 54	55,870	115
55 to 64	25,600	85
65 and over	2,550	23
Occupation		
Management, business, and financial	2,280	21
Professional and related	3,310	14
Service	4,580	9
Sales and related	980	15
Office and administrative support	8,310	—
Farming, fishing, and forestry	810	5
Construction and extractive	7,650	24
Installation, maintenance, and repair	15,830	53
Production	140,160	192
Transportation and material moving	41,790	127
Military occupations	—	—
Race or ethnic origin[b]		
White, non-Hispanic	124,430	326
Black, non-Hispanic	17,450	48
Hispanic	33,520	76
Other, multiple, and not reported	50,700	13
Nature of injury, illness		
Sprains, strains	80,800	—
Fractures	18,470	—
Cuts, lacerations, punctures	25,600	41
Bruises, contusions	18,840	—
Heat burns	3,850	17
Chemical burns	2,060	—
Amputations	3,640	—
Carpal tunnel syndrome	6,470	—
Tendonitis	2,440	—
Multiple injuries	7,720	135
Soreness, Pain	15,200	—
Back pain	4,710	—
All other	40,990	258

Characteristic	Nonfatal Cases	Fatalities
Part of body affected		
Head	15,920	111
Eye	9,720	—
Neck	2,620	8
Trunk	73,670	103
Back	40,540	—
Shoulder	16,120	—
Upper extremities	73,520	—
Finger	32,430	—
Hand, except finger	10,600	—
Wrist	14,070	—
Lower extremities	41,410	6
Knee	14,710	—
Foot, toe	10,590	—
Body systems	2,050	71
Multiple	15,640	163
All other	1,240	—
Source of injury, illness		
Chemicals, chemical products	4,420	9
Containers	27,720	20
Furniture, fixtures	5,970	—
Machinery	28,370	109
Parts and materials	40,620	48
Worker motion or position	39,790	—
Floor, ground surfaces	27,840	41
Handtools	12,750	5
Vehicles	12,060	164
Health care patient	—	—
All other	26,550	66
Event or exposure		
Contact with object, equipment	80,620	164
Struck by object	34,910	64
Struck against object	16,520	—
Caught in object, equipment, material	22,910	98
Fall to lower level	9,300	40
Fall on same level	20,550	5
Slips, trips	5,030	—
Overexertion	53,910	—
Overexertion in lifting	28,000	—
Repetitive motion	17,730	—
Exposed to harmful substance	10,590	36
Transportation accidents	4,980	143
Highway accident	1,930	83
Nonhighway accident, except air, rail, water	1,290	17
Pedestrian, nonpassenger struck by vehicle, mobile equipment	1,670	19
Fires, explosions	750	28
Assault, violent act	620	42
By person	370	16
By other	260	25
All other	22,020	—

Source: National Safety Council tabulations of Bureau of Labor Statistics data.
Note: Because of rounding and data exclusion of nonclassifiable responses, data may not sum to the totals. Dashes (—) indicate data that do not meet publication guidelines.

[a]Days away from work include those that result in days away from work with or without restricted work activity or job transfer.
[b]In the fatalities column, non-Hispanic categories include cases with Hispanic origin not reported.

WHOLESALE TRADE

Establishments in Wholesale Trade generally sell merchandise to other businesses. The merchandise includes the outputs of agriculture, mining, manufacturing, and certain information industries, such as publishing.

Wholesale Trade employed 4,600,000 people in 2004 of which 4,396,000 were private sector employees.

NUMBER OF NONFATAL OCCUPATIONAL INJURIES AND ILLNESSES INVOLVING DAYS AWAY FROM WORK[a] AND FATAL OCCUPATIONAL INJURIES BY SELECTED WORKER AND CASE CHARACTERISTICS, UNITED STATES, WHOLESALE TRADE, 2004

Characteristic	Nonfatal Cases	Fatalities
Total	**81,140**	**205**
Sex		
Men	71,420	194
Women	9,720	11
Age		
Under 16	—	—
16 to 19	1,530	6
20 to 24	9,020	17
25 to 34	21,910	30
35 to 44	23,020	47
45 to 54	16,660	53
55 to 64	6,650	33
65 and over	1,330	19
Occupation		
Management, business, and financial	1,520	10
Professional and related	1,030	—
Service	1,320	—
Sales and related	6,630	45
Office and administrative support	7,610	—
Farming, fishing, and forestry	660	—
Construction and extractive	2,020	—
Installation, maintenance, and repair	10,620	18
Production	7,470	14
Transportation and material moving	42,190	111
Military occupations	—	—
Race or ethnic origin[b]		
White, non-Hispanic	40,570	137
Black, non-Hispanic	7,190	19
Hispanic	11,590	41
Other, multiple, and not reported	21,750	8
Nature of injury, illness		
Sprains, strains	35,700	—
Fractures	6,310	—
Cuts, lacerations, punctures	6,320	16
Bruises, contusions	7,100	—
Heat burns	490	16
Chemical burns	310	—
Amputations	470	—
Carpal tunnel syndrome	800	—
Tendonitis	360	—
Multiple injuries	2,950	71
Soreness, Pain	8,100	—
Back pain	3,300	—
All other	12,240	98

Characteristic	Nonfatal Cases	Fatalities
Part of body affected		
Head	4,580	43
Eye	1,810	—
Neck	1,330	5
Trunk	32,370	35
Back	22,260	—
Shoulder	4,570	—
Upper extremities	14,290	—
Finger	5,530	—
Hand, except finger	2,850	—
Wrist	2,740	—
Lower extremities	20,410	—
Knee	6,340	—
Foot, toe	5,660	—
Body systems	460	25
Multiple	7,240	92
All other	450	—
Source of injury, illness		
Chemicals, chemical products	690	—
Containers	15,260	—
Furniture, fixtures	1,980	—
Machinery	5,080	17
Parts and materials	9,730	16
Worker motion or position	12,940	—
Floor, ground surfaces	13,100	13
Handtools	2,590	—
Vehicles	12,040	127
Health care patient	—	—
All other	7,710	24
Event or exposure		
Contact with object, equipment	22,130	35
Struck by object	11,750	19
Struck against object	5,080	—
Caught in object, equipment, material	4,100	16
Fall to lower level	5,800	11
Fall on same level	7,690	—
Slips, trips	3,280	—
Overexertion	21,350	—
Overexertion in lifting	13,290	—
Repetitive motion	2,190	—
Exposed to harmful substance	1,950	7
Transportation accidents	6,270	119
Highway accident	3,590	86
Nonhighway accident, except air, rail, water	1,260	14
Pedestrian, nonpassenger struck by vehicle, mobile equipment	1,050	16
Fires, explosions	160	12
Assault, violent act	390	19
By person	170	10
By other	220	9
All other	9,940	—

Source: National Safety Council tabulations of Bureau of Labor Statistics data.
Note: Because of rounding and data exclusion of nonclassifiable responses, data may not sum to the totals. Dashes (—) indicate data that do not meet publication guidelines.

[a]Days away from work include those that result in days away from work with or without restricted work activity or job transfer.
[b]In the fatalities column, non-Hispanic categories include cases with Hispanic origin not reported.

RETAIL TRADE

Establishments in Retail Trade generally sell merchandise in small quantities for personal or household consumption. This sector includes both store and nonstore retailers.

Retail Trade employed 16,269,000 people in 2004 of which 15,204,000 were private sector employees.

NUMBER OF NONFATAL OCCUPATIONAL INJURIES AND ILLNESSES INVOLVING DAYS AWAY FROM WORK[a] AND FATAL OCCUPATIONAL INJURIES BY SELECTED WORKER AND CASE CHARACTERISTICS, UNITED STATES, RETAIL TRADE, 2004

Characteristic	Nonfatal Cases	Fatalities
Total	**178,760**	**377**
Sex		
Men	107,230	333
Women	71,280	44
Age		
Under 16	70	—
16 to 19	9,490	14
20 to 24	26,410	29
25 to 34	39,150	54
35 to 44	41,760	65
45 to 54	34,420	90
55 to 64	18,720	60
65 and over	5,580	65
Occupation		
Management, business, and financial	3,020	10
Professional and related	2,270	—
Service	15,890	18
Sales and related	61,900	225
Office and administrative support	24,640	14
Farming, fishing, and forestry	100	—
Construction and extractive	2,490	—
Installation, maintenance, and repair	18,550	23
Production	10,020	—
Transportation and material moving	39,610	81
Military occupations	—	—
Race or ethnic origin[b]		
White, non-Hispanic	83,120	256
Black, non-Hispanic	9,120	42
Hispanic	14,550	39
Other, multiple, and not reported	71,940	40
Nature of injury, illness		
Sprains, strains	79,700	—
Fractures	11,830	7
Cuts, lacerations, punctures	17,640	162
Bruises, contusions	17,940	—
Heat burns	1,700	—
Chemical burns	1,120	—
Amputations	1,000	—
Carpal tunnel syndrome	2,110	—
Tendonitis	930	—
Multiple injuries	6,250	87
Soreness, Pain	14,510	—
Back pain	*4,950*	—
All other	24,030	117

Characteristic	Nonfatal Cases	Fatalities
Part of body affected		
Head	10,760	117
Eye	*4,020*	—
Neck	3,320	10
Trunk	66,970	88
Back	*42,780*	*9*
Shoulder	*12,010*	—
Upper extremities	38,950	—
Finger	*15,260*	—
Hand, except finger	*6,280*	—
Wrist	*7,740*	—
Lower extremities	39,720	6
Knee	*14,080*	—
Foot, toe	*11,040*	—
Body systems	1,950	33
Multiple	15,930	120
All other	1,160	—
Source of injury, illness		
Chemicals, chemical products	2,230	8
Containers	38,750	—
Furniture, fixtures	11,360	—
Machinery	12,390	9
Parts and materials	15,100	15
Worker motion or position	23,160	—
Floor, ground surfaces	32,720	37
Handtools	8,250	20
Vehicles	14,680	115
Health care patient	—	—
All other	20,080	165
Event or exposure		
Contact with object, equipment	50,810	22
Struck by object	*29,610*	*14*
Struck against object	*12,100*	—
Caught in object, equipment, material	*5,830*	*8*
Fall to lower level	9,640	22
Fall on same level	24,760	13
Slips, trips	4,860	—
Overexertion	51,950	—
Overexertion in lifting	*32,770*	—
Repetitive motion	5,150	—
Exposed to harmful substance	5,530	15
Transportation accidents	5,950	106
Highway accident	*3,300*	*74*
Nonhighway accident, except air, rail, water	*680*	*13*
Pedestrian, nonpassenger struck by vehicle, mobile equipment	*1,710*	*16*
Fires, explosions	210	8
Assault, violent act	1,970	188
By person	*1,470*	*163*
By other	*490*	*25*
All other	17,930	—

Source: National Safety Council tabulations of Bureau of Labor Statistics data.
Note: Because of rounding and data exclusion of nonclassifiable responses, data may not sum to the totals. Dashes (—) indicate data that do not meet publication guidelines.

[a]*Days away from work include those that result in days away from work with or without restricted work activity or job transfer.*
[b]*In the fatalities column, non-Hispanic categories include cases with Hispanic origin not reported.*

TRANSPORTATION AND WAREHOUSING

This industry sector includes transportation of cargo and passengers, warehousing and storage of goods, scenic and sightseeing transportation, and support activities related to transportation by rail, highway, air, water, or pipeline.

Employment in the Transportation and Warehousing industry sector totaled 5,844,000 in 2004 of which 4,245,000 were private sector employees.

NUMBER OF NONFATAL OCCUPATIONAL INJURIES AND ILLNESSES INVOLVING DAYS AWAY FROM WORK[a] AND FATAL OCCUPATIONAL INJURIES BY SELECTED WORKER AND CASE CHARACTERISTICS, UNITED STATES, TRANSPORTATION AND WAREHOUSING,[b] 2004

Characteristic	Nonfatal Cases	Fatalities
Total	**120,010**	**840**
Sex		
Men	92,760	809
Women	23,190	31
Age		
Under 16	—	—
16 to 19	1,420	—
20 to 24	7,750	24
25 to 34	28,680	137
35 to 44	35,520	224
45 to 54	29,070	239
55 to 64	14,520	160
65 and over	2,020	52
Occupation		
Management, business, and financial	1,560	7
Professional and related	340	—
Service	8,220	6
Sales and related	350	—
Office and administrative support	9,670	16
Farming, fishing, and forestry	—	—
Construction and extractive	1,020	—
Installation, maintenance, and repair	9,130	17
Production	3,000	6
Transportation and material moving	86,560	782
Military occupations	—	—
Race or ethnic origin[c]		
White, non-Hispanic	37,850	573
Black, non-Hispanic	8,110	113
Hispanic	8,370	101
Other, multiple, and not reported	65,640	53
Nature of injury, illness		
Sprains, strains	57,850	—
Fractures	7,440	—
Cuts, lacerations, punctures	5,020	55
Bruises, contusions	13,540	—
Heat burns	510	33
Chemical burns	360	—
Amputations	140	—
Carpal tunnel syndrome	870	—
Tendonitis	590	—
Multiple injuries	5,140	399
Soreness, Pain	11,520	—
Back pain	3,530	—
All other	17,010	346

Characteristic	Nonfatal Cases	Fatalities
Part of body affected		
Head	7,990	131
Eye	2,810	—
Neck	2,840	20
Trunk	47,150	111
Back	27,980	5
Shoulder	9,840	—
Upper extremities	20,070	—
Finger	4,940	—
Hand, except finger	3,670	—
Wrist	4,430	—
Lower extremities	27,580	8
Knee	9,850	—
Foot, toe	5,470	—
Body systems	960	108
Multiple	12,970	442
All other	450	20
Source of injury, illness		
Chemicals, chemical products	930	17
Containers	25,640	12
Furniture, fixtures	3,260	—
Machinery	3,300	13
Parts and materials	8,690	31
Worker motion or position	16,390	—
Floor, ground surfaces	18,820	32
Handtools	2,100	—
Vehicles	26,870	666
Health care patient	90	—
All other	13,910	66
Event or exposure		
Contact with object, equipment	26,290	83
Struck by object	13,270	63
Struck against object	7,320	—
Caught in object, equipment, material	3,520	20
Fall to lower level	7,640	30
Fall on same level	12,170	—
Slips, trips	3,700	—
Overexertion	34,150	—
Overexertion in lifting	16,740	—
Repetitive motion	2,850	—
Exposed to harmful substance	2,510	24
Transportation accidents	15,270	636
Highway accident	8,780	438
Nonhighway accident, except air, rail, water	3,220	10
Pedestrian, nonpassenger struck by vehicle, mobile equipment	2,000	70
Fires, explosions	120	—
Assault, violent act	810	61
By person	580	49
By other	230	12
All other	14,490	—

Source: National Safety Council tabulations of Bureau of Labor Statistics data.
Note: Because of rounding and data exclusion of nonclassifiable responses, data may not sum to the totals. Dashes (—) indicate data that do not meet publication guidelines.
[a]Days away from work include those that result in days away from work with or without restricted work activity or job transfer.

[b]Data for employees in railroad transportation are provided to BLS by the Federal Railroad Administration, U.S. Department of Transportation. FRA data do not reflect the changes in OSHA record-keeping requirements in 2002.
[c]In the fatalities column, non-Hispanic categories include cases with Hispanic origin not reported.

UTILITIES

The Utilities sector includes establishments that provide electric power generation, transmission, and distribution; natural gas distribution; steam supply; water treatment and distribution; and sewage collection, treatment, and disposal.

The Utilities sector employed 1,168,000 people in 2004 of which 836,000 were private sector employees.

NUMBER OF NONFATAL OCCUPATIONAL INJURIES AND ILLNESSES INVOLVING DAYS AWAY FROM WORK[a] AND FATAL OCCUPATIONAL INJURIES BY SELECTED WORKER AND CASE CHARACTERISTICS, UNITED STATES, UTILITIES, 2004

Characteristic	Nonfatal Cases	Fatalities
Total	**7,740**	**51**
Sex		
Men	6,880	51
Women	860	—
Age		
Under 16	—	—
16 to 19	—	—
20 to 24	310	—
25 to 34	1,520	7
35 to 44	2,510	14
45 to 54	2,210	22
55 to 64	1,080	6
65 and over	30	—
Occupation		
Management, business, and financial	70	—
Professional and related	380	6
Service	140	—
Sales and related	130	—
Office and administrative support	1,400	—
Farming, fishing, and forestry	—	—
Construction and extractive	960	5
Installation, maintenance, and repair	3,400	25
Production	920	6
Transportation and material moving	310	—
Military occupations	—	—
Race or ethnic origin[b]		
White, non-Hispanic	3,700	46
Black, non-Hispanic	520	—
Hispanic	270	—
Other, multiple, and not reported	3,220	—
Nature of injury, illness		
Sprains, strains	3,890	—
Fractures	540	—
Cuts, lacerations, punctures	410	—
Bruises, contusions	630	—
Heat burns	170	5
Chemical burns	—	—
Amputations	20	—
Carpal tunnel syndrome	70	—
Tendonitis	—	—
Multiple injuries	340	17
Soreness, Pain	500	—
Back pain	230	—
All other	1,170	27

Characteristic	Nonfatal Cases	Fatalities
Part of body affected		
Head	530	6
Eye	200	—
Neck	80	—
Trunk	3,150	7
Back	1,880	—
Shoulder	730	—
Upper extremities	1,170	—
Finger	410	—
Hand, except finger	190	—
Wrist	140	—
Lower extremities	1,770	—
Knee	860	—
Foot, toe	230	—
Body systems	110	14
Multiple	810	23
All other	120	—
Source of injury, illness		
Chemicals, chemical products	40	—
Containers	280	—
Furniture, fixtures	40	—
Machinery	460	—
Parts and materials	890	17
Worker motion or position	1,790	—
Floor, ground surfaces	1,670	8
Handtools	490	—
Vehicles	590	13
Health care patient	—	—
All other	1,490	10
Event or exposure		
Contact with object, equipment	1,610	—
Struck by object	720	—
Struck against object	550	—
Caught in object, equipment, material	160	—
Fall to lower level	520	8
Fall on same level	1,210	—
Slips, trips	220	—
Overexertion	1,420	—
Overexertion in lifting	620	—
Repetitive motion	220	—
Exposed to harmful substance	380	14
Transportation accidents	390	13
Highway accident	300	8
Nonhighway accident, except air, rail, water	40	—
Pedestrian, nonpassenger struck by vehicle, mobile equipment	40	—
Fires, explosions	70	9
Assault, violent act	140	—
By person	—	—
By other	110	—
All other	1,570	—

Source: National Safety Council tabulations of Bureau of Labor Statistics data.
Note: Because of rounding and data exclusion of nonclassifiable responses, data may not sum to the totals. Dashes (—) indicate data that do not meet publication guidelines.

[a]Days away from work include those that result in days away from work with or without restricted work activity or job transfer.
[b]In the fatalities column, non-Hispanic categories include cases with Hispanic origin not reported.

INFORMATION

The Information sector includes establishments that (a) produce and distribute information and cultural products, (b) provide the means to transmit or distribute these products as well as data or communications, and (c) process data. Included are both traditional and Internet publishing and broadcasting, motion pictures and sound recordings, telecommunications, Internet service providers, Web search portals, data processing, and information services.

The Information sector employed 3,463,000 people in 2004 of which 3,138,000 were private sector employees.

NUMBER OF NONFATAL OCCUPATIONAL INJURIES AND ILLNESSES INVOLVING DAYS AWAY FROM WORK[a] AND FATAL OCCUPATIONAL INJURIES BY SELECTED WORKER AND CASE CHARACTERISTICS, UNITED STATES, INFORMATION, 2004

Characteristic	Nonfatal Cases	Fatalities
Total	**21,150**	**55**
Sex		
Men	14,890	41
Women	6,260	14
Age		
Under 16	—	—
16 to 19	500	—
20 to 24	1,230	5
25 to 34	5,020	15
35 to 44	5,390	10
45 to 54	6,150	11
55 to 64	2,320	8
65 and over	410	6
Occupation		
Management, business, and financial	1,120	—
Professional and related	3,290	—
Service	830	7
Sales and related	1,210	18
Office and administrative support	3,720	—
Farming, fishing, and forestry	—	—
Construction and extractive	430	—
Installation, maintenance, and repair	6,940	10
Production	1,960	—
Transportation and material moving	1,600	10
Military occupations	—	—
Race or ethnic origin[b]		
White, non-Hispanic	8,010	42
Black, non-Hispanic	920	7
Hispanic	1,000	6
Other, multiple, and not reported	11,200	—
Nature of injury, illness		
Sprains, strains	9,310	—
Fractures	1,260	—
Cuts, lacerations, punctures	840	6
Bruises, contusions	2,060	—
Heat burns	50	—
Chemical burns	—	—
Amputations	90	—
Carpal tunnel syndrome	550	—
Tendonitis	230	—
Multiple injuries	1,260	21
Soreness, Pain	2,290	—
Back pain	780	—
All other	3,200	26

Characteristic	Nonfatal Cases	Fatalities
Part of body affected		
Head	990	11
Eye	390	—
Neck	460	—
Trunk	7,190	8
Back	4,590	—
Shoulder	1,660	—
Upper extremities	4,010	—
Finger	1,080	—
Hand, except finger	530	—
Wrist	1,170	—
Lower extremities	3,980	—
Knee	1,750	—
Foot, toe	580	—
Body systems	380	11
Multiple	3,970	24
All other	160	—
Source of injury, illness		
Chemicals, chemical products	120	—
Containers	2,740	—
Furniture, fixtures	470	—
Machinery	1,100	—
Parts and materials	1,330	—
Worker motion or position	4,140	—
Floor, ground surfaces	4,980	—
Handtools	430	—
Vehicles	2,180	38
Health care patient	—	—
All other	3,660	8
Event or exposure		
Contact with object, equipment	3,930	—
Struck by object	1,940	—
Struck against object	1,040	—
Caught in object, equipment, material	720	—
Fall to lower level	1,890	—
Fall on same level	3,280	—
Slips, trips	780	—
Overexertion	4,700	—
Overexertion in lifting	2,500	—
Repetitive motion	1,660	—
Exposed to harmful substance	860	8
Transportation accidents	1,800	37
Highway accident	1,580	27
Nonhighway accident, except air, rail, water	110	—
Pedestrian, nonpassenger struck by vehicle, mobile equipment	60	—
Fires, explosions	—	—
Assault, violent act	160	6
By person	60	5
By other	110	—
All other	2,100	—

Source: National Safety Council tabulations of Bureau of Labor Statistics data.
Note: Because of rounding and data exclusion of nonclassifiable responses, data may not sum to the totals. Dashes (—) indicate data that do not meet publication guidelines.

[a]Days away from work include those that result in days away from work with or without restricted work activity or job transfer.
[b]In the fatalities column, non-Hispanic categories include cases with Hispanic origin not reported.

FINANCIAL ACTIVITIES

Financial Activities includes the Finance and Insurance sector and the Real Estate and Rental and Leasing sector. Included are banks and other savings institutions; securities and commodities brokers, dealers, exchanges, and services; insurance carriers, brokers, and agents; real estate operators, developers, agents, and brokers; and establishments that rent and lease goods such as automobiles, computers, and household and industrial machinery and equipment.

Financial Activities had 9,969,000 workers in 2004 of which 8,963,000 were private sector employees.

NUMBER OF NONFATAL OCCUPATIONAL INJURIES AND ILLNESSES INVOLVING DAYS AWAY FROM WORK[a] AND FATAL OCCUPATIONAL INJURIES BY SELECTED WORKER AND CASE CHARACTERISTICS, UNITED STATES, FINANCIAL ACTIVITIES, 2004

Characteristic	Nonfatal Cases	Fatalities
Total	**34,930**	**116**
Sex		
Men	19,580	92
Women	15,350	24
Age		
Under 16	—	—
16 to 19	550	—
20 to 24	2,930	—
25 to 34	7,830	19
35 to 44	9,160	23
45 to 54	8,090	26
55 to 64	4,390	28
65 and over	1,470	16
Occupation		
Management, business, and financial	4,170	45
Professional and related	1,120	—
Service	8,350	7
Sales and related	2,790	30
Office and administrative support	8,600	9
Farming, fishing, and forestry	—	—
Construction and extractive	820	—
Installation, maintenance, and repair	4,250	5
Production	680	—
Transportation and material moving	4,100	16
Military occupations	—	—
Race or ethnic origin[b]		
White, non-Hispanic	15,110	87
Black, non-Hispanic	3,190	15
Hispanic	4,450	10
Other, multiple, and not reported	12,180	—
Nature of injury, illness		
Sprains, strains	13,750	—
Fractures	3,160	—
Cuts, lacerations, punctures	2,590	37
Bruises, contusions	2,820	—
Heat burns	230	—
Chemical burns	190	—
Amputations	30	—
Carpal tunnel syndrome	1,330	—
Tendonitis	270	—
Multiple injuries	1,940	33
Soreness, Pain	3,080	—
Back pain	*1,030*	—
All other	5,540	42

Characteristic	Nonfatal Cases	Fatalities
Part of body affected		
Head	2,030	31
Eye	*570*	—
Neck	520	—
Trunk	11,450	20
Back	*7,620*	—
Shoulder	*1,940*	—
Upper extremities	7,230	—
Finger	*1,720*	—
Hand, except finger	*1,000*	—
Wrist	*2,730*	—
Lower extremities	8,280	—
Knee	*3,390*	—
Foot, toe	*1,560*	—
Body systems	840	16
Multiple	4,490	45
All other	110	—
Source of injury, illness		
Chemicals, chemical products	430	—
Containers	3,190	—
Furniture, fixtures	1,780	—
Machinery	1,930	—
Parts and materials	1,980	7
Worker motion or position	5,770	—
Floor, ground surfaces	9,500	14
Handtools	1,360	6
Vehicles	3,120	38
Health care patient	140	—
All other	5,740	45
Event or exposure		
Contact with object, equipment	6,530	—
Struck by object	*3,590*	—
Struck against object	*2,080*	—
Caught in object, equipment, material	*510*	—
Fall to lower level	3,680	10
Fall on same level	6,520	—
Slips, trips	1,170	—
Overexertion	7,200	—
Overexertion in lifting	*4,120*	—
Repetitive motion	2,590	—
Exposed to harmful substance	1,160	7
Transportation accidents	2,150	37
Highway accident	*1,550*	*29*
Nonhighway accident, except air, rail, water	*190*	—
Pedestrian, nonpassenger struck by vehicle, mobile equipment	*350*	—
Fires, explosions	30	5
Assault, violent act	610	48
By person	*400*	*37*
By other	*210*	*11*
All other	3,300	—

Source: National Safety Council tabulations of Bureau of Labor Statistics data.
Note: Because of rounding and data exclusion of nonclassifiable responses, data may not sum to the totals. Dashes (—) indicate data that do not meet publication guidelines.

[a]Days away from work include those that result in days away from work with or without restricted work activity or job transfer.
[b]In the fatalities column, non-Hispanic categories include cases with Hispanic origin not reported.

PROFESSIONAL AND BUSINESS SERVICES

The Professional and Business Services sector includes legal, accounting, architectural, engineering, computer, consulting, research, advertising, photographic, translation and interpretation, veterinary, and other professional scientific and technical services. Also included are business management and administrative and support activities and waste management and remediation services.

Professional and Business Services employed 14,108,000 people in 2004 of which 11,759,000 were private sector employees.

NUMBER OF NONFATAL OCCUPATIONAL INJURIES AND ILLNESSES INVOLVING DAYS AWAY FROM WORK[a] AND FATAL OCCUPATIONAL INJURIES BY SELECTED WORKER AND CASE CHARACTERISTICS, UNITED STATES, PROFESSIONAL AND BUSINESS SERVICES, 2004

Characteristic	Nonfatal Cases	Fatalities
Total	**90,500**	**452**
Sex		
Men	60,100	430
Women	30,390	22
Age		
Under 16	—	—
16 to 19	1,930	15
20 to 24	9,820	55
25 to 34	26,690	81
35 to 44	24,520	119
45 to 54	17,060	90
55 to 64	6,970	62
65 and over	1,830	29
Occupation		
Management, business, and financial	2,650	23
Professional and related	7,750	35
Service	35,240	244
Sales and related	2,940	8
Office and administrative support	9,690	6
Farming, fishing, and forestry	1,340	—
Construction and extractive	3,430	22
Installation, maintenance, and repair	4,780	15
Production	5,810	13
Transportation and material moving	16,440	82
Military occupations	—	—
Race or ethnic origin[b]		
White, non-Hispanic	38,360	282
Black, non-Hispanic	9,090	61
Hispanic	18,830	91
Other, multiple, and not reported	24,140	18
Nature of injury, illness		
Sprains, strains	33,180	—
Fractures	6,550	—
Cuts, lacerations, punctures	7,980	39
Bruises, contusions	9,470	—
Heat burns	490	8
Chemical burns	570	—
Amputations	240	—
Carpal tunnel syndrome	1,810	—
Tendonitis	440	—
Multiple injuries	4,530	173
Soreness, Pain	7,620	—
Back pain	2,830	—
All other	17,620	226

Characteristic	Nonfatal Cases	Fatalities
Part of body affected		
Head	6,500	108
Eye	2,560	—
Neck	1,600	7
Trunk	28,210	66
Back	17,560	5
Shoulder	5,010	—
Upper extremities	21,790	—
Finger	6,620	—
Hand, except finger	4,200	—
Wrist	4,760	—
Lower extremities	18,630	9
Knee	6,780	—
Foot, toe	3,120	—
Body systems	1,630	78
Multiple	11,080	184
All other	1,050	—
Source of injury, illness		
Chemicals, chemical products	1,530	12
Containers	10,910	5
Furniture, fixtures	2,920	—
Machinery	4,580	33
Parts and materials	6,050	22
Worker motion or position	11,850	—
Floor, ground surfaces	18,340	71
Handtools	3,160	16
Vehicles	11,380	197
Health care patient	870	—
All other	18,920	93
Event or exposure		
Contact with object, equipment	21,450	73
Struck by object	9,480	49
Struck against object	5,870	—
Caught in object, equipment, material	3,860	21
Fall to lower level	5,970	70
Fall on same level	14,010	5
Slips, trips	2,690	—
Overexertion	17,370	—
Overexertion in lifting	10,990	—
Repetitive motion	3,510	—
Exposed to harmful substance	4,440	55
Transportation accidents	8,380	191
Highway accident	6,120	105
Nonhighway accident, except air, rail, water	870	18
Pedestrian, nonpassenger struck by vehicle, mobile equipment	1,250	55
Fires, explosions	220	—
Assault, violent act	4,010	52
By person	860	31
By other	3,150	21
All other	8,440	—

Source: National Safety Council tabulations of Bureau of Labor Statistics data.
Note: Because of rounding and data exclusion of nonclassifiable responses, data may not sum to the totals. Dashes (—) indicate data that do not meet publication guidelines.

[a] Days away from work include those that result in days away from work with or without restricted work activity or job transfer.
[b] In the fatalities column, non-Hispanic categories include cases with Hispanic origin not reported.

EDUCATIONAL AND HEALTH SERVICES

Educational services includes instruction and training through schools, colleges, universities, and training centers. Health services includes ambulatory health care facilities, hospitals, nursing and residential care facilities, and social assistance for individuals, families, and communities.

Educational and Health Services employed 28,719,000 people in 2004 of which 17,371,000 were private sector employees.

NUMBER OF NONFATAL OCCUPATIONAL INJURIES AND ILLNESSES INVOLVING DAYS AWAY FROM WORK[a] AND FATAL OCCUPATIONAL INJURIES BY SELECTED WORKER AND CASE CHARACTERISTICS, UNITED STATES, EDUCATIONAL AND HEALTH SERVICES, 2004

Characteristic	Nonfatal Cases	Fatalities
Total	**189,980**	**157**
Sex		
Men	39,410	97
Women	150,550	60
Age		
Under 16	—	—
16 to 19	3,190	—
20 to 24	16,360	7
25 to 34	43,450	29
35 to 44	48,150	34
45 to 54	47,740	38
55 to 64	23,640	31
65 and over	4,460	14
Occupation		
Management, business, and financial	5,030	7
Professional and related	60,120	—
Service	103,930	97
Sales and related	480	—
Office and administrative support	10,900	10
Farming, fishing, and forestry	60	—
Construction and extractive	980	—
Installation, maintenance, and repair	2,650	—
Production	1,970	—
Transportation and material moving	3,780	36
Military occupations	—	—
Race or ethnic origin[b]		
White, non-Hispanic	85,560	121
Black, non-Hispanic	30,940	15
Hispanic	15,590	9
Other, multiple, and not reported	57,900	12
Nature of injury, illness		
Sprains, strains	99,790	—
Fractures	10,210	—
Cuts, lacerations, punctures	5,290	20
Bruises, contusions	17,200	—
Heat burns	1,990	—
Chemical burns	1,150	—
Amputations	50	—
Carpal tunnel syndrome	2,150	—
Tendonitis	830	—
Multiple injuries	6,890	76
Soreness, Pain	19,230	—
Back pain	7,970	—
All other	25,200	53

Characteristic	Nonfatal Cases	Fatalities
Part of body affected		
Head	9,850	33
Eye	3,350	—
Neck	4,310	—
Trunk	81,220	15
Back	57,260	—
Shoulder	13,330	—
Upper extremities	30,140	—
Finger	7,970	—
Hand, except finger	4,070	—
Wrist	8,770	—
Lower extremities	35,610	—
Knee	15,580	—
Foot, toe	5,590	—
Body systems	3,130	20
Multiple	24,460	83
All other	1,270	—
Source of injury, illness		
Chemicals, chemical products	3,250	13
Containers	10,590	—
Furniture, fixtures	9,390	—
Machinery	4,210	—
Parts and materials	2,290	—
Worker motion or position	25,530	—
Floor, ground surfaces	38,410	14
Handtools	2,190	—
Vehicles	9,520	94
Health care patient	55,800	—
All other	28,800	29
Event or exposure		
Contact with object, equipment	24,880	—
Struck by object	12,180	—
Struck against object	8,490	—
Caught in object, equipment, material	2,890	—
Fall to lower level	5,820	7
Fall on same level	33,670	6
Slips, trips	5,980	—
Overexertion	67,790	—
Overexertion in lifting	32,130	—
Repetitive motion	5,720	—
Exposed to harmful substance	8,800	12
Transportation accidents	5,860	93
Highway accident	4,870	40
Nonhighway accident, except air, rail, water	370	—
Pedestrian, nonpassenger struck by vehicle, mobile equipment	410	5
Fires, explosions	50	—
Assault, violent act	12,820	33
By person	12,230	23
By other	590	10
All other	18,610	—

Source: National Safety Council tabulations of Bureau of Labor Statistics data.
Note: Because of rounding and data exclusion of nonclassifiable responses, data may not sum to the totals. Dashes (—) indicate data that do not meet publication guidelines.

[a]Days away from work include those that result in days away from work with or without restricted work activity or job transfer.
[b]In the fatalities column, non-Hispanic categories include cases with Hispanic origin not reported.

LEISURE AND HOSPITALITY

The Leisure sector includes establishments that provide arts, entertainment, and recreation experiences such as theatre, dance, music, and spectator sports, museums, zoos, amusement and theme parks, casinos, golf courses, ski areas, marinas, and fitness and sports centers. The Hospitality sector includes hotels and other traveler accommodations, food services, and drinking places.

The Leisure and Hospitality sector employed 11,820,000 people in 2004 of which 10,706,000 were private sector employees.

NUMBER OF NONFATAL OCCUPATIONAL INJURIES AND ILLNESSES INVOLVING DAYS AWAY FROM WORK[a] AND FATAL OCCUPATIONAL INJURIES BY SELECTED WORKER AND CASE CHARACTERISTICS, UNITED STATES, LEISURE AND HOSPITALITY, 2004

Characteristic	Nonfatal Cases	Fatalities
Total	**95,380**	**247**
Sex		
Men	47,040	199
Women	48,270	48
Age		
Under 16	80	—
16 to 19	8,790	10
20 to 24	17,490	28
25 to 34	20,820	43
35 to 44	19,150	53
45 to 54	15,190	62
55 to 64	9,560	31
65 and over	2,110	19
Occupation		
Management, business, and financial	3,250	55
Professional and related	3,530	—
Service	71,080	137
Sales and related	3,210	—
Office and administrative support	1,790	—
Farming, fishing, and forestry	—	—
Construction and extractive	410	—
Installation, maintenance, and repair	2,680	11
Production	2,840	—
Transportation and material moving	6,520	36
Military occupations	—	—
Race or ethnic origin[b]		
White, non-Hispanic	37,260	162
Black, non-Hispanic	7,170	25
Hispanic	14,650	30
Other, multiple, and not reported	36,300	30
Nature of injury, illness		
Sprains, strains	32,720	—
Fractures	5,920	—
Cuts, lacerations, punctures	14,200	88
Bruises, contusions	9,420	—
Heat burns	6,490	—
Chemical burns	430	—
Amputations	210	—
Carpal tunnel syndrome	770	—
Tendonitis	150	—
Multiple injuries	3,680	59
Soreness, Pain	7,960	—
Back pain	2,850	—
All other	13,440	96

Characteristic	Nonfatal Cases	Fatalities
Part of body affected		
Head	5,660	63
Eye	2,030	—
Neck	930	8
Trunk	25,900	60
Back	15,710	6
Shoulder	5,180	—
Upper extremities	28,490	—
Finger	11,890	—
Hand, except finger	6,540	—
Wrist	4,190	—
Lower extremities	21,290	—
Knee	8,080	—
Foot, toe	4,560	—
Body systems	1,080	28
Multiple	11,330	84
All other	720	—
Source of injury, illness		
Chemicals, chemical products	1,280	9
Containers	14,810	—
Furniture, fixtures	4,660	—
Machinery	6,060	11
Parts and materials	2,130	6
Worker motion or position	12,440	—
Floor, ground surfaces	24,970	22
Handtools	7,110	14
Vehicles	4,820	70
Health care patient	—	—
All other	17,100	113
Event or exposure		
Contact with object, equipment	25,810	21
Struck by object	14,250	10
Struck against object	7,220	—
Caught in object, equipment, material	2,430	7
Fall to lower level	4,030	18
Fall on same level	22,480	—
Slips, trips	3,770	—
Overexertion	15,460	—
Overexertion in lifting	9,740	—
Repetitive motion	2,080	—
Exposed to harmful substance	8,890	15
Transportation accidents	2,940	72
Highway accident	1,840	31
Nonhighway accident, except air, rail, water	500	18
Pedestrian, nonpassenger struck by vehicle, mobile equipment	470	9
Fires, explosions	150	—
Assault, violent act	1,200	112
By person	880	88
By other	320	24
All other	8,570	—

Source: National Safety Council tabulations of Bureau of Labor Statistics data.
Note: Because of rounding and data exclusion of nonclassifiable responses, data may not sum to the totals. Dashes (—) indicate data that do not meet publication guidelines.

[a]Days away from work include those that result in days away from work with or without restricted work activity or job transfer.
[b]In the fatalities column, non-Hispanic categories include cases with Hispanic origin not reported.

The Other Services sector includes repair and maintenance of equipment and machinery and personal and household goods, personal care and laundry services, and religious, grant making, civic, professional, and similar organizations.

The Other Services sector employed 6,903,000 people in 2004 of which 5,827,000 were private sector employees.

NUMBER OF NONFATAL OCCUPATIONAL INJURIES AND ILLNESSES INVOLVING DAYS AWAY FROM WORK[a] AND FATAL OCCUPATIONAL INJURIES BY SELECTED WORKER AND CASE CHARACTERISTICS, UNITED STATES, OTHER SERVICES (EXCEPT PUBLIC ADMINISTRATION), 2004

Characteristic	Nonfatal Cases	Fatalities
Total	**31,350**	**207**
Sex		
Men	21,790	181
Women	9,560	26
Age		
Under 16	—	—
16 to 19	1,280	5
20 to 24	3,470	17
25 to 34	7,070	29
35 to 44	7,740	42
45 to 54	7,340	44
55 to 64	3,360	32
65 and over	890	37
Occupation		
Management, business, and financial	1,370	14
Professional and related	1,480	—
Service	6,550	59
Sales and related	800	6
Office and administrative support	1,740	—
Farming, fishing, and forestry	—	—
Construction and extractive	600	—
Installation, maintenance, and repair	9,440	88
Production	4,100	11
Transportation and material moving	5,100	22
Military occupations	—	—
Race or ethnic origin[b]		
White, non-Hispanic	17,770	142
Black, non-Hispanic	2,370	24
Hispanic	4,020	30
Other, multiple, and not reported	7,140	11
Nature of injury, illness		
Sprains, strains	11,880	—
Fractures	2,230	—
Cuts, lacerations, punctures	2,940	43
Bruises, contusions	2,450	—
Heat burns	660	6
Chemical burns	190	—
Amputations	470	—
Carpal tunnel syndrome	360	—
Tendonitis	140	—
Multiple injuries	1,460	46
Soreness, Pain	2,520	—
Back pain	1,130	—
All other	6,080	109

Characteristic	Nonfatal Cases	Fatalities
Part of body affected		
Head	2,600	50
Eye	1,340	—
Neck	560	5
Trunk	10,590	42
Back	6,600	—
Shoulder	2,080	—
Upper extremities	7,130	—
Finger	2,670	—
Hand, except finger	1,470	—
Wrist	1,320	—
Lower extremities	6,510	—
Knee	2,550	—
Foot, toe	1,140	—
Body systems	410	44
Multiple	3,220	64
All other	320	—
Source of injury, illness		
Chemicals, chemical products	570	10
Containers	2,540	—
Furniture, fixtures	830	—
Machinery	1,820	5
Parts and materials	3,500	20
Worker motion or position	5,340	—
Floor, ground surfaces	6,110	22
Handtools	1,750	8
Vehicles	3,630	77
Health care patient	260	—
All other	4,990	62
Event or exposure		
Contact with object, equipment	8,490	35
Struck by object	4,600	29
Struck against object	1,920	—
Caught in object, equipment, material	1,280	5
Fall to lower level	1,830	15
Fall on same level	4,470	5
Slips, trips	970	—
Overexertion	5,970	—
Overexertion in lifting	3,470	—
Repetitive motion	1,210	—
Exposed to harmful substance	1,540	25
Transportation accidents	2,060	52
Highway accident	1,340	22
Nonhighway accident, except air, rail, water	220	—
Pedestrian, nonpassenger struck by vehicle, mobile equipment	380	16
Fires, explosions	80	10
Assault, violent act	690	63
By person	230	40
By other	450	23
All other	4,020	—

Source: National Safety Council tabulations of Bureau of Labor Statistics data.
Note: Because of rounding and data exclusion of nonclassifiable responses, data may not sum to the totals. Dashes (—) indicate data that do not meet publication guidelines.

[a]Days away from work include those that result in days away from work with or without restricted work activity or job transfer.
[b]In the fatalities column, non-Hispanic categories include cases with Hispanic origin not reported.

GOVERNMENT

Government includes public employees at all levels from federal (civilian and military) to state, county, and municipal.

Government employment totaled 21,302,000 in 2004.

NUMBER OF NONFATAL OCCUPATIONAL INJURIES AND ILLNESSES INVOLVING DAYS AWAY FROM WORK[a] AND FATAL OCCUPATIONAL INJURIES BY SELECTED WORKER AND CASE CHARACTERISTICS, UNITED STATES, GOVERNMENT, 2004

Characteristic	Nonfatal Cases	Fatalities
Total	[b]	535
Sex		
Men		461
Women		74
Age		
Under 16		—
16 to 19		9
20 to 24		34
25 to 34		124
35 to 44		126
45 to 54		135
55 to 64		79
65 and over		27
Occupation		
Management, business, and financial		34
Professional and related		16
Service		262
Sales and related		—
Office and administrative support		21
Farming, fishing, and forestry		—
Construction and extractive		52
Installation, maintenance, and repair		20
Production		7
Transportation and material moving		49
Military occupations		71
Race or ethnic origin[c]		
White, non-Hispanic		424
Black, non-Hispanic		53
Hispanic		42
Other, multiple, and not reported		16
Nature of injury, illness		
Sprains, strains		—
Fractures		—
Cuts, lacerations, punctures		92
Bruises, contusions		—
Heat burns		8
Chemical burns		—
Amputations		—
Carpal tunnel syndrome		—
Tendonitis		—
Multiple injuries		203
Soreness, Pain		—
Back pain		—
All other		222

Characteristic	Nonfatal Cases	Fatalities
Part of body affected		
Head		128
Eye		—
Neck		12
Trunk		80
Back		—
Shoulder		—
Upper extremities		—
Finger		—
Hand, except finger		—
Wrist		—
Lower extremities		7
Knee		—
Foot, toe		—
Body systems		68
Multiple		238
All other		—
Source of injury, illness		
Chemicals, chemical products		9
Containers		6
Furniture, fixtures		—
Machinery		22
Parts and materials		14
Worker motion or position		—
Floor, ground surfaces		35
Handtools		—
Vehicles		305
Health care patient		—
All other		137
Event or exposure		
Contact with object, equipment		39
Struck by object		28
Struck against object		—
Caught in object, equipment, material		10
Fall to lower level		29
Fall on same level		7
Slips, trips		—
Overexertion		—
Overexertion in lifting		—
Repetitive motion		—
Exposed to harmful substance		32
Transportation accidents		304
Highway accident		169
Nonhighway accident, except air, rail, water		20
Pedestrian, nonpassenger struck by vehicle, mobile equipment		52
Fires, explosions		15
Assault, violent act		103
By person		70
By other		33
All other		6

Source: National Safety Council tabulations of Bureau of Labor Statistics data.
Note: Because of rounding and data exclusion of nonclassifiable responses, data may not sum to the totals. Dashes (—) indicate data that do not meet publication guidelines.
[a]Days away from work include those that result in days away from work with or without restricted work activity or job transfer.

[b]Data for government entities not collected in the national BLS Survey of Occupational Injuries and Illnesses.
[c]In the fatalities column, non-Hispanic categories include cases with Hispanic origin not reported.

OCCUPATIONAL HEALTH

Skin diseases or disorders were the most common illness with over 40,000 new cases in 2005.

Approximately 242,500 occupational illnesses were recognized or diagnosed by private employers in 2005 according to the Bureau of Labor Statistics (BLS), an increase of 2.6% from 2004. The overall incidence rate of occupational illness for all workers was 26.7 per 10,000 full-time workers. Of the major industry sectors, manufacturing had the highest overall rate for total cases in 2005, 66.1 per 10,000 full-time workers. Utilities had the second highest incidence rate, 46.1, followed by education and health services with a rate of 36.7. Workers in agriculture, forestry, fishing, and hunting had the highest illness rates for skin diseases and disorders and for poisoning, while workers in education and health services had the highest rate for respiratory conditions. Workers in manufacturing had the highest rates in the hearing loss and "all other illnesses" categories.

Manufacturing accounted for about 39% of new illness cases in 2005. Skin diseases or disorders were the most common illness with 40,100 new cases, followed by

hearing loss with 26,900, respiratory conditions with 20,200, and poisonings with 2,800. Since the revised recordkeeping guidelines that became effective January 1, 2002, no longer provide categories to separately record cases such as disorders associated with repeated trauma or disorders due to physical agents, these cases are now being captured in the "all other illnesses" category, which accounted for 152,400 or about 63% of all new illness cases in 2005.

The table below shows the number of occupational illnesses and the incidence rate per 10,000 full-time workers as measured by the 2005 BLS survey. To convert these to incidence rates per 100 full-time workers, which are comparable to other published BLS rates, divide the rates in the table by 100. The BLS survey records illnesses only for the year in which they are recognized or diagnosed as work-related. Since only recognized cases are included, the figures underestimate the incidence of occupational illness.

NONFATAL OCCUPATIONAL ILLNESS INCIDENCE RATES AND NUMBER OF ILLNESSES BY TYPE OF ILLNESS AND INDUSTRY SECTOR, 2005

Industry Sector	All Illnesses	Skin Diseases, Disorders	Respiratory Conditions	Poisoning	Hearing Loss	All Other Occupational Illnesses
Incidence Rate per 10,000 Full-Time Workers						
Private Sector[a,b]	**26.7**	**4.4**	**2.2**	**0.3**	**3.0**	**16.8**
Goods Producing[a,b]	48.5	6.3	2.6	0.3	10.3	29.1
Agriculture, forestry, fishing & hunting[a]	35.9	13.5	4.2	0.9	(c)	15.2
Mining[b,d]	10.4	0.9	0.9	(e)	1.5	6.9
Construction	15.7	4.3	1.7	0.3	0.5	8.9
Manufacturing	66.1	7.0	(c)	0.3	15.7	40.2
Service Providing	19.6	3.8	2.1	0.3	0.6	12.8
Wholesale trade	12.4	(c)	0.9	0.3	0.9	7.1
Retail trade	12.9	2.2	1.5	0.3	0.1	8.8
Transportation and warehousing	27.2	2.3	1.4	0.6	4.2	18.7
Utilities	46.1	8.9	(c)	(c)	12.4	19.4
Information	19.1	2.1	1.0	0.2	0.9	14.8
Financial Activities	13.1	1.1	1.5	0.1	(f)	10.4
Professional and Business Services	13.8	3.3	1.3	0.3	0.4	8.5
Education and Health Services	36.7	6.6	4.8	0.2	0.1	25.0
Leisure and Hospitality	17.2	5.8	2.4	0.4	0.1	8.6
Other Services	17.4	5.1	1.1	0.6	0.2	10.3
Number of Illnesses (in thousands)						
Private Sector[a,b]	**242.5**	**40.1**	**20.2**	**2.8**	**26.9**	**152.4**
Goods Producing[a,d]	108.1	13.9	5.7	0.8	22.9	64.8
Agriculture, forestry, fishing & hunting[a]	3.2	1.2	0.4	0.1	(c)	1.4
Mining[c,d]	0.6	0.1	0.1	(e)	0.1	0.4
Construction	10.3	2.8	1.1	0.2	0.3	5.9
Manufacturing	94.0	9.9	(c)	0.5	22.3	57.2
Service Providing	134.4	26.2	14.5	2.0	4.1	87.6
Wholesale trade	6.8	—	0.5	0.2	0.5	3.9
Retail trade	15.5	2.6	1.8	0.3	0.1	10.6
Transportation and warehousing	10.9	0.9	0.5	0.2	1.7	7.5
Utilities	2.5	0.5	(c)	(c)	0.7	1.1
Information	5.3	0.6	0.3	0.1	0.3	4.1
Financial Activities	9.5	0.8	1.1	0.1	(g)	7.5
Professional and Business Services	17.1	4.1	1.6	0.3	0.5	10.5
Education and Health Services	47.0	8.4	6.1	0.3	0.1	32.0
Leisure and Hospitality	14.6	4.9	2.0	0.3	0.1	7.3
Other Services	5.1	1.5	0.3	0.2	0.1	3.0

Source: Bureau of Labor Statistics, U.S. Department of Labor. Components may not add to totals due to rounding.
[a] Private sector includes all industries except government, but excludes farms with less than 11 employees.
[b] Data for mining do not reflect the changes OSHA made to its recordkeeping requirements effective January 1, 2002; therefore, estimates for this industry are not comparable with estimates for other industries.
[c] Standard error of estimate exceeded publication guidelines.
[d] Mining includes quarrying and oil and gas extraction.
[e] Fewer than 15 cases.
[f] Incidence rate less than 0.05.
[g] Fewer than 50 cases.

MOTOR VEHICLE

INJURY FACTS®

NATIONAL SAFETY COUNCIL

Between 1912 and 2004, motor-vehicle deaths per 10,000 registered vehicles were reduced 94%, from 33 to about 2. In 1912, there were 3,100 fatalities when the number of registered vehicles totaled only 950,000. In 2005, there were 45,800 fatalities, but registrations soared to 246 million.

While mileage data were not available in 1912, the 2005 mileage death rate of 1.54 per 100,000,000 vehicle miles was up 1% from the revised 2004 rate of 1.53, which is the lowest on record. Disabling injuries in motor-vehicle accidents totaled 2,400,000 in 2005, and total motor-vehicle costs were estimated at $247.7 billion. Costs include wage and productivity losses, medical expenses, administrative expenses, motor-vehicle property damage, and employer costs.

Motor-vehicle deaths increased 1% from 2004 to 2005 and increased 2% from 2003 to 2005. Miles traveled

was up less than 0.5%, the number of registered vehicles increased 1%, and the population increased 1%. As a result, the mileage death rate was up 1%, the registration death rate was unchanged, and the population death rate was up 1% from 2004 to 2005.

Compared with 1995, 2005 motor-vehicle deaths increased by about 6%. However, mileage, registration, and population death rates were all sharply lower in 2005 compared to 1995 (see chart on next page).

The word "accident" may be used in this section as well as the word "crash." When used, "accident" has a specific meaning as defined in the Manual on Classification of Motor Vehicle Traffic Accidents, ANSI D16.2-1996. "Crash" is generally used by the National Highway Traffic Safety Administration to mean the same as accident, but it is not formally defined.

Deaths **45,800**
Disabling injuries **2,400,000**
Cost . . . . **$247.7 billion**
Motor-vehicle mileage . . . . **2,967 billion**
Registered vehicles in the United States **245,700,000**
Licensed drivers in the United States **201,500,000**
Death rate per 100,000,000 vehicle miles **1.54**
Death rate per 10,000 registered vehicles **1.86**
Death rate per 100,000 population **15.5**

MOTOR-VEHICLE ACCIDENT OUTCOMES, UNITED STATES, 2005

Severity of Accident	Deaths or Injuries	Accidents or Crashes	Drivers (Vehicles) Involved
Fatal (within 1 year)	45,800	41,300	62,300
Disabling injury	2,400,000	1,600,000	2,800,000
Property damage (including unreported) and nondisabling injury		9,100,000	15,500,000
Total		**10,700,000**	**18,400,000**
Fatal (within 30 days)	43,443	39,189	59,104
Injury (disabling and nondisabling)	2,699,000	1,816,000	3,282,000
Police-reported property damage		4,304,000	7,492,000
Total		**6,159,000**	**10,832,000**

Source: National Safety Council estimates (top half) and National Highway Traffic Safety Administration (bottom half).

TRAVEL, DEATHS, AND DEATH RATES, UNITED STATES, 1925–2005

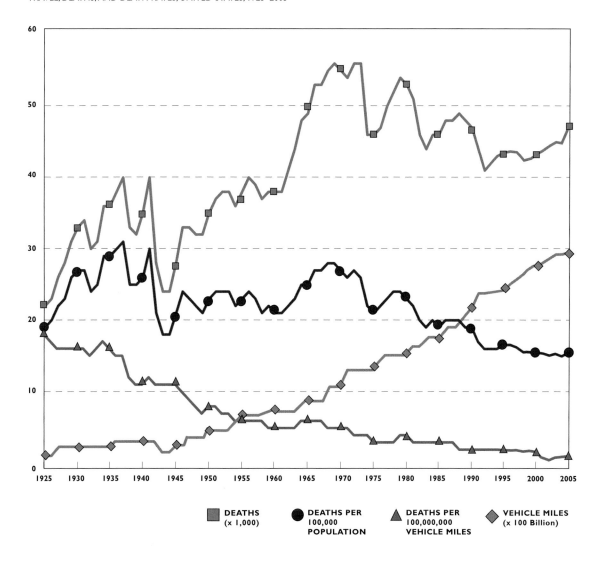

DEATHS DUE TO MOTOR-VEHICLE ACCIDENTS, 2005

TYPE OF EVENT AND AGE OF VICTIM

All Motor-Vehicle Accidents

Includes deaths involving mechanically or electrically powered highway-transport vehicles in motion (except those on rails), both on and off the highway or street.

	Total	Change from 2004	Death Rate[a]
Deaths	45,800	+1%	15.5
Nonfatal injuries	2,400,000		

Age	0–4	5–14	15–24	25–44	45–64	65–74	75+
Deaths	700	1,500	11,000	14,200	10,900	3,100	4,400

Collision Between Motor Vehicles

Includes deaths from collisions of two or more motor vehicles. Motorized bicycles and scooters, trolley buses, and farm tractors or road machinery traveling on highways are motor vehicles.

	Total	Change from 2004	Death Rate[a]
Deaths	19,200	–1%	6.5
Nonfatal injuries	1,800,000		

Age	0–4	5–14	15–24	25–44	45–64	65–74	75+
Deaths	250	450	4,000	5,400	4,900	1,700	2,500

Collision with Fixed Object

Includes deaths from collisions in which the first harmful event is the striking of a fixed object such as a guardrail, abutment, impact attenuator, etc.

	Total	Change from 2004	Death Rate[a]
Deaths	13,700	+1%	4.6
Nonfatal injuries	360,000		

Age	0–4	5–14	15–24	25–44	45–64	65–74	75+
Deaths	150	350	4,500	4,600	2,700	600	800

Pedestrian Accidents

Includes all deaths of persons struck by motor vehicles, either on or off a street or highway, regardless of the circumstances of the accident.

	Total	Change from 2004	Death Rate[a]
Deaths	6,200	+3%	2.1
Nonfatal injuries	70,000		

Age	0–4	5–14	15–24	25–44	45–64	65–74	75+
Deaths	250	300	750	1,900	1,700	500	800

See footnotes on page 89.

Noncollision Accidents

Includes deaths from accidents in which the first injury or damage-producing event was an overturn, jackknife, or other type of noncollision.

	Total	Change from 2004	Death Rate[a]
Deaths	5,300	+4%	1.8
Nonfatal injuries	110,000		

Collision with Pedalcycle

Includes deaths of pedalcyclists and motor-vehicle occupants from collisions between pedalcycles and motor vehicles on streets, highways, private driveways, parking lots, etc.

	Total	Change from 2004	Death Rate[a]
Deaths	1,000	+11%	0.3
Nonfatal injuries	51,000		

Collision with Railroad Train

Includes deaths from collisions of motor vehicles (moving or stalled) and railroad vehicles at public or private grade crossings. In other types of accidents, classification requires motor vehicle to be in motion.

	Total	Change from 2004	Death Rate[a]
Deaths	300	0%	0.1
Nonfatal injuries	1,000		

Other Collision

Includes deaths from motor-vehicle collisions not specified in other categories above. Most of the deaths arose out of accidents involving animals or animal-drawn vehicles.

	Total	Change from 2004	Death Rate[a]
Deaths	100	0%	(c)
Nonfatal Injuries	8,000		

Note: Procedures and benchmarks for estimating deaths by type of accident and age were changed in 1990. Estimates for 1987 and later years are not comparable to earlier years. The noncollision and fixed object categories were most affected by the changes.
[a]Deaths per 100,000 population.
[b]Deaths per 100,000 population in each age group.
[c]Death rate was less than 0.05.

Motor-vehicle crashes are the leading cause of death for people between the ages of 2 and 33. Motor-vehicle crashes are also the leading cause of unintentional-injury (accidental) death for persons of each single year of age from 3 to 42, for those aged 45, and again for each single year of age from 48 to 74. This is a summary of the most important issues that affect traffic safety.

Occupant protection. Forty-nine states and the District of Columbia have mandatory belt use laws in effect, with the laws in twenty-five of the states and the District of Columbia allowing standard (primary) enforcement. Safety belt use reached an all-time high of 82% in 2005 and was at a significantly high 85% in states with standard enforcement laws. The latest observational surveys show motorcycle helmet use declined to 48% in 2005, a statistically significant drop from the rate as observed in 2000 that corresponds to a 79% increase in nonuse.

Alcohol. Although all states and the District of Columbia have 21-year-old minimum drinking age laws and have by law created a threshold making it illegal to drive with a BAC of 0.08 g/dl or higher, traffic fatalities in alcohol-related crashes fell by only 0.2% from 2004 to 2005 and declined just 5% from 1995–2005. About 39% of all traffic fatalities in 2005 involved an intoxicated or alcohol-impaired driver or nonoccupant and there was an average of one alcohol-related fatality every 31 minutes.

Speeding. Excessive speed was a factor in 30% of all traffic fatalities in 2005 and, similar to alcohol, the number of crashes attributable to speeding has not changed appreciably over the last decade. Nearly half of all speeding-related fatalities in 2005 occurred on roads where the posted speed limit was 55 miles per hour or greater. It has been estimated that speeding-related crashes cost the nation over $40 billion annually.

Distracted driving. Driver distractions from all sources contribute to about 1.5 million crashes per year. Observational surveys indicate that about 10% of all drivers on the road at any given time are engaged in some type of inappropriate cell phone use while driving,

whether it be holding a phone their ear, using a head set, or manipulating a hand-held device. The rates of inappropriate cell phone use increased across all three of these categories from 2004 to 2005.

Motorcycles. Fatalities among motorcycle riders and passengers have more than doubled between 1995 and 2005, while nonfatal injuries have increased by 53% over the same period. With the number of registered motorcycles increasing by 50% from 1995 through 2004 and miles traveled up only slightly, the death rate per 100 million miles driven has increased by 76%. In contrast to earlier years, almost half of fatally injured riders are now over 40 years of age.

Large trucks. Over 12% of traffic fatalities in 2005 resulted from a crash involving a large truck (gross vehicle weight rating greater than 10,000 pounds) and over three-quarters of the deaths were occupants of vehicles other than the large truck. Large trucks were more likely to be involved in a multiple vehicle fatal crash than passenger vehicles — 83% vs. 63%, respectively.

Young drivers. Total fatalities in crashes involving drivers 15 to 20 years old numbered 8,193 in 2005. Although the 7,460 15 to 20 year old drivers involved in fatal crashes in 2005 represented a 7% decrease from the 7,979 involved in 1995, driver fatalities among this age group increased by 4% over the same time period. According to the latest 2003 mortality figures, motor-vehicle crashes are the leading cause of death for 15 to 20 year olds. In 2005, 12.6% of all the drivers involved in fatal crashes were between 15 and 20 years old, a figure far out of proportion to this age group's 6.3% of all licensed drivers in 2004.

Pedestrians. There were about 6,200 pedestrian deaths and 70,000 injuries in motor-vehicle accidents in 2005. The majority (over 60%) of pedestrian deaths and injuries occur when pedestrians improperly cross roadways or intersections or dart/run into streets. Pedestrians in age groups beginning with those aged 15 and older are more likely to cross improperly, while those in younger age groups are more likely to dart/run into the roadway.

ESTIMATING MOTOR-VEHICLE CRASH COSTS

There are two methods commonly used to measure the costs of motor-vehicle crashes. One is the *economic cost* framework and the other is the *comprehensive cost* framework.

Economic costs may be used by a community or state to estimate the economic impact of motor-vehicle crashes that occurred within its jurisdiction in a given time period. It is a measure of the productivity lost and expenses incurred because of the crashes. Economic costs, however, should not be used for cost-benefit analysis because they do not reflect what society is willing to pay to prevent a statistical fatality or injury.

There are five economic cost components: (a) wage and productivity losses, which include wages, fringe benefits, household production, and travel delay; (b) medical expenses including emergency service costs; (c) administrative expenses, which include the administrative cost of private and public insurance plus police and legal costs; (d) motor-vehicle damage including the value of damage to property; and (e) uninsured employer costs for crashes involving workers.

The information below shows the average economic costs in 2005 per death (*not* per fatal crash), per injury (*not* per injury crash), and per property damage crash.

ECONOMIC COSTS, 2005

Death	**$1,150,000**
Nonfatal Disabling Injury	**$52,900**
Incapacitating injury[a]	$60,500
Nonincapacitating evident injury[a]	$19,600
Possible injury[a]	$11,100
Property Damage Crash (including minor injuries)	**$7,500**

Comprehensive costs include not only the economic cost components, but also a measure of the value of lost quality of life associated with the deaths and injuries, that is, what society is willing to pay to prevent them. The values of lost quality of life were obtained through empirical studies of what people actually pay to reduce their safety and health risks, such as through the purchase of air bags or smoke detectors. Comprehensive costs should be used for cost-benefit analysis, but because the lost quality of life represents only a dollar equivalent of intangible qualities, they do not represent real economic losses and should not be used to determine the economic impact of past crashes.

The information below shows the average comprehensive costs in 2005 on a per person basis.

COMPREHENSIVE COSTS, 2005

Death	**$3,840,000**
Incapacitating injury[a]	$193,800
Nonincapacitating evident injury[a]	$49,500
Possible injury[a]	$23,600
No Injury	**$2,200**

Source: National Safety Council estimates (see the Technical Appendix) and Children's Safety Network Economics and Insurance Resource Center, Pacific Institute for Research and Evaluation.
Note: The National Safety Council's cost-estimating procedures were extensively revised for the 1993 edition, and additional revisions were made this year (see page 4). The costs are not comparable to those of prior years.
[a] Committee on Motor Vehicle Traffic Accident Classification. (1997). Manual on Classification of Motor Vehicle Traffic Accidents, ANSI D16.1–1996 (6th ed.). Itasca, IL: National Safety Council.

All states and the District of Columbia have 21-year-old drinking age and child safety seat laws. Breath alcohol ignition interlock device laws are in effect in 43 states. Mandatory belt use laws are in effect in 49 states plus the District of Columbia, of which 25 states and D.C. are standard enforcement. Graduated licensing is in effect in some form in 48 states and the District of Columbia

STATE LAWS

State	Alcohol Laws				Mandatory Belt Use Law		Graduated Licensing Laws				
	Administrative License Revocation[a]	BAC Limit[b]	Zero Tolerance Limit[c] for Minors	Alcohol Ignition Interlock Device[d]	Enforcement	Seating Positions Covered by Law	Minimum Instructional Permit Period[e]	Minimum Hours of Supervised Driving[f]	Passenger Restrictions	Nighttime Driving Restrictions	Unrestricted License Minimum Age[g]
Alabama	1996	0.08	0.02	no	standard	front	6 mo.	30/–	yes	yes	16 yrs.
Alaska	1983	0.08	0.00	yes	standard	all	6 mo.	none	yes	yes	16 yrs.
Arizona	1992	0.08	0.00	yes[h]	secondary	front	6 mo.	25/5	no	no	16 yrs.
Arkansas	1995	0.08	0.02	yes	secondary	front	until 16 yrs.	none	no	no	18 yrs.
California	1989	0.08	0.01	yes[h]	standard	all	6 mo.	50/10	yes	yes	16 yrs.
Colorado	1983	0.08	0.02	yes[h]	secondary	front	12 mo.	50/10	yes	yes	17 yrs.
Connecticut	1990	0.08	0.02	yes[h]	standard	front[i]	6 mo.	none	yes	no	16 yrs., 4 mo.
Delaware	yes	0.08	0.02	yes[h]	standard	all	12 mo.	50/10	yes	yes	17 yrs.
Dist. of Columbia	yes	0.08	0.00	no	standard	all	6 mo.	40+10[j]	yes	yes	18 yrs.
Florida	1990	0.08	0.02	yes[h]	secondary[k]	front	12 mo.	50/10	no	yes	18 yrs.
Georgia	1995	0.08	0.02	yes[h]	standard	front[i]	12 mo.	40/6	yes	yes	18 yrs.
Hawaii	1990	0.08	0.02	no	standard	front[i]	6 mo.	50/10	yes	yes	17 yrs.
Idaho	1994	0.08	0.02	yes	secondary	all	4 mo.	50/10	no	yes	16 yrs.
Illinois	1986	0.08	0.00	yes[h]	standard	front	3 mo.	50/10	yes	yes	18 yrs.
Indiana	yes	0.08	0.02	yes[h]	standard	front	2 mo.	none	yes	yes	18 yrs.
Iowa	1982	0.08	0.02	yes	standard	front	6 mo.	20/2	no	yes	17 yrs.
Kansas	1988	0.08	0.02	yes[h]	secondary	front	6 mo.	50/10	no	no	16 yrs.
Kentucky	no	0.08	0.02	yes[h]	standard	all	6 mo.	60/10	yes	yes[m]	17 yrs.
Louisiana	1984	0.08	0.02	yes	standard	front[i]	3 mo.	none	yes	yes	17 yrs.
Maine	1984	0.08	0.00	no	secondary	all	6 mo.	35/5	yes	yes	16 yrs., 6 mo.
Maryland	1989	0.08[l]	0.02	yes[h]	standard	front[i]	6 mo.	60/10	yes	yes	17 yrs., 9 mo.
Massachusetts	1994	0.08	0.02	no	secondary	all	6 mo.	12/–	yes	yes	18 yrs.
Michigan	no	0.08	0.02	yes[h]	standard	front[i]	6 mo.	50/10	no	yes	17 yrs.
Minnesota	1976	0.08	0.00	no	secondary	front[i]	6 mo.	30/10	no	no	17 yrs.
Mississippi	1983	0.08	0.02	yes[h]	standard	front	6 mo.	none	no	yes	16 yrs.
Missouri	1987	0.08	0.02	yes[h]	secondary	front[i]	6 mo.	40/10	yes	yes	18 yrs.
Montana	no	0.08	0.02	yes	secondary	all	6 mo.	50/10	yes	yes	18 yrs.
Nebraska	1993	0.08	0.02	yes	secondary	front[i]	none	50/–	no	yes	17 yrs.
Nevada	1983	0.08	0.02	yes[h]	secondary	all	6 mo.	50/10	yes	yes	18 yrs.
New Hampshire	1993	0.08	0.02	yes[h]	(k)	(k)	6 mo.	20/–	no	yes	18 yrs.
New Jersey	no	0.08	0.01	yes[h]	standard	front	12 mo.	none	yes	yes	18 yrs.
New Mexico	1984	0.08	0.02	yes	standard	all	6 mo.	50/10	yes	yes	16 yrs., 6mo.
New York	1994[n]	0.08[l]	0.02	yes[h]	standard	front[i]	6 mo.	20/–	no	yes	18 yrs.
North Carolina	1983	0.08	0.00	yes[h]	standard	all	12 mo.	none	yes	yes	16 yrs., 6mo.
North Dakota	1983	0.08	0.02	yes[h]	secondary	front	6 mo.	none	no	no	16 yrs.
Ohio	1993	0.08	0.02	yes	secondary	front	6 mo.	50/10	no	yes	18 yrs.
Oklahoma	1983	0.08	0.00	yes	standard	front	6 mo.	40/10	yes	yes	18 yrs.
Oregon	1983	0.08	0.00	yes	standard	all	6 mo.	100/–	yes	yes	18 yrs.
Pennsylvania	no	0.08	0.02	yes[h]	secondary	front[i]	6 mo.	50/–	yes	yes	17 yrs., 6mo.
Rhode Island	no	0.08	0.02	yes[h]	secondary	all	6 mo.	50/10	yes	yes	17 yrs.
South Carolina	1998	0.08	0.02	yes	standard	front[o]	180 days	40/10	yes	yes	17 yrs.
South Dakota	no	0.08	0.02	no	secondary	front	6 mo.	none	no	yes	16 yrs.
Tennessee	no	0.08	0.02	yes	standard	all	180 days	50/10	yes	yes	18 yrs.
Texas	1995	0.08	0.00	yes[h]	standard	front[i]	6 mo.	none	yes	yes	18 yrs.
Utah	1983	0.08	0.00	yes	secondary[k]	all	none	40/10	yes	yes	17 yrs.
Vermont	1969[n]	0.08	0.02	no	secondary	all	12 mo.	40/10	yes	no	16 yrs., 6 mo.
Virginia	1995	0.08	0.02	yes	secondary	front[i]	9 mo.	40/10	yes	yes	18 yrs.
Washington	1998	0.08	0.02	yes	standard	all	6 mo.	50/10	yes	yes	18 yrs.
West Virginia	1981	0.08	0.02	yes	secondary	front[i]	6 mo.	30/–	yes	yes	18 yrs.
Wisconsin	1988	0.08	0.00	yes[h]	secondary	front[o]	12 mo.	30/10	yes	yes	18 yrs.
Wyoming	1973	0.08	0.02	yes	secondary	all	10 days	50/10	yes	yes	17 yrs.

Source: National Safety Council survey of state officials. Laws as of July 2006.
Note: Michigan and Minnesota did not respond to the 2006 survey. Data for these states are for 2005.
[a] *Year original law became effective, not when grandfather clauses expired.*
[b] *Blood alcohol concentration that constitutes the threshold of legal intoxication.*
[c] *Blood alcohol concentration that constitutes "zero tolerance" threshold for minors (<21 years of age unless otherwise noted).*
[d] *Instruments designed to prevent drivers from starting their cars when breath alcohol content is at or above a set point.*
[e] *Minimum instructional periods often include time spent in driver's education classes.*
[f] *Figures shown as follows: Total hours/Nighttime hours. For example, 25/5 means 25 hours of supervised driving, 5 of which must be at night. Some states (GA, MD, OR, WV) have lower requirements if driver ed it taken.*

[g] *Minimum age to obtain unrestricted license provided driver is crash and violation free. Alcohol restrictions still apply at least until 21.*
[h] *Primarily for repeat offenders.*
[i] *Required for certain ages at all seating positions.*
[j] *40 hours of supervised driving during learner's stage; 10 hours at night during intermediate stage.*
[k] *Standard enforcement law in effect for ages under 18 (FL, NH), under 19 (UT).*
[l] *BAC of 0.07 is prima facie evidence of DUI (MD). BAC of 0.05 –0.07 constitutes driving while ability impaired (NY).*
[m] *During permit period only.*
[n] *Revocation by judicial action (NY) or Department of Motor Vehicles (VT).*
[o] *Belt use required in rear seat if lap/shoulder belt is available.*
[p] *Belt use required in rear seat if lap/shoulder belt is available.*

Safety belt use in the United States reached 82% in June 2005, the highest level yet recorded and a statistically significant increase over the 80% use rate observed the previous year. This result is from the National Occupant Protection Use Survey (NOPUS), which provides the only probability-based observed data on safety belt use in the United States.

The increase in use during 2004–2005 occurred in several areas, most notably in two that were the focus of a national campaign by the National Highway Traffic Safety Administration and the States to increase safety belt use — pickup trucks and rural areas (see chart below). Safety belt use increased by a statically significant 3 percentage points in both of these categories. Other significant increases in safety belt use

occurred among drivers, in States with primary enforcement laws (see page 94), in cars, vans and SUVs, and for motorists traveling during both the weekday rush hour and the weekday nonrush hour.

The nation's highest use rate, a significantly high 85%, was achieved in states with primary enforcement laws. In these states (AL, CA, CT, DE, GA, HI, IL, IN, IA, LA, MD, MI, NJ, NM, NY, NC, OK, OR, SC, TN, TX, WA, and the District of Columbia) motorists can be ticketed simply for not using their belts. This high use rate was also matched by motorists in vans and SUVs.

Glassbrenner, D. (2005). Safety Belt Use in 2005 — Overall Results (DOT HS 809 932, August). *Washington, DC: National Center for Statistics and Analysis.*

SAFETY BELT USE BY VEHICLE TYPE, URBANIZATION, AND ENFORCEMENT TYPE, UNITED STATES, 2005

OCCUPANT PROTECTION

Safety Belts

- When used, lap/shoulder safety belts reduce the risk of fatal injury to front seat passenger car occupants by 45% and reduce the risk of moderate-to-critical injury by 50%.

- For light truck occupants, safety belts reduce the risk of fatal injury by 60% and moderate-to-critical injury by 65%.

- Forty-nine states and the District of Columbia have mandatory belt use laws in effect, the only exception being New Hampshire. Twenty-four of the states with belt use laws in effect in 2005 specified secondary enforcement (i.e., police officers are permitted to write a citation only after a vehicle is stopped for some other traffic infraction). Twenty-five states and the District of Columbia had laws that allowed primary enforcement, enabling officers to stop vehicles and write citations whenever they observe violations of the belt law.

- Safety belts saved an estimated 15,632 lives in 2005 among passenger vehicle occupants over 4 years old. An additional 5,328 lives could have been saved in 2005 if all passenger vehicle occupants over age 4 wore safety belts. From 1975 through 2005, an estimated 211,128 lives were saved by safety belts.

- Safety belts provide the greatest protection against occupant ejection. Among crashes in which a fatality occurred in 2005, only 1% of restrained passenger car occupants were ejected, compared to 30% of unrestrained occupants.

- The results of a 1995 study by the National Highway Traffic Safety Administration (NHTSA) suggest that belt use among fatally injured occupants was at least 15% higher in states with primary enforcement laws.

Air Bags

- Air bags, combined with lap/shoulder belts, offer the best available protection for passenger vehicle occupants. Recent analyses indicate a fatality-reducing effectiveness for air bags of 14% when no safety belt was used and 11% when a safety belt was used in conjunction with air bags.

- Lap/shoulder belts should always be used, even in a vehicle with an air bag. Air bags are a supplemental form of protection and most are designed to deploy only in moderate-to-severe *frontal* crashes.

- Children in rear-facing child seats should not be placed in the front seat of vehicles equipped with passenger-side air bags. The impact of the deploying air bag could result in injury to the child.

- An estimated 2,741 lives were saved by air bags in 2005 and a total of 19,659 lives were saved from 1987 through 2005.

- Beginning September 1997, all new passenger cars were required to have driver and passenger side air bags. In 1998, the same requirement went into effect for light trucks.

Child Restraints

- Child restraints saved an estimated 420 lives in 2005 among children under the age of 5. Of the 420 lives saved, 382 were attributed to the use of child safety seats while 38 lives were spared with the use of adult belts.

- At 100% child safety seat use for children under the age of 5, an estimated 98 *additional* lives could have been saved in 2005.

- All states and the District of Columbia have had child restraint use laws in effect since 1985.

- Research has shown that child safety seats reduce fatal injury in passenger cars by 71% for infants (less than 1 year old), and by 54% for toddlers (1-4 years old). For infants and toddlers in light trucks, the corresponding reductions are 58% and 59%, respectively.

- In 2005, there were 361 occupant fatalities among children less than 4 years of age. Of the 344 fatalities in this age group for which restraint use was known, 32% were totally unrestrained. Of the 304 fatalities among children 4 to 7 years of age for which restraint use was known, 45% were unrestrained.

- An estimated 7,896 lives have been saved by child restraints from 1975 through 2005.

ESTIMATED NUMBER OF LIVES SAVED BY RESTRAINT SYSTEMS, 1975–2005

Restraint Type	1975–97	1998	1999	2000	2001	2002	2003	2004	2005
Seat Belts	100,851	11,680	11,941	12,882	13,295	14,264	15,095	15,548	15,632
Air Bags	3,022	1,208	1,491	1,716	1,978	2,324	2,519	2,660	2,741
Child Restraints	4,439	438	447	479	388	383	447	455	420

Motorcycle Helmets

- Technological changes over the past 15 years have led to improvements in helmet design and materials that have resulted in an increase in the effectiveness of helmets in preventing fatalities. The effectiveness of motorcycle helmets has increased from 29% in 1982 through 1987 to 37% over the years 1993 through 2005.

- Based on this new effectiveness data, it was estimated that motorcycle helmets saved the lives of 1,546 motorcyclists in 2005. An additional 728 lives could have been saved if all motorcyclists had worn helmets.

- Reported helmet use rates for fatally injured motorcyclists in 2005 were 58% for operators and 50% for passengers, compared with the corresponding rates of 56% and 47%, respectively, in 2004.

- In 2005, 20 states, the District of Columbia, and Puerto Rico required helmet use by all motorcycle operators and passengers. In another 27 states, only persons under a specific age, usually 18, were required to wear helmets. Three states had no laws requiring helmet use.

Safety Belt and Helmet Use

- According to the latest observational survey by the National Highway Traffic Safety Administration, the national safety belt use rate was 82% in 2005, the highest rate yet observed and a continuation of the relatively steady pattern of increased use since belt use was first measured by a national survey at 58% in 1994.

- Belt use rates in states with primary enforcement of belt laws ranged from 74% to 95% in 2005, while use rates in states with secondary enforcement ranged from 61% to 95%.

- In 2005, safety belt use in the United States ranged from 61% in Mississippi to 95% in Hawaii, Nevada, and Washington. Nine states and territories achieved usage rates of 90% or higher, namely Arizona, Hawaii, California, Maryland, Michigan, Nevada, Oregon, Washington, and Puerto Rico. Nevada, Texas, and West Virginia showed the greatest improvement, each reducing belt nonuse by 30% or more during the period 2004–2005.

- Women continue to use safety belts more than men do, with 84% of female motorists observed as belted in 2005, compared to 80% for males. Drivers and right-front-seat passengers who appeared to be aged 16–24 had significantly lower belt use rates than other age groups. Drivers with no passengers had significantly lower use rates than those with at least one or more passengers, while those with at least one passenger had significantly higher use rates. Males, white motorists, and drivers with no passengers all showed significant increases in their belt use rates from 2004–2005. Passengers in the second row of seats in passenger vehicles had a belt use rate of 68% in 2005, compared to 82% in the front seat. Motorists in second row seats who appeared to be aged 70 or older had significantly higher belt use rates than other age groups, while those who appeared to be aged 16–24 had lower rates. Motorists who appeared to be white had significantly higher rates than other racial groups. A significantly high 76% use rate among motorists in second row seats was observed in States with laws requiring belts be used in all seating positions, while those in States with laws requiring belts be used in the front seat only had a significantly lower belt use rate of 64%. Motorists who appeared to be members of races other than white or black showed a significant increase in their belt use rate from 2004 to 2005.

- Helmet use declined to 48% in 2005, representing a decline of 23 percentage points from the 71% use rate measured in 2000. This drop is statistically significant and corresponds to a notable 79% increase in nonuse.

See page 93 for additional information on safety belt use.

Source: National Center for Statistics and Analysis. (2006, September). Traffic Safety Facts 2005 Data — Occupant Protection (DOT HS 810 621); Traffic Safety Facts 2005 Data — Motorcycles (DOT HS 810 620), Washington, DC: Author. Glassbrenner, D. (2006). Safety Belt Use in 2005 — Use Rates in the States and Territories (DOT HS 809 970, March), Washington, DC: National Center for Statistics and Analysis. Glassbrenner, D. (2005). Safety Belt Use in 2005 — Demographic Results (DOT HS 809 969, December), Washington, DC: National Center for Statistics and Analysis.

SAFETY BELT USE BY GENDER. 2004–2005

ALCOHOL

According to studies conducted by the National Highway Traffic Safety Administration (NHTSA), about 39% of all traffic fatalities in 2005 involved an intoxicated or alcohol-impaired driver or nonmotorist. In 2005, 34% of all traffic fatalities occurred in crashes where at least one driver or nonoccupant was intoxicated (blood alcohol concentration [BAC] of 0.08 grams per deciliter [g/dl] or greater). Of the 14,539 people killed in such crashes, 71% were themselves intoxicated. The other 29% were passengers, nonintoxicated drivers, or nonintoxicated nonoccupants. The following data summarizes the extent of alcohol involvement in motor-vehicle crashes:

• Traffic fatalities in alcohol-related crashes fell by 0.2% from 2004 to 2005 and declined by 5% from 1995 to 2005. (See corresponding chart.) In 1995, alcohol-related fatalities accounted for 42% of all traffic deaths.

• According to NHTSA, alcohol was involved in 39% of fatal crashes and 7% of all crashes, both fatal and nonfatal, in 2005.

• Over 1.4 million drivers were arrested in 2004 for driving under the influence of alcohol or narcotics.

• There were 16,885 alcohol-related traffic fatalities in 2005, an average of one alcohol-related fatality every 31 minutes. An average of one person every 2 minutes is injured in a crash where alcohol is present.

• In 2005, alcohol was present in 30% of all fatal crashes on weekdays, compared to 52% on weekends. The rate of alcohol involvement in fatal crashes during the day is 18%, compared to 59% at night.

PERCENT OF TOTAL TRAFFIC FATALITIES WITH ALCOHOL PRESENT, BY STATE, 2005

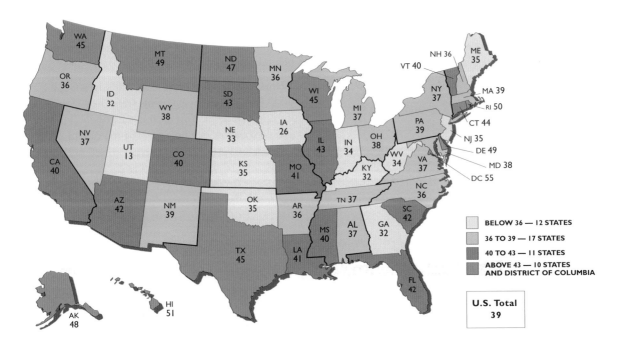

BELOW 36 — 12 STATES
36 TO 39 — 17 STATES
40 TO 43 — 11 STATES
ABOVE 43 — 10 STATES AND DISTRICT OF COLUMBIA

U.S. Total
39

ALCOHOL (CONT.)

- From 1995 to 2005, the change in the percentage of drivers involved in fatal crashes with BAC 0.08 g/dl or higher showed decreases for drivers in the 25–34, 35–44, 55-64, and 65–74 year age groups, increased for drivers in the 45–54 age group, and remained unchanged for drivers in the 16–20, 21–24, and 75 and over age groups. The greatest decrease was for drivers 55–64 years of age (–14%), followed by drivers 65–74 years old (–13%) and drivers in the 35–44 year age group (–12%). The increase for drivers in the 45–54 age group was +6%.

- All states and the District of Columbia now have 21-year-old minimum drinking age laws. In 2005, all states plus the District of Columbia had by law created a threshold making it illegal to drive with a BAC of 0.08 g/dl or higher.

- Safety belts were used by only 28% of fatally injured intoxicated drivers, compared to 44% of fatally injured alcohol-impaired drivers (BAC of 0.01 to 0.07 g/dl) and 56% of fatally injured sober drivers (BAC of 0.00 g/dl).

- The driver, pedestrian, or both were intoxicated in 44% of all fatal pedestrian crashes in 2005. In these crashes, the intoxication rate for pedestrians was nearly triple the rate for drivers.

- The cost of alcohol-related motor-vehicle crashes is estimated by the National Safety Council at $36.1 billion in 2005.

Source: National Center for Statistics and Analysis. (2006). Traffic Safety Facts 2005 Data — Alcohol. *Washington, DC: National Highway Traffic Safety Administration.*

PERCENT OF ALL TRAFFIC FATALITIES THAT OCCURRED IN ALCOHOL-RELATED CRASHES, 1995–2005

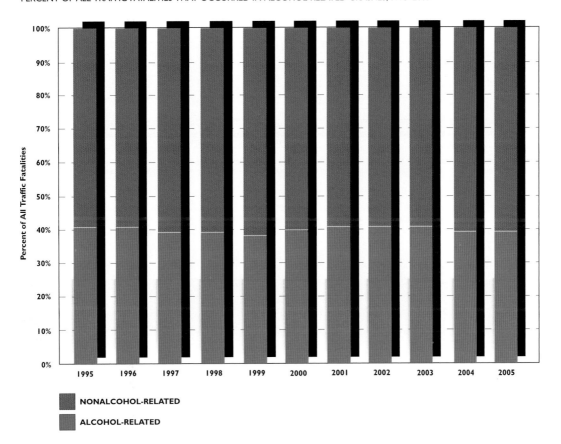

TYPE OF MOTOR-VEHICLE ACCIDENT

Although motor-vehicle deaths occur more often in collisions between motor vehicles than any other type of accident, this type represents only about 42% of the total. Collisions between a motor vehicle and a fixed object were the next most common type, with about 30% of the deaths, followed by pedestrian accidents and noncollisions (rollovers, etc.).

While collisions between motor vehicles accounted for less than half of motor-vehicle fatalities, this accident type represented 75% of injuries, 68% of injury accidents, and 70% of all accidents. Single-vehicle accidents involving collisions with fixed objects, pedestrians, and noncollisions, on the other hand,

accounted for a greater proportion of fatalities and fatal accidents compared to less serious accidents. These three accident types made up 55% of fatalities and 54% of fatal accidents, but 29% or less of injuries, injury accidents, or all accidents.

Of collisions between motor vehicles, angle collisions cause the greatest number of deaths, about 10,700 in 2005 and the greatest number of nonfatal injuries as well as fatal and injury accidents. The table below shows the estimated number of motor-vehicle deaths, injuries, fatal accidents, injury accidents, and all accidents for various types of accidents.

MOTOR-VEHICLE DEATHS AND INJURIES AND NUMBER OF ACCIDENTS BY TYPE OF ACCIDENT, 2005

Type of Accident	Deaths	Nonfatal Injuries	Fatal Accidents	Injury Accidents	All Accidents
Total	**45,800**	**2,400,000**	**41,300**	**1,600,000**	**10,700,000**
Collision with—					
Pedestrian	6,200	70,000	4,400	53,000	108,000
Other motor vehicle	19,200	1,800,000	18,000	1,090,000	7,540,000
Angle collision	*10,700*	*901,000*	*10,100*	*519,000*	*3,200,000*
Head-on collision	*5,500*	*107,000*	*4,900*	*56,000*	*220,000*
Rear-end collision	*2,000*	*699,000*	*2,000*	*454,000*	*3,280,000*
Sideswipe and other two-vehicle collisions	*1,000*	*93,000*	*1,000*	*61,000*	*840,000*
Railroad train	300	1,000	200	1,000	2,000
Pedalcycle	1,000	51,000	800	40,000	90,000
Animal, animal-drawn vehicle	100	8,000	100	8,000	490,000
Fixed object	13,700	360,000	12,800	320,000	2,120,000
Noncollision	**5,300**	**110,000**	**5,000**	**88,000**	**350,000**

Source: National Safety Council estimates, based on data from the National Highway Traffic Safety Administration Fatality Analysis Reporting System and General Estimates System. Procedures for estimating the number of accidents by type were changed for the 1998 edition and are not comparable to estimates in previous editions (See Technical Appendix).

SPEEDING

Speeding is one of the major factors contributing to the occurrence of deaths, injuries, and property damage related to motor-vehicle crashes. The role of speeding in crash causation can be described in terms of its effect on the driver, the vehicle, and the road. Excessive-speed driving reduces the amount of time the driver has to react in a dangerous situation to avoid a crash. Speeding increases vehicle stopping distance and also reduces the ability of road safety structures such as guardrails, impact attenuators, crash cushions, median dividers, and concrete barriers to protect vehicle occupants in a crash.

The National Highway Traffic Safety Administration (NHTSA) estimates that speeding-related crashes[a] cost the nation $40.4 billion, or 18% of the entire cost of motor-vehicle crashes in the United States. These economic losses are equivalent to $110.7 million per day or $4.6 million per hour.

Speeding was a factor in 30% of all traffic fatalities in 2005, killing an average of 36 vehicle occupants per day. The total number of motor-vehicle crashes attributable to speeding has not changed appreciably over the last decade with over 10,000 fatal crashes occurring every year.

Forty-two percent of all speeding-related fatalities in 2005 occurred on roads where the posted speed limit was 55–65 miles per hour and an additional 7% occurred on roads with the posted speed limit of 65 miles per hour or more.

There were 79 fewer speeding-related traffic deaths in 2005 (13,113 deaths), a decline of 0.6% compared to 2004 (13,192 deaths).

The state map below shows the percent of all traffic deaths where speeding was involved. In 2005, Maine and Hawaii had the highest proportion of speeding-related fatalities, whereas Florida and Iowa had the lowest. From 2004 to 2005, Mississippi, Iowa, and New Hampshire showed the greatest improvement, each reducing speeding-related fatalities by 25% or more, while the number of speeding-related fatalities in Florida more than doubled.

[a]A crash is considered speeding related if the driver was charged with a speeding-related offense or if racing, driving too fast for conditions, or exceeding the posted speed limit was indicated as a contributing factor in the crash.

Source: National Center for Statistics and Analysis. (2006). Traffic Safety Facts 2005 — Speeding. Washington, DC: National Highway Traffic Safety Administration. DOT HS 810 629.

PERCENT OF TOTAL TRAFFIC FATALITIES INVOLVING SPEEDING, BY STATE, 2005

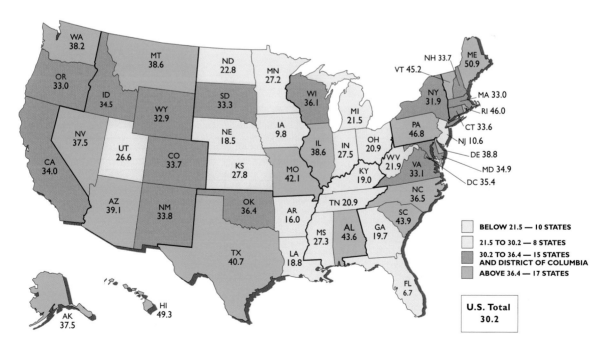

CELL PHONE USE WHILE DRIVING

Driver distractions from all sources, including cell phones, contribute to approximately 25% of all police-reported crashes, or about 1.5 million crashes per year.[a]

The National Occupant Protection Use Survey (NOPUS) is the only available source of data on cell phone use while driving that includes a nationally representative sample of American drivers. The survey is conducted annually between 8:00 A.M. and 6:00 P.M. through direct observations of stopped vehicles and their occupants at intersections controlled by a stop sign or stoplight. The survey methodology differentiates between drivers who are observed to be holding phones to their ears, using a headset, and manipulating a handheld device.

According to the 2005 NOPUS survey, which included 43,000 vehicles observed at 1,200 sites across the country, 10% of all drivers on the road at any given time are engaged in some type of inappropriate cell phone use while driving.

In 2005, 6% of all drivers were observed holding a phone to their ears while driving, 0.7% using a headset, and 0.2% manipulating a handheld device. Higher percentages of males than females were observed holding a phone to their ears and using a headset. All three behaviors of interest were higher among younger drivers. Drivers traveling alone were more likely to be engaged in some type of inappropriate cell phone use compared to those traveling with passengers, while drivers transporting children under the age of 8 years were more likely to be holding a phone to their ears or using a headset than those whose passengers were at least 8 years old.

From 2004 to 2005, the rates of inappropriate cell phone use while driving increased across all three observation categories.[b]

PERCENT OF DRIVERS ENGAGED IN CELL PHONE USE WHILE DRIVING, UNITED STATES, 2004–2005[b]

Characteristic	Holding Phone to Their Ears			Using a Headset			Manipulating Handheld Device[d]
	2004	2005	2004–2005 Change	2004	2005	2004–2005 Change	2005
Total	**5.0%**	**6.0%**	**1.0%**	**0.4%**	**0.7%**	**0.3%**	**0.2%**
Sex							
Male	4.0	5.0	1.0	0.5	0.7	0.2	0.1
Female	6.0	8.0	2.0[e]	0.2	0.6	0.4[e]	0.2
Driver Age							
16–24 years	8.0	10.0	2.0[e]	0.8	1.3	0.5	0.3
25–69 years	5.0	6.0	1.0	0.3	0.6	0.3[e]	0.1
70 years and older	1.0	1.0	0.0	(c)	(c)	—	(c)
Race							
Black	5.0	6.0	1.0	0.8	1.3	0.5	0.1
White	5.0	6.0	1.0	0.3	0.6	0.3	0.2
Other	3.0	6.0	3.0[e]	0.2	0.7	0.5	0.2
Vehicle Type							
Passenger Cars	4.0	6.0	2.0[e]	0.4	0.7	0.3	0.2
Vans & SUVs	6.0	7.0	1.0	0.3	1.0	0.7[e]	0.2
Pickup Trucks	5.0	5.0	0.0	0.4	0.3	−0.1	0.1
Region							
Northeast	3.0	4.0	1.0	1.0	0.9	−0.1	0.3
Midwest	5.0	8.0	3.0	0.2	1.7	1.5[e]	0.1
South	6.0	5.0	−1.0	0.4	0.4	0.0	0.2
West	6.0	8.0	2.0[e]	0.3	0.3	0.0	0.1
Area							
Urban	7.0	7.0	0.0	0.9	0.9	0.0	0.1
Suburban	4.0	7.0	3.0[e]	0.2	0.7	0.5[e]	0.2
Rural	6.0	3.0	−3.0	0.4	0.5	0.1	0.1
Day of Week/Time of Day							
Weekdays	5.0	7.0	2.0	0.4	0.8	0.4[e]	0.2
Rush Hours	*5.0*	*8.0*	*3.0[e]*	*0.6*	*0.8*	*0.2*	*0.1*
Nonrush Hours	*5.0*	*6.0*	*1.0*	*0.3*	*0.8*	*0.5[e]*	*0.2*
Weekends	3.0	4.0	1.0[e]	0.2	0.2	0.0	0.2
Passengers							
None	6.0	8.0	2.0	0.5	0.8	0.3	0.2
One or more	2.0	2.0	0.0	0.1	0.4	0.3	0.0
Age of Passenger							
0–7 years	7.0	6.0	−1.0	(c)	1.0	—	(c)
8 and older	2.0	2.0	0.0	0.1	0.3	−0.7	0.0

[a] National Highway Traffic Safety Administration. (2005). NHTSA Vehicle safety rulemaking and supporting research priorities: 2005–2009. Retrieved from http://www.nhtsa.gov/cars/rules/rulings/PriorityPlan-2005.html
[b] Gassbranner, D. (2005). Driver Cell Phone Use in 2005 — Overall Results. Washington, DC: National Highway Traffic Safety Administration. DOT HS 809 967.
[c] Estimate is not shown because it does not meet standard of reliability or precision.
[d] 2004 data not available.
[e] Statistical confidence in a 2004–2005 change of 90% or higher.

IMPROPER DRIVING

In most motor-vehicle accidents, factors are present relating to the driver, the vehicle and the road, and it is the interaction of these factors that often sets up the series of events that result in an accident. The table below relates only to the driver, and shows the principal kinds of improper driving in accidents in 2005 as reported by police.

Exceeding the posted speed limit or driving at an unsafe speed was the most common error in fatal accidents. Right-of-way violations predominated in the injury accidents and all accidents categories.

While some drivers were under the influence of alcohol or other drugs, this represents the driver's physical condition — not a driving error. See page 96 for a discussion of alcohol involvement in traffic accidents.

Correcting the improper practices listed below could reduce the number of accidents. This does not mean, however, that road and vehicle conditions can be disregarded.

IMPROPER DRIVING REPORTED IN ACCIDENTS, 2005

Kind of Improper Driving	Fatal Accidents	Injury Accidents	All Accidents
Total	**100.0%**	**100.0%**	**100.0%**
Improper driving	**62.7**	**62.7**	**58.5**
Speed too fast or unsafe	18.1	15.0	12.7
Right of way	12.2	17.5	14.3
Failed to yield	*8.0*	*12.5*	*10.8*
Disregarded signal	*1.4*	*2.5*	*1.7*
Passed stop sign	*2.8*	*2.5*	*1.8*
Drove left of center	8.0	2.2	1.6
Made improper turn	4.5	4.2	4.5
Improper overtaking	1.4	0.6	0.8
Followed too closely	1.0	6.8	8.7
Other improper driving	17.5	16.4	15.9
No improper driving stated	**37.3**	**37.3**	**41.5**

Source: Based on reports from 20 state traffic authorities. Percents may not add to totals due to rounding.

MOTORCYCLES

Fatalities among motorcycle riders and passengers have increased 104% between 1995 and 2005. Nonfatal injuries increased, too, from 57,000 to 87,000.

Exposure has also increased. From 1995 through 2004 (the latest year available), the number of registered motorcycles increased 48% from 3.9 million to 5.8 million. Miles traveled, however, is up only 2.6% from 9.8 billion to 10.0 billion. Consequently, the death rate has increased 76% from 22.73 to 40.09 deaths per 100 million miles traveled.

In 1995, 50% of fatally injured riders were younger than 30 and 25% were 40 years old or older. In 2005, 32% were under 30 and 47% were 40 or older. Compared to other vehicle drivers, fatally injured motorcycle operators are more likely to be involved in a fixed object collision, more likely to have an invalid license, and more likely to be intoxicated. See page 95 for data on motorcycle helmet use and effectiveness.

Source: National Center for Statistics and Analysis. (2006). Traffic Safety Facts 2005 Data: Motorcycles. DOT HS 810 620. Washington, DC: National Highway Traffic Safety Administration.

MOTORCYCLIST DEATHS AND DEATH RATES, UNITED STATES, 1995–2005

LARGE TRUCKS

In 2005, one out of eight traffic fatalities resulted from a crash involving a large truck and 76% of these 5,212 deaths were occupants of vehicles other than the large truck. An estimated 113,000 people were injured in large truck crashes in 2005. A large truck is one with gross vehicle weight rating greater than 10,000 pounds.

Large trucks were more likely to be involved in a multiple-vehicle fatal crash than passenger vehicles. Eighty three percent of large trucks in fatal crashes were in multiple-vehicle crashes compared to 61% of passenger vehicles.

Thirty percent of fatal crashes involving a large truck and another vehicle were front-to-front collisions. The truck was struck in the rear 2.6 times more often than the other vehicle (18% and 7%, respectively) while the other vehicle was struck on the right side 2.3 times more often than the large truck (14% and 6%, respectively).

Most large truck fatal crashes occurred in rural areas (61%) and on weekdays (81%). Nearly three quarters (74%) of the fatal crashes happened during the daytime on weekdays while on weekends 60% occurred at night.

Only 1% of large truck drivers in fatal crashes were intoxicated compared to 22% for drivers of passenger cars, 21% for light trucks, and 27% for motorcycles.

Source: National Center for Statistics and Analysis. (2006). Traffic Safety Facts 2005 Data: Large Trucks. DOT HS 810 619. Washington, DC: National Highway Traffic Safety Administration.

FATALITIES IN CRASHES INVOLVING LARGE TRUCKS, UNITED STATES, 2005

School bus-related crashes killed 134 persons nationwide in 2005, according to data from the National Highway Traffic Safety Administration.

A school bus-related crash is defined by NHTSA to be any crash in which a vehicle, regardless of body design, used as a school bus is directly or indirectly involved, such as a crash involving school children alighting from a vehicle.

Over the period from 2000–2005, about 70% of the deaths in school bus-related crashes were occupants of vehicles other than the school bus and 19% were pedestrians. About 5% were school bus passengers and 4% were school bus drivers.

Of the pedestrians killed in school bus-related crashes over this period, approximately 83% were struck by the school bus.

Out of the people injured in school bus-related crashes from 2000 through 2004, about 46% were school bus passengers, 8% were school bus drivers, and another 41% were occupants of other vehicles. The remainder were pedestrians, pedalcyclists, and other or unknown type persons.

Characteristics of school bus transportation

Forty-eight states reported that about 24.4 million public school pupils were transported at public expense and 33 states reported that public funds were used to transport another 1.0 million private school pupils. These data are prepared by School Bus Fleet (vol. 52, no. 1) for the 2003-2004 school year with 10 states reporting for prior school years. This compares to estimates from the U.S. Department of Education of enrollments in fall 2003 in grades K–12 of about 48.5 million public school pupils and 6.3 million private school pupils nationwide. Fifty states employed a total of 470,371 school buses, and the buses in 42 states traveled about 3.9 billion route miles.

DEATHS AND INJURIES IN SCHOOL BUS–RELATED CRASHES, UNITED STATES, 2000–2005

	2000	2001	2002	2003	2004	2005
Deaths						
Total	**147**	**141**	**129**	**140**	**133**	**134**
School bus driver	8	6	1	6	3	5
School bus passenger	13	12	2	5	4	5
Pedestrian	26	22	20	27	30	30
Pedalcyclist	1	4	5	2	3	6
Occupant of other vehicle	99	95	100	100	93	87
Other or Unknown	0	2	1	0	0	1
Injuries						
Total	**20,000**	**13,000**	**18,000**	**19,000**	**17,000**	**11,000**
School bus driver	2,000	1,000	1,000	2,000	1,000	1,000
School bus passenger	8,000	6,000	9,000	9,000	8,000	4,000
Pedestrian	1,000	(a)	1,000	(a)	1,000	(a)
Pedalcyclist	(a)	(a)	(a)	(a)	(a)	(a)
Occupant of other vehicle	9,000	5,000	7,000	8,000	7,000	6,000
Other or Unknown	(a)	(a)	(a)	(a)	(a)	(a)

Source: National Highway Traffic Safety Administration.
[a] *Less than 500.*

AGE OF DRIVER

The table below shows the total number of licensed drivers and drivers involved in accidents by selected ages and age groups. The figures in the last two columns indicate the rate of accident involvement on the basis of the number of drivers in each age group. The fatal accident involvement rates per 100,000 drivers in each age group ranged from a low of 22 for drivers 55 to 64 years of age to a high of 71 for drivers aged 16. The all accident involvement rates per 100 drivers in each age group ranged from 4 for drivers in the 75 and over age group to 32 for drivers aged 16.

On the basis of miles driven by each age group, however, involvement rates (not shown in the table) are highest for young and old drivers. For drivers aged 16 to 19, the fatal involvement rate per 100 million vehicle miles traveled was 9.2 in 1990, about three times the overall rate for all drivers in passenger vehicles, 3.0. The rate for drivers aged 75 and over was 11.5, the highest of all age groups. The same basic "U"-shaped curve is found for injury accident involvement rates.[a]

[a]Massie, D., Campbell, K., & Williams, A. (1995). Traffic accident involvement rates by driver age and gender. Accident Analysis and Prevention, 27 (1), 73–87.

AGE OF DRIVER — TOTAL NUMBER AND NUMBER IN ACCIDENTS, 2005

| Age Group | Licensed Drivers | | Drivers in ... | | | | | |
| | | | Fatal Accidents | | | All Accidents | | |
	Number	Percent	Number	Percent	Rate[a]	Number	Percent	Rate[b]
Total	201,500,000	100.0%	62,300	100.0%	31	18,400,000	100.0%	9
Under 16	52,000	(c)	400	0.6	(d)	250,000	1.4	(d)
16	1,271,000	0.6	900	1.4	71	410,000	2.2	32
17	2,197,000	1.1	1,300	2.1	59	570,000	3.1	26
18	2,758,000	1.4	1,800	2.9	65	650,000	3.5	24
19	3,118,000	1.6	1,900	3.0	61	610,000	3.3	20
19 and under	9,396,000	4.7	6,300	10.1	67	2,490,000	13.5	27
20	3,217,000	1.6	1,800	2.9	56	610,000	3.3	19
21	3,245,000	1.6	1,900	3.0	59	540,000	2.9	17
22	3,394,000	1.7	1,900	3.0	56	500,000	2.7	15
23	3,460,000	1.7	1,700	2.7	49	500,000	2.7	14
24	3,570,000	1.8	1,600	2.6	45	490,000	2.7	14
20–24	16,886,000	8.4	8,900	14.3	53	2,640,000	14.3	16
25–34	36,003,000	17.9	11,300	18.1	31	3,820,000	20.8	11
35–44	40,394,000	20.0	10,400	16.7	26	3,420,000	18.6	8
45–54	39,851,000	19.8	9,600	15.4	24	3,060,000	16.6	8
55–64	29,685,000	14.7	6,600	10.6	22	1,610,000	8.8	5
65–74	16,492,000	8.2	4,200	6.7	25	800,000	4.3	5
75 and over	12,793,000	6.4	5,000	8.0	39	560,000	3.0	4

Source: National Safety Council estimates. Drivers in accidents based on data from National Highway Traffic Safety Administration's Fatality Analysis Reporting System and General Estimates System. Total licensed drivers from the Federal Highway Administration; age distribution by National Safety Council.
Note: Percents may not add to total due to rounding.
[a]Drivers in fatal accidents per 100,000 licensed drivers in each age group.
[b]Drivers in all accidents per 100 licensed drivers in each age group.
[c]Less than 0.05.
[d]Rates for drivers under age 16 are substantially overstated due to the high proportion of unlicensed drivers involved.

Motor-vehicle crashes are the leading cause of death for young people 15–20 years old. In 2003 (the latest year available), according to a National Safety Council analysis of National Center for Health Statistics mortality data, 6,543 young people died in crashes. More than half of them (56%) were drivers.

In 2005, 7,460 young drivers were involved in fatal crashes and 1.7 million were involved in police-reported crashes of all severities according to National Highway Traffic Safety Administration data. Young drivers represent 6.3% of all licensed drivers but 12.6% of drivers in fatal crashes and 16% of drivers in all crashes.

In 2005, 3,467 young drivers were killed in crashes (see the graph below) and another 281,000 were injured.

Twenty percent of young drivers involved in fatal crashes had been drinking. Four percent had a BAC between .01 and .07 g/dL and 16% were intoxicated (BAC .08 or greater). Of those who were fatally injured, 23% were intoxicated.

Source: National Center for Statistics and Analysis. (2006). Traffic Safety Facts 2005 Data: Young Drivers. DOT HS 810 630. Washington, DC: National Highway Traffic Safety Administration.

FATALITIES IN CRASHES INVOLVING DRIVERS 15–20 YEARS OLD, UNITED STATES, 2005

Occupants of other vehicles 1,933

Nonoccupants 622

Passengers in young drivers' vehicles 2,171

Young drivers 3,467

Graduated driver licensing (GDL) is an effective way to reduce the impact of motor-vehicle crashes on the lives of young drivers. GDL is a three-stage licensing system for beginning drivers consisting of a learner's permit that allows driving only while supervised by a fully licensed driver, an intermediate license that allows unsupervised driving with certain restrictions (usually on young passengers and night time operation), and a full license. Both the learner's permit and intermediate license have minimum age requirements and must be held for a specified minimum time period.

Evaluations of GDL laws as implemented in 13 states and 4 Canadian provinces have reported positive findings, with reductions for all types of crashes among all teenage drivers. The size of the reductions varied as did the specific features of the laws.

Two studies looked at the United States as a whole. Williams, Ferguson, and Wells (2005) analyzed fatality data from 1993 to 2003 during which time GDL was implemented in 46 states and the District of Columbia. They found that the per capita crash rate for 16 year old drivers decreased 26% over this period, compared to an 11% reduction for 17 year old drivers, 6% for 18-19 year old drivers, and 7% for drivers 20-49 years old. Young passenger restrictions for 16 year old drivers appeared to be effective but night time restriction did

not. Baker, Chen, and Li (2006) examined 16 year old drivers in fatal crashes from 1994 through 2004 and found that the most comprehensive GDL programs reduced their fatal crash involvement rate by about 20%. The most beneficial GDL components were a three month minimum learner's permit period, a night time driving restriction, and either 30 or more hours of supervised driving or a passenger restriction.

Morrisey, Grabowski, Dee, and Campbell (2006) compared GDL programs based on their quality as defined by the Insurance Institute for Highway Safety. "Good" laws were found to reduce traffic deaths among 15-17 year olds by 19%. "Fair" laws reduced night time fatalities by 13% but had no effect on day time fatalities. "Marginal" laws had no effect.

Summary articles on the science behind GDL and annual updates on GDL research may be found at www.nsc.org/gdlsym.

References

Baker, S.P., Chen, L-H, & Li, G. (2006). National evaluation of graduated driver licensing programs. DOT HS 810 614. Washington, DC: National Highway Traffic Safety Administration.

Morrisey, M.A., Grabowski, D.C., Dee, T.S., & Campbell, C. (2006). The strength of graduated driver's license programs and fatalities among teen drivers and passengers. Accident Analysis and Prevention, 38(1), 135–141.

Williams, A.F., Ferguson, S.A., & Wells, J.K. (2005). The 16-year-old driver crash problem in the United States in 2003. Arlington, VA: Insurance Institute for Highway Safety.

PEDESTRIANS

In 2005, there were an estimated 6,200 pedestrian deaths and 70,000 injuries in motor-vehicle accidents. About 63% of these deaths and injuries occur when pedestrians improperly cross roadways or intersections or dart/run into streets. Playing, working, standing, etc. in the roadway accounted for over 9% of pedestrian deaths and injuries, while walking with traffic accounted for over 4%.

The distribution of pedestrian deaths and injuries by action varies for persons of different ages. Darting/

running into the road was the leading type for the three youngest age groups, varying from 40% for those aged 5 to 9 years to 75% for those aged 10 to 14 years. Improper crossing of the roadway or intersection was the leading type for the 15 to 19, 20 to 24, 25 to 44, 45 to 64, and 65 and over age groups, ranging from 30% for those aged 15 to 19 years to over 44% for those aged 45 to 64 years.

DEATHS AND INJURIES OF PEDESTRIANS BY AGE AND ACTION, 2005

		Age of Persons Killed or Injured							
	Total[a]	0–4	5–9	10–14	15–19	20–24	25–44	45–64	65 & Over
All Actions	100.0%	6.4%	15.6%	9.8%	11.2%	10.1%	22.8%	17.6%	6.6%
Totals	**100.0%**	**100.0%**	**100.0%**	**100.0%**	**100.0%**	**100.0%**	**100.0%**	**100.0%**	**100.0%**
Improper crossing of roadway or intersection	32.2%	4.5%	35.7%	16.7%	29.7%	32.2%	33.9%	44.5%	39.6%
Darting or running into roadway	31.1%	70.2%	40.3%	74.8%	25.9%	25.9%	13.2%	22.8%	7.6%
Walking with traffic	4.5%	0.0%	0.4%	2.7%	5.7%	4.8%	9.8%	2.7%	5.4%
Walking against traffic	1.9%	0.5%	5.5%	0.8%	3.0%	1.4%	1.4%	0.5%	0.0%
Playing/working/standing, etc. in roadway	9.5%	13.7%	6.1%	2.2%	5.9%	7.6%	14.7%	9.9%	14.2%
Nonmotorist pushing a vehicle in roadway	0.5%	0.0%	0.0%	0.0%	0.3%	0.0%	2.3%	0.0%	0.0%
Inattentive — talking, eating, etc.	2.0%	0.7%	1.3%	0.0%	9.3%	1.6%	2.1%	0.7%	0.0%
Other action	11.6%	2.0%	9.8%	1.8%	11.7%	17.1%	16.5%	12.4%	12.0%
Not stated	6.6%	8.4%	0.9%	1.1%	8.5%	9.5%	6.2%	6.6%	21.2%

Source: National Highway Traffic Safety Administration, General Estimates System, 2005.
[a]Total includes "Age Unknown."

PEDESTRIAN DEATHS AND DEATH RATES BY SEX AND AGE GROUP, UNITED STATES, 2003

Source: National Safety Council based on National Center for Health Statistics data.

DEATHS AND MILEAGE DEATH RATES BY MONTH

Motor-vehicle deaths in 2005 were at their lowest level in February and increased to their highest level in July. In 2005, the highest monthly mileage death rate of 1.69 deaths per 100,000,000 vehicle miles occurred in October. The overall rate for the year was 1.54.

Source: Deaths — National Safety Council estimates. Mileage — Federal Highway Administration, Traffic Volume Trends.

MOTOR-VEHICLE DEATHS AND MILEAGE DEATH RATES BY MONTH, 2005

HOLIDAYS

Holidays are traditionally a time of travel for families across the United States and many choose the automobile — with the highest fatality rate of any of the major forms of transportation based on fatalities per passenger mile (see page 134) — as their mode of travel and therefore increase their risk of dying in a motor- vehicle crash. In addition, holidays are often the cause for celebrations that include the drinking of alcohol, which is a major contributing factor to motor-vehicle crashes. Alcohol-related fatalities in 2005 represented 39% of the total traffic fatalities for the year.

MOTOR-VEHICLE DEATHS AND PERCENT ALCOHOL-RELATED DURING HOLIDAY PERIODS, 2000–2005

| Year | Holiday Period[a] | | | | | | | | | | | |
| | New Year's Day | | Memorial Day | | Independence Day | | Labor Day | | Thanksgiving | | Christmas | |
	Deaths[b]	Alcohol-Related[c] %	Deaths[b]	Alcohol-Related[c] %	Deaths[b]	Alcohol-Related[c] %	Deaths[b]	Alcohol-Related[c] %	Deaths[b]	Alcohol-Related[c] %	Deaths[b]	Alcohol-Related[c] %
2000	458 (3)	58	451 (3)	55	683 (4)	49	514 (3)	54	497 (4)	53	419 (3)	51
2001	338 (3)	51	499 (3)	55	173 (1)	62	432 (3)	51	580 (4)	48	575 (4)	48
2002	554 (3)	52	484 (3)	47	662 (4)	48	536 (3)	57	527 (4)	47	114 (1)	54
2003	203 (1)	63	472 (3)	48	500 (3)	55	490 (3)	51	544 (4)	45	488 (4)	46
2004	549 (4)	50	496 (3)	49	502 (3)	49	480 (3)	49	556 (4)	42	370 (3)	49
2005	449 (3)	50	512 (3)	48	565 (3)	51	500 (3)	51	605 (4)	44	383 (3)	45

Source: National Highway Traffic Safety Administration (NHTSA), Fatality Analysis Reporting System and National Highway Traffic Safety Administration, Traffic Safety Facts, 2005 edition.
[a]The length of the holiday period depends on the day of the week on which the holiday falls. Memorial Day and Labor Day are always 3.25 days, Thanksgiving is always 4.25 days, and New Year's, Independence Day, and Christmas are 3.25 days if the holiday falls on Friday thru Monday, 4.25 days if it falls on Tuesday or Thursday, and 1.25 days if it falls on Wednesday.
[b]Number in parentheses refers to the number of whole days in the holiday period.
[c]Blood alcohol concentration (BAC) of .01 grams per deciliter (g/dl) or greater. The holiday periods used to calculate the percentages conform to the NHTSA holiday period definitions that add another quarter day to the periods noted in footnote (a).

WORK ZONE DEATHS AND INJURIES

In 2005 there were 1,074 people killed and 37,653 people injured in work zone crashes (see table below). Compared to 2004, work zone fatalities increased 1% and injuries decreased 21%. Of the 1,074 people killed in work zones, 872 were in construction zones, 98 were in maintenance zones, 17 were in utility zones, and 87 were in an unknown type of work zone.

Over the 10 years from 1996 through 2005, work zone deaths have ranged from 658 to 1,181 and averaged 954 per year.

Based on a National Safety Council survey in August 2006, 31 states reported having work zone speed laws and 49 states had special penalties for traffic violations in work zones, such as increased or doubled fines. Hawaii and District of Columbia were the only jurisdictions with neither.

PERSONS KILLED AND INJURED IN WORK ZONES, UNITED STATES, 2005

	Total	Vehicle Occupants	Pedestrians	Pedalcyclists	Other Nonmotorists
Killed	1,074	916	137	12	9
Injured	37,653	36,252	1,148	125	128

Source: National Safety Council analysis of data from National Highway Traffic Safety Administration Fatality Analysis Reporting System (FARS) and General Estimates Systems (GES).

EMERGENCY VEHICLES

CRASHES INVOLVING EMERGENCY VEHICLES, UNITED STATES, 2005

	Ambulance		Fire Truck/Car		Police Car	
	Total	Emergency Use[a]	Total	Emergency Use[a]	Total	Emergency Use[a]
Emergency vehicles in fatal crashes	43	24	27	17	100	40
Emergency vehicles in injury crashes	1,820	1,147	914	537	7,316	3,726
Emergency vehicles in all crashes	**4,815**	**2,060**	**3,332**	**1,794**	**27,200**	**12,415**
Emergency vehicle drivers killed	4	2	4	2	27	6
Emergency vehicle passengers killed	11	7	2	1	4	2
Other vehicle occupants killed	29	17	20	14	60	28
Nonmotorists killed	5	1	3	2	22	13
Total killed in crashes	**49**	**27**	**29**	**19**	**113**	**49**
Total injured in crashes	**3,835**	**2,687**	**1,571**	**1,145**	**12,442**	**7,120**

Source: National Safety Council analysis of data from National Highway Traffic Safety Administration Fatality Analysis Reporting System (FARS) and General Estimates Systems (GES).
[a]Emergency lights and/or sirens in use.

The National Safety Council and the National Highway Traffic Safety Administration (NHTSA) count motor-vehicle crash deaths using somewhat different criteria. The Council counts total motor-vehicle-related fatalities — both traffic and nontraffic — that occur within one year of the crash. This is consistent with the data compiled from death certificates by the National Center for Health Statistics (NCHS). The Council uses the NCHS death certificate data as the final count of deaths from all causes.

NHTSA counts only traffic fatalities that occur within 30 days of the crash in its Fatality Analysis Reporting System (FARS). This means that the FARS count omits about 800 to 1,000 motor-vehicle-related deaths each year that occur more than 30 days after the crash. Nontraffic fatalities (those that do not occur on public highways; e.g., parking lots, private roads and driveways), which account for 900 to 1,400 deaths annually, are also omitted. By using a 30-day cut off, NHTSA can issue a "final" count about eight months after the reference year.

Because of the time it takes to process 2.4 million deaths certificates, the NCHS data are not available until about 22 months after the reference year. This means, for example, that this edition of Injury Facts includes the 2003 NCHS final counts by cause of death including motor-vehicle crashes and estimates of the totals for 2004 and 2005. For motor-vehicle deaths, these estimates are based on data supplied by traffic authorities in 48 states and the District of Columbia so they are fairly reliable. For other causes of death, the estimates are based on data supplied by state vital statistics authorities. See the Technical Appendix for more information on estimation procedures.

The graph below shows the NCHS death certificate counts of total motor-vehicle deaths through 2003 and the NSC estimates for 2004 and 2005 compared to the NHTSA FARS counts of traffic deaths.

MOTOR-VEHICLE DEATHS: NSC AND NHTSA, 1992–2005

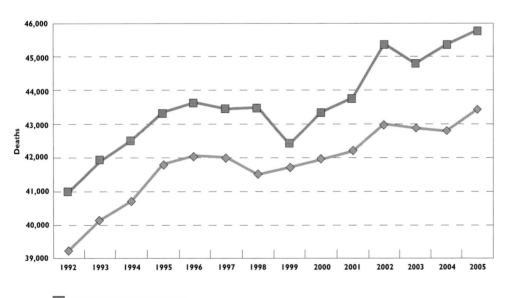

■ NATIONAL SAFETY COUNCIL

◆ NATIONAL HIGHWAY TRAFFIC SAFETY ADMINISTRATION

MOTOR-VEHICLE DEATHS AND RATES

MOTOR-VEHICLE DEATHS AND RATES, UNITED STATES, 1913–2005

Year	No. of Deaths	Estimated No. of Vehicles (Millions)	Estimated Vehicle Miles (Billions)	Estimated No. of Drivers (Millions)	Death Rates		
					Per 10,000 Motor Vehicles	Per 100,000,000 Vehicle Miles	Per 100,000 Population
1913	4,200	1.3	(a)	2.0	33.38	(a)	4.4
1914	4,700	1.8	(a)	3.0	26.65	(a)	4.8
1915	6,600	2.5	(a)	3.0	26.49	(a)	6.6
1916	8,200	3.6	(a)	5.0	22.66	(a)	8.1
1917	10,200	5.1	(a)	7.0	19.93	(a)	10.0
1918	10,700	6.2	(a)	9.0	17.37	(a)	10.3
1919	11,200	7.6	(a)	12.0	14.78	(a)	10.7
1920	12,500	9.2	(a)	14.0	13.53	(a)	11.7
1921	13,900	10.5	(a)	16.0	13.25	(a)	12.9
1922	15,300	12.3	(a)	19.0	12.47	(a)	13.9
1923	18,400	15.1	85	22.0	12.18	21.65	16.5
1924	19,400	17.6	104	26.0	11.02	18.65	17.1
1925	21,900	20.1	122	30.0	10.89	17.95	19.1
1926	23,400	22.2	141	33.0	10.54	16.59	20.1
1927	25,800	23.3	158	34.0	11.07	16.33	21.8
1928	28,000	24.7	173	37.0	11.34	16.18	23.4
1929	31,200	26.7	197	40.0	11.69	15.84	25.7
1930	32,900	26.7	206	40.0	12.32	15.97	26.7
1931	33,700	26.1	216	39.0	12.91	15.60	27.2
1932	29,500	24.4	200	36.0	12.09	14.75	23.6
1933	31,363	24.2	201	35.0	12.96	15.60	25.0
1934	36,101	25.3	216	37.0	14.27	16.71	28.6
1935	36,369	26.5	229	39.0	13.72	15.88	28.6
1936	38,089	28.5	252	42.0	13.36	15.11	29.7
1937	39,643	30.1	270	44.0	13.19	14.68	30.8
1938	32,582	29.8	271	44.0	10.93	12.02	25.1
1939	32,386	31.0	285	46.0	10.44	11.35	24.7
1940	34,501	32.5	302	48.0	10.63	11.42	26.1
1941	39,969	34.9	334	52.0	11.45	11.98	30.0
1942	28,309	33.0	268	49.0	8.58	10.55	21.1
1943	23,823	30.9	208	46.0	7.71	11.44	17.8
1944	24,282	30.5	213	45.0	7.97	11.42	18.3
1945	28,076	31.0	250	46.0	9.05	11.22	21.2
1946	33,411	34.4	341	50.0	9.72	9.80	23.9
1947	32,697	37.8	371	53.0	8.64	8.82	22.8
1948	32,259	41.1	398	55.0	7.85	8.11	22.1
1949	31,701	44.7	424	59.3	7.09	7.47	21.3
1950	34,763	49.2	458	62.2	7.07	7.59	23.0
1951	36,996	51.9	491	64.4	7.13	7.53	24.1
1952	37,794	53.3	514	66.8	7.10	7.36	24.3
1953	37,956	56.3	544	69.9	6.74	6.97	24.0
1954	35,586	58.6	562	72.2	6.07	6.33	22.1
1955	38,426	62.8	606	74.7	6.12	6.34	23.4
1956	39,628	65.2	631	77.9	6.07	6.28	23.7
1957	38,702	67.6	647	79.6	5.73	5.98	22.7
1958	36,981	68.8	665	81.5	5.37	5.56	21.3
1959	37,910	72.1	700	84.5	5.26	5.41	21.5
1960	38,137	74.5	719	87.4	5.12	5.31	21.2
1961	38,091	76.4	738	88.9	4.98	5.16	20.8
1962	40,804	79.7	767	92.0	5.12	5.32	22.0
1963	43,564	83.5	805	93.7	5.22	5.41	23.1
1964	47,700	87.3	847	95.6	5.46	5.63	25.0
1965	49,163	91.8	888	99.0	5.36	5.54	25.4
1966	53,041	95.9	930	101.0	5.53	5.70	27.1
1967	52,924	98.9	962	103.2	5.35	5.50	26.8
1968	54,862	103.1	1,016	105.4	5.32	5.40	27.5
1969	55,791	107.4	1,071	108.3	5.19	5.21	27.7
1970	54,633	111.2	1,120	111.5	4.92	4.88	26.8
1971	54,381	116.3	1,186	114.4	4.68	4.57	26.3
1972	56,278	122.3	1,268	118.4	4.60	4.43	26.9
1973	55,511	129.8	1,309	121.6	4.28	4.24	26.3
1974	46,402	134.9	1,290	125.6	3.44	3.59	21.8
1975	45,853	137.9	1,330	129.8	3.33	3.45	21.3
1976	47,038	143.5	1,412	133.9	3.28	3.33	21.6

See source and footnotes on page 111.

MOTOR-VEHICLE DEATHS AND RATES, UNITED STATES, 1913–2005, Cont.

Year	No. of Deaths	Estimated No. of Vehicles (Millions)	Estimated Vehicle Miles (Billions)	Estimated No. of Drivers (Millions)	Death Rates		
					Per 10,000 Motor Vehicles	Per 100,000,000 Vehicle Miles	Per 100,000 Population
1977	49,510	148.8	1,477	138.1	3.33	3.35	22.5
1978	52,411	153.6	1,548	140.8	3.41	3.39	23.6
1979	53,524	159.6	1,529	143.3	3.35	3.50	23.8
1980	53,172	161.6	1,521	145.3	3.29	3.50	23.4
1981	51,385	164.1	1,556	147.1	3.13	3.30	22.4
1982	45,779	165.2	1,592	150.3	2.77	2.88	19.8
1983	44,452	169.4	1,657	154.2	2.62	2.68	19.0
1984	46,263	171.8	1,718	155.4	2.69	2.69	19.6
1985	45,901	177.1	1,774	156.9	2.59	2.59	19.3
1986	47,865	181.4	1,835	159.5	2.63	2.60	19.9
1987	48,290	183.9	1,924	161.8	2.63	2.51	19.9
1988	49,078	189.0	2,026	162.9	2.60	2.42	20.1
1989	47,575	191.7	2,107	165.6	2.48	2.26	19.3
1990	46,814	192.9	2,148	167.0	2.43	2.18	18.8
1991	43,536	192.5	2,172	169.0	2.26	2.00	17.3
1992	40,982	194.4	2,240	173.1	2.11	1.83	16.1
1993	41,893	198.0	2,297	173.1	2.12	1.82	16.3
1994	42,524	201.8	2,360	175.4	2.11	1.80	16.3
1995	43,363	205.3	2,423	176.6	2.11	1.79	16.5
1996	43,649	210.4	2,486	179.5	2.07	1.76	16.5
1997	43,458	211.5	2,562	182.7	2.05	1.70	16.2
1998	43,501	215.0	2,632	185.2	2.02	1.65	16.1
1999	42,401	220.5	2,691	187.2	1.92	1.58	15.5
2000	43,354	225.8	2,747	190.6	1.92	1.58	15.8
2001	43,788	235.3	2,797	191.3	1.86	1.57	15.4
2002	45,380	234.6	2,856	194.3	1.93	1.59	15.8
2003[b]	44,757	236.8	2,890	196.2	1.89	1.55	15.4
2004[b]	45,300	243.0	2,962	198.9	1.86	1.53	15.4
2005[c]	45,800	245.7	2,967	201.5	1.86	1.54	15.5
Changes							
1995 to 2005	+6%	+20%	+22%	+14%	−12%	−14%	−6%
2004 to 2005	+1%	+1%	(d)	+1%	0%	+1%	(d)

Source: Deaths from National Center for Health Statistics except 1964, 2004, and 2005, which are National Safety Council estimates based on data from the National Highway Traffic Safety Administration's Fatality Analysis Reporting System. See Technical Appendix for comparability. Motor-vehicle registrations, mileage and drivers estimated by Federal Highway Administration except 2005 registrations and drivers which are National Safety Council estimates.
[a]Mileage data inadequate prior to 1923.
[b]Revised.
[c]Preliminary.
[d]Change less than 0.5%.

MOTOR-VEHICLE
DEATHS BY TYPE OF ACCIDENT

MOTOR-VEHICLE DEATHS BY TYPE OF ACCIDENT, UNITED STATES, 1913–2005

Year	Total Deaths	Deaths from Collision with —							Deaths from Noncollision Accidents	Nontraffic Deaths[a]
		Pedestrians	Other Motor Vehicles	Railroad Trains	Streetcars	Pedal-cycles	Animal-Drawn Vehicle or Animal	Fixed Objects		
1913	4,200	(b)	(b)	(b)	(b)	(b)	(b)	(b)	(b)	(c)
1914	4,700	(b)	(b)	(b)	(b)	(b)	(b)	(b)	(b)	(c)
1915	6,600	(b)	(b)	(b)	(b)	(b)	(b)	(b)	(b)	(c)
1916	8,200	(b)	(b)	(b)	(b)	(b)	(b)	(b)	(b)	(c)
1917	10,200	(b)	(b)	(b)	(b)	(b)	(b)	(b)	(b)	(c)
1918	10,700	(b)	(b)	(b)	(b)	(b)	(b)	(b)	(b)	(c)
1919	11,200	(b)	(b)	(b)	(b)	(b)	(b)	(b)	(b)	(c)
1920	12,500	(b)	(b)	(b)	(b)	(b)	(b)	(b)	(b)	(c)
1921	13,900	(b)	(b)	(b)	(b)	(b)	(b)	(b)	(b)	(c)
1922	15,300	(b)	(b)	(b)	(b)	(b)	(b)	(b)	(b)	(c)
1923	18,400	(b)	(b)	(b)	(b)	(b)	(b)	(b)	(b)	(c)
1924	19,400	(b)	(b)	1,130	410	(b)	(b)	(b)	(b)	(c)
1925	21,900	(b)	(b)	1,410	560	(b)	(b)	(b)	(b)	(c)
1926	23,400	(b)	(b)	1,730	520	(b)	(b)	(b)	(b)	(c)
1927	25,800	10,820	3,430	1,830	520	(b)	(b)	(b)	(b)	(c)
1928	28,000	11,420	4,310	2,140	570	(b)	(b)	540	8,070	(c)
1929	31,200	12,250	5,400	2,050	530	(b)	(b)	620	9,380	(c)
1930	32,900	12,900	5,880	1,830	480	(b)	(b)	720	9,970	(c)
1931	33,700	13,370	6,820	1,710	440	(b)	(b)	870	9,570	(c)
1932	29,500	11,490	6,070	1,520	320	350	400	800	8,500	(c)
1933	31,363	12,840	6,470	1,437	318	400	310	900	8,680	(c)
1934	36,101	14,480	8,110	1,457	332	500	360	1,040	9,820	(c)
1935	36,369	14,350	8,750	1,587	253	450	250	1,010	9,720	(c)
1936	38,089	15,250	9,500	1,697	269	650	250	1,060	9,410	(c)
1937	39,643	15,500	10,320	1,810	264	700	200	1,160	9,690	(c)
1938	32,582	12,850	8,900	1,490	165	720	170	940	7,350	(c)
1939	32,386	12,400	8,700	1,330	150	710	200	1,000	7,900	(c)
1940	34,501	12,700	10,100	1,707	132	750	210	1,100	7,800	(c)
1941	39,969	13,550	12,500	1,840	118	910	250	1,350	9,450	(c)
1942	28,309	10,650	7,300	1,754	124	650	240	850	6,740	(c)
1943	23,823	9,900	5,300	1,448	171	450	160	700	5,690	(c)
1944	24,282	9,900	5,700	1,663	175	400	140	700	5,600	(c)
1945	28,076	11,000	7,150	1,703	163	500	130	800	6,600	(c)
1946	33,411	11,600	9,400	1,703	174	450	130	950	8,900	(c)
1947	32,697	10,450	9,900	1,736	102	550	150	1,000	8,800	(c)
1948	32,259	9,950	10,200	1,474	83	500	100	1,000	8,950	(c)
1949	31,701	8,800	10,500	1,452	56	550	140	1,100	9,100	838
1950	34,763	9,000	11,650	1,541	89	440	120	1,300	10,600	900
1951	36,996	9,150	13,100	1,573	46	390	100	1,400	11,200	966
1952	37,794	8,900	13,500	1,429	32	430	130	1,450	11,900	970
1953	37,956	8,750	13,400	1,506	26	420	120	1,500	12,200	1,026
1954	35,586	8,000	12,800	1,289	28	380	90	1,500	11,500	1,004
1955	38,426	8,200	14,500	1,490	15	410	90	1,600	12,100	989
1956	39,628	7,900	15,200	1,377	11	440	100	1,600	13,000	888
1957	38,702	7,850	15,400	1,376	13	460	80	1,700	11,800	1,016
1958	36,981	7,650	14,200	1,316	9	450	80	1,650	11,600	929
1959	37,910	7,850	14,900	1,202	6	480	70	1,600	11,800	948
1960	38,137	7,850	14,800	1,368	5	460	80	1,700	11,900	995
1961	38,091	7,650	14,700	1,267	5	490	80	1,700	12,200	1,065
1962	40,804	7,900	16,400	1,245	3	500	90	1,750	12,900	1,029
1963	43,564	8,200	17,600	1,385	10	580	80	1,900	13,800	990
1964	47,700	9,000	19,600	1,580	5	710	100	2,100	14,600	1,123
1965	49,163	8,900	20,800	1,556	5	680	120	2,200	14,900	1,113
1966	53,041	9,400	22,200	1,800	2	740	100	2,500	16,300	1,108
1967	52,924	9,400	22,000	1,620	3	750	100	2,350	16,700	1,165
1968	54,862	9,900	22,400	1,570	4	790	100	2,700	17,400	1,061
1969	55,791	10,100	23,700	1,495	2	800	100	3,900[d]	15,700[d]	1,155
1970	54,633	9,900	23,200	1,459	3	780	100	3,800	15,400	1,140
1971	54,381	9,900	23,100	1,378	2	800	100	3,800	15,300	1,015
1972	56,278	10,300	23,900	1,260	2	1,000	100	3,900	15,800	1,064
1973	55,511	10,200	23,600	1,194	2	1,000	100	3,800	15,600	1,164
1974	46,402	8,500	19,700	1,209	1	1,000	100	3,100	12,800	1,088
1975	45,853	8,400	19,550	979	1	1,000	100	3,130	12,700	1,033
1976	47,038	8,600	20,100	1,033	2	1,000	100	3,200	13,000	1,026

See source and footnotes on page 113.

MOTOR-VEHICLE DEATHS BY TYPE OF ACCIDENT, UNITED STATES, 1913–2005, Cont.

Year	Total Deaths	Pedestrians	Other Motor Vehicles	Railroad Trains	Streetcars	Pedal-cycles	Animal-Drawn Vehicle or Animal	Fixed Objects	Deaths from Noncollision Accidents	Nontraffic Deaths[a]
					Deaths from Collision with —					
1977	49,510	9,100	21,200	902	3	1,100	100	3,400	13,700	1,053
1978	52,411	9,600	22,400	986	1	1,200	100	3,600	14,500	1,074
1979	53,524	9,800	23,100	826	1	1,200	100	3,700	14,800	1,271
1980	53,172	9,700	23,000	739	1	1,200	100	3,700	14,700	1,242
1981	51,385	9,400	22,200	668	1	1,200	100	3,600	14,200	1,189
1982	45,779	8,400	19,800	554	1	1,100	100	3,200	12,600	1,066
1983	44,452	8,200	19,200	520	1	1,100	100	3,100	12,200	1,024
1984	46,263	8,500	20,000	630	0	1,100	100	3,200	12,700	1,055
1985	45,901	8,500	19,900	538	2	1,100	100	3,200	12,600	1,079
1986	47,865	8,900	20,800	574	2	1,100	100	3,300	13,100	998
1987	48,290	7,500[e]	20,700	554	1	1,000[e]	100	13,200[e]	5,200[e]	993
1988	49,078	7,700	20,900	638	2	1,000	100	13,400	5,300	1,054
1989	47,575	7,800	20,300	720	2	900	100	12,900	4,900	989
1990	46,814	7,300	19,900	623	2	900	100	13,100	4,900	987
1991	43,536	6,600	18,200	541	1	800	100	12,600	4,700	915
1992	40,982	6,300	17,600	521	2	700	100	11,700	4,100	997
1993	41,893	6,400	18,300	553	3	800	100	11,500	4,200	994
1994	42,524	6,300	18,900	549	1	800	100	11,500	4,400	1,017
1995	43,363	6,400	19,000	514	(c)	800	100	12,100	4,400	1,032
1996	43,649	6,100	19,600	373	(c)	800	100	12,100	4,600	1,127
1997	43,458	5,900	19,900	371	(c)	800	100	12,000	4,400	1,118
1998	43,501	5,900	19,700	309	(c)	700	100	12,200	4,600	1,310
1999	42,401	6,100	18,600	314	1	800	100	11,800	4,700	1,436
2000	43,354	5,900	19,100	321	(c)	800	100	12,300	4,800	1,360
2001	43,788	6,100	18,800	324	3	800	100	12,800	4,900	1,345
2002	45,380	6,100	19,200	283	(c)	800	100	13,600	5,300	1,315
2003[f]	44,757	6,000	19,300	245	(c)	800	100	13,100	5,200	1,417
2004[f]	45,300	6,000	19,400	300	(c)	900	100	13,500	5,100	1,400
2005[g]	45,800	6,200	19,200	300	(c)	1,000	100	13,700	5,300	1,400
Changes in Deaths										
1995 to 2005	+6%	−3%	+1%	−42%	—	+25%	0%	+13%	+20%	+36%
2004 to 2005	+1%	+3%	−1%	0%	—	+11%	0%	+1%	+4%	0%

Source: Total deaths from National Center for Health Statistics except 1964 and 2004-2005, which are National Safety Council estimates based on data from the National Highway Traffic Safety Administration's Fatality Analysis Reporting System. Most totals by type are estimated and may not add to the total deaths. See Technical Appendix for comparability.
[a]*See definition, page 175. Nontraffic deaths are included in appropriate accident type totals in table; in 2003, 46% of the nontraffic deaths were pedestrians.*
[b]*Insufficient data for approximations.*
[c]*Data not available.*
[d]*1969 through 1986 totals are not comparable to previous years.*
[e]*Procedures and benchmarks for estimating deaths for certain types of accidents were changed for the 1990 edition. Estimates for 1987 and later years are not comparable to earlier years.*
[f]*Revised.*
[g]*Preliminary.*

MOTOR-VEHICLE DEATHS BY AGE

MOTOR-VEHICLE DEATHS BY AGE, UNITED STATES, 1913–2005

Year	All Ages	Under 5 Years	5–14 Years	15–24 Years	25–44 Years	45–64 Years	65–74 Years	75 & Over[a]
1913	4,200	300	1,100	600	1,100	800	300	
1914	4,700	300	1,200	700	1,200	900	400	
1915	6,600	400	1,500	1,000	1,700	1,400	600	
1916	8,200	600	1,800	1,300	2,100	1,700	700	
1917	10,200	700	2,400	1,400	2,700	2,100	900	
1918	10,700	800	2,700	1,400	2,500	2,300	1,000	
1919	11,200	900	3,000	1,400	2,500	2,100	1,300	
1920	12,500	1,000	3,300	1,700	2,800	2,300	1,400	
1921	13,900	1,100	3,400	1,800	3,300	2,700	1,600	
1922	15,300	1,100	3,500	2,100	3,700	3,100	1,800	
1923	18,400	1,200	3,700	2,800	4,600	3,900	2,200	
1924	19,400	1,400	3,800	2,900	4,700	4,100	2,500	
1925	21,900	1,400	3,900	3,600	5,400	4,800	2,800	
1926	23,400	1,400	3,900	3,900	5,900	5,200	3,100	
1927	25,800	1,600	4,000	4,300	6,600	5,800	3,500	
1928	28,000	1,600	3,800	4,900	7,200	6,600	3,900	
1929	31,200	1,600	3,900	5,700	8,000	7,500	4,500	
1930	32,900	1,500	3,600	6,200	8,700	8,000	4,900	
1931	33,700	1,500	3,600	6,300	9,100	8,200	5,000	
1932	29,500	1,200	2,900	5,100	8,100	7,400	4,800	
1933	31,363	1,274	3,121	5,649	8,730	7,947	4,642	
1934	36,101	1,210	3,182	6,561	10,232	9,530	5,386	
1935	36,369	1,253	2,951	6,755	10,474	9,562	5,374	
1936	38,089	1,324	3,026	7,184	10,807	10,089	5,659	
1937	39,643	1,303	2,991	7,800	10,877	10,475	6,197	
1938	32,582	1,122	2,511	6,016	8,772	8,711	5,450	
1939	32,386	1,192	2,339	6,318	8,917	8,292	5,328	
1940	34,501	1,176	2,584	6,846	9,362	8,882	5,651	
1941	39,969	1,378	2,838	8,414	11,069	9,829	6,441	
1942	28,309	1,069	1,991	5,932	7,747	7,254	4,316	
1943	23,823	1,132	1,959	4,522	6,454	5,996	3,760	
1944	24,282	1,203	2,093	4,561	6,514	5,982	3,929	
1945	28,076	1,290	2,386	5,358	7,578	6,794	4,670	
1946	33,411	1,568	2,508	7,445	8,955	7,532	5,403	
1947	32,697	1,502	2,275	7,251	8,775	7,468	5,426	
1948	32,259	1,635	2,337	7,218	8,702	7,190	3,173	2,004
1949	31,701	1,667	2,158	6,772	8,892	7,073	3,116	2,023
1950	34,763	1,767	2,152	7,600	10,214	7,728	3,264	2,038
1951	36,996	1,875	2,300	7,713	11,253	8,276	3,444	2,135
1952	37,794	1,951	2,295	8,115	11,380	8,463	3,472	2,118
1953	37,956	2,019	2,368	8,169	11,302	8,318	3,508	2,271
1954	35,586	1,864	2,332	7,571	10,521	7,848	3,247	2,203
1955	38,426	1,875	2,406	8,656	11,448	8,372	3,455	2,214
1956	39,628	1,770	2,640	9,169	11,551	8,573	3,657	2,268
1957	38,702	1,785	2,604	8,667	11,230	8,545	3,560	2,311
1958	36,981	1,791	2,710	8,388	10,414	7,922	3,535	2,221
1959	37,910	1,842	2,719	8,969	10,358	8,263	3,487	2,272
1960	38,137	1,953	2,814	9,117	10,189	8,294	3,457	2,313
1961	38,091	1,891	2,802	9,088	10,212	8,267	3,467	2,364
1962	40,804	1,903	3,028	10,157	10,701	8,812	3,696	2,507
1963	43,564	1,991	3,063	11,123	11,356	9,506	3,786	2,739
1964	47,700	2,120	3,430	12,400	12,500	10,200	4,150	2,900
1965	49,163	2,059	3,526	13,395	12,595	10,509	4,077	3,002
1966	53,041	2,182	3,869	15,298	13,282	11,051	4,217	3,142
1967	52,924	2,067	3,845	15,646	12,987	10,902	4,285	3,192
1968	54,862	1,987	4,105	16,543	13,602	11,031	4,261	3,333
1969	55,791	2,077	4,045	17,443	13,868	11,012	4,210	3,136
1970	54,633	1,915	4,159	16,720	13,446	11,099	4,084	3,210
1971	54,381	1,885	4,256	17,103	13,307	10,471	4,108	3,251
1972	56,278	1,896	4,258	17,942	13,758	10,836	4,138	3,450
1973	55,511	1,998	4,124	18,032	14,013	10,216	3,892	3,236
1974	46,402	1,546	3,332	15,905	11,834	8,159	3,071	2,555
1975	45,853	1,576	3,286	15,672	11,969	7,663	3,047	2,640
1976	47,038	1,532	3,175	16,650	12,112	7,770	3,082	2,717

See source and footnotes on page 115.

MOTOR-VEHICLE DEATHS BY AGE, UNITED STATES, 1913–2005, Cont.

Year	All Ages	Under 5 Years	5–14 Years	15–24 Years	25–44 Years	45–64 Years	65–74 Years	75 & Over[a]
1977	49,510	1,472	3,142	18,092	13,031	8,000	3,060	2,713
1978	52,411	1,551	3,130	19,164	14,574	8,048	3,217	2,727
1979	53,524	1,461	2,952	19,369	15,658	8,162	3,171	2,751
1980	53,172	1,426	2,747	19,040	16,133	8,022	2,991	2,813
1981	51,385	1,256	2,575	17,363	16,447	7,818	3,090	2,836
1982	45,779	1,300	2,301	15,324	14,469	6,879	2,825	2,681
1983	44,452	1,233	2,241	14,289	14,323	6,690	2,827	2,849
1984	46,263	1,138	2,263	14,738	15,036	6,954	3,020	3,114
1985	45,901	1,195	2,319	14,277	15,034	6,885	3,014	3,177
1986	47,865	1,188	2,350	15,227	15,844	6,799	3,096	3,361
1987	48,290	1,190	2,397	14,447	16,405	7,021	3,277	3,553
1988	49,078	1,220	2,423	14,406	16,580	7,245	3,429	3,775
1989	47,575	1,221	2,266	12,941	16,571	7,287	3,465	3,824
1990	46,814	1,123	2,059	12,607	16,488	7,282	3,350	3,905
1991	43,536	1,076	2,011	11,664	15,082	6,616	3,193	3,894
1992	40,982	1,020	1,904	10,305	14,071	6,597	3,247	3,838
1993	41,893	1,081	1,963	10,500	14,283	6,711	3,116	4,239
1994	42,524	1,139	2,026	10,660	13,966	7,097	3,385	4,251
1995	43,363	1,004	2,055	10,600	14,618	7,428	3,300	4,358
1996	43,649	1,035	1,980	10,576	14,482	7,749	3,419	4,408
1997	43,458	933	1,967	10,208	14,167	8,134	3,370	4,679
1998	43,501	921	1,868	10,026	14,095	8,416	3,410	4,765
1999	42,401	834	1,771	10,128	13,516	8,342	3,276	4,534
2000	43,354	819	1,772	10,560	13,811	8,867	3,038	4,487
2001	43,788	770	1,686	10,725	14,020	9,029	2,990	4,568
2002	45,380	733	1,614	11,459	14,169	9,701	3,113	4,591
2003[b]	44,757	766	1,642	10,972	13,794	10,032	2,967	4,584
2004[b]	45,300	800	1,700	11,100	13,800	10,400	3,000	4,500
2005[c]	45,800	700	1,500	11,000	14,200	10,900	3,100	4,400
Changes in Deaths								
1995 to 2005	+6%	−30%	−27%	+4%	−3%	+47%	−6%	+1%
2004 to 2005	+1%	−1%	−12%	−1%	+3%	+5%	+3%	−2%

Source: 1913 to 1932 calculated from National Center for Health Statistics data for registration states; 1933 to 1963, 1965 to 2003 are NCHS totals. All other figures are National Safety Council estimates. See Technical Appendix for comparability.
[a] Includes "age unknown." In 2003 these deaths numbered 16.
[b] Revised.
[c] Preliminary.

MOTOR-VEHICLE DEATH RATES BY AGE

MOTOR-VEHICLE DEATH RATES[a] BY AGE, UNITED STATES, 1913–2005

Year	All Ages	Under 5 Years	5–14 Years	15–24 Years	25–44 Years	45–64 Years	65–74 Years	75 & Over
1913	4.4	2.3	5.5	3.1	3.8	5.3	8.5	
1914	4.8	2.5	5.7	3.5	4.1	6.2	9.3	
1915	6.6	3.5	7.3	5.0	5.6	8.8	13.5	
1916	8.1	4.7	8.6	6.0	7.0	10.7	15.8	
1917	10.0	5.6	10.6	7.4	8.6	12.6	18.6	
1918	10.3	6.9	12.3	7.7	8.3	13.7	21.2	
1919	10.7	7.5	13.9	7.5	8.1	12.4	24.1	
1920	11.7	8.6	14.6	8.7	8.8	13.5	27.0	
1921	12.9	9.0	14.5	9.2	10.2	15.4	31.0	
1922	13.9	9.2	15.0	10.8	11.1	17.2	34.9	
1923	16.5	9.7	15.6	13.4	13.6	21.0	40.5	
1924	17.1	11.1	16.1	14.3	13.7	21.8	43.7	
1925	19.1	11.0	15.6	17.2	15.8	25.0	48.9	
1926	20.1	11.0	15.9	18.6	17.1	26.3	51.4	
1927	21.8	12.8	16.0	20.0	18.8	28.9	56.9	
1928	23.4	12.7	15.5	21.9	20.2	32.4	62.2	
1929	25.7	13.4	15.6	25.6	22.3	35.6	68.6	
1930	26.7	13.0	14.7	27.4	23.9	37.0	72.5	
1931	27.2	13.3	14.5	27.9	24.8	37.4	70.6	
1932	23.6	11.3	12.0	22.6	22.0	32.9	63.6	
1933	25.0	12.0	12.7	24.8	23.4	34.7	63.1	
1934	28.6	11.7	13.0	28.6	27.2	40.7	71.0	
1935	28.6	12.3	12.2	29.2	27.6	39.9	68.9	
1936	29.7	13.2	12.6	30.8	28.2	41.3	70.5	
1937	30.8	13.0	12.7	33.2	28.2	42.0	75.1	
1938	25.1	11.0	10.8	25.4	22.5	34.3	64.1	
1939	24.7	11.2	10.4	26.5	22.6	32.2	60.2	
1940	26.1	11.1	11.5	28.7	23.5	33.9	62.1	
1941	30.0	12.7	12.6	35.7	27.5	37.0	68.6	
1942	21.1	9.5	8.8	25.8	19.2	26.9	44.5	
1943	17.8	9.4	8.6	20.6	16.1	21.9	37.6	
1944	18.3	9.6	9.1	22.5	16.6	21.6	38.2	
1945	21.2	10.0	10.3	27.8	19.7	24.2	44.1	
1946	23.9	11.9	10.8	34.4	21.1	26.4	49.6	
1947	22.8	10.5	9.7	32.8	20.3	25.7	48.2	
1948	22.1	11.0	9.8	32.5	19.8	24.3	39.6	55.4
1949	21.3	10.7	9.0	30.7	19.9	23.4	37.8	53.9
1950	23.0	10.8	8.8	34.5	22.5	25.1	38.8	52.4
1951	24.1	10.9	9.2	36.0	24.7	26.5	39.5	53.0
1952	24.3	11.3	8.7	38.6	24.7	26.7	38.5	50.8
1953	24.0	11.5	8.5	39.1	24.5	25.8	37.7	52.6
1954	22.1	10.4	8.1	36.2	22.6	24.0	33.9	49.0
1955	23.4	10.2	8.0	40.9	24.5	25.2	35.1	47.1
1956	23.7	9.4	8.4	42.9	24.6	25.3	36.2	46.4
1957	22.7	9.2	8.0	39.7	23.9	24.8	34.4	45.5
1958	21.3	9.1	8.1	37.0	22.3	22.6	33.5	42.3
1959	21.5	9.1	7.9	38.2	22.2	23.2	32.3	41.8
1960	21.2	9.6	7.9	37.7	21.7	22.9	31.3	41.1
1961	20.8	9.2	7.6	36.5	21.8	22.5	30.7	40.5
1962	22.0	9.3	8.1	38.4	22.9	23.7	32.2	41.7
1963	23.1	9.8	8.0	40.0	24.3	25.2	32.6	44.3
1964	25.0	10.5	8.8	42.6	26.8	26.6	35.5	45.2
1965	25.4	10.4	8.9	44.2	27.0	27.0	34.6	45.4
1966	27.1	11.4	9.7	48.7	28.5	27.9	35.4	46.2
1967	26.8	11.2	9.5	48.4	27.8	27.1	35.6	45.4
1968	27.5	11.1	10.1	49.8	28.8	27.0	35.1	46.0
1969	27.7	12.0	9.9	50.7	29.1	26.6	34.3	42.0
1970	26.8	11.2	10.2	46.7	27.9	26.4	32.7	42.2
1971	26.3	10.9	10.5	45.7	27.4	24.7	32.4	41.3
1972	26.9	11.1	10.7	47.1	27.4	25.3	32.0	42.6
1973	26.3	11.9	10.5	46.3	27.2	23.6	29.4	39.1
1974	21.8	9.4	8.6	40.0	22.4	18.8	22.6	30.1
1975	21.3	9.8	8.6	38.7	22.1	17.5	21.9	30.1
1976	21.6	9.8	8.4	40.3	21.8	17.6	21.6	30.1

See source and footnotes on page 117.

MOTOR-VEHICLE DEATH RATES[a] BY AGE, UNITED STATES, 1913–2005, Cont.

Year	All Ages	Under 5 Years	5–14 Years	15–24 Years	25–44 Years	45–64 Years	65–74 Years	75 & Over
1977	22.5	9.5	8.5	43.3	22.7	18.1	20.9	29.3
1978	23.6	9.9	8.6	45.4	24.6	18.2	21.5	28.7
1979	23.8	9.1	8.3	45.6	25.6	18.4	20.7	28.1
1980	23.4	8.7	7.9	44.8	25.5	18.0	19.1	28.0
1981	22.4	7.4	7.5	41.1	25.2	17.6	19.4	27.5
1982	19.8	7.5	6.7	36.8	21.5	15.5	17.5	25.2
1983	19.0	7.0	6.6	34.8	20.6	15.0	17.2	26.0
1984	19.6	6.4	6.7	36.4	21.0	15.6	18.2	27.7
1985	19.3	6.7	6.9	35.7	20.5	15.4	17.9	27.5
1986	19.9	6.6	7.0	38.5	21.0	15.2	18.1	28.3
1987	19.9	6.6	7.1	37.1	21.3	15.7	18.8	29.1
1988	20.1	6.7	7.1	37.8	21.2	15.9	19.5	30.2
1989	19.3	6.6	6.5	34.6	20.8	15.9	19.4	29.8
1990	18.8	6.0	5.8	34.2	20.4	15.7	18.5	29.7
1991	17.3	5.6	5.6	32.1	18.3	14.2	17.5	28.9
1992	16.1	5.2	5.2	28.5	17.1	13.6	17.6	27.8
1993	16.3	5.5	5.3	29.1	17.3	13.5	16.7	30.0
1994	16.3	5.8	5.4	29.5	16.8	13.9	18.1	29.4
1995	16.5	5.1	5.4	29.3	17.5	14.2	17.6	29.4
1996	16.5	5.4	5.2	29.2	17.3	14.4	18.3	29.0
1997	16.2	4.9	5.1	27.9	17.0	14.7	18.2	29.9
1998	16.1	4.9	4.8	26.9	16.9	14.7	18.5	29.8
1999	15.5	4.4	4.5	26.8	16.3	14.1	18.0	27.8
2000	15.7	4.3	4.5	27.5	16.8	14.5	16.7	27.0
2001	15.4	4.0	4.1	26.8	16.5	14.0	16.3	26.8
2002	15.8	3.7	3.9	28.2	16.8	14.6	17.0	26.5
2003[b]	15.4	3.9	4.0	26.6	16.4	14.6	16.2	26.0
2004[b]	15.4	4.0	4.2	26.6	16.4	14.7	16.3	25.2
2005[c]	15.5	3.4[c]	3.7	26.1	16.9	15.0	16.6	24.2
Changes in Rates								
1995 to 2005	–6%	–33%	–31%	–11%	–3%	+6%	–6%	–18%
2004 to 2005	+1%	–15%	–12%	–2%	+3%	+2%	+2%	–4%

Source: 1913 to 1932 calculated from National Center for Health Statistics data for registration states; 1933 to 1963, 1965 to 2003 are NCHS totals. All other figures are National Safety Council estimates. See Technical Appendix for comparability.
[a] *Death rates are deaths per 100,000 population in each age group.*
[b] *Revised.*
[c] *Preliminary.*

INJURY FACTS®

NATIONAL SAFETY COUNCIL

HOME AND COMMUNITY, 2005

The Home and Community venue is the combination of the Home class and the Public class. Home and Community together with the Occupational and Transportation venues make up the totality of unintentional injuries. Home and Community includes all unintentional injuries that are not work related and do not involve motor vehicles on streets and highways.

In 2005, an estimated 64,600 unintentional-injury deaths occurred in the Home and Community venue, or 57% of all unintentional-injury deaths that year. The number of deaths was up about 1% from the revised 2004 total of 64,000. Another 18,100,000 people suffered nonfatal disabling injuries. The death rate per 100,000 population was 21.8, no change from the revised 2004 rate.

About 1 out of 16 people experienced an unintentional injury in the Home and Community venue and about 1 out of 4,600 people died from such an injury. About 39% of the deaths and 55% of the disabling injuries involved workers while they were away from work (off the job).

The graph on the next page shows the five leading causes of unintentional-injury deaths in the Home and Community venue and the broad age groups (children, youths and adults, and the elderly) affected by them. This is one way to prioritize issues in this venue. Below is a graph of the trend in deaths and death rates from 1995 to the present. Similar graphs for the Public and Home classes are on pages 122 and 126.

The Council adopted the Bureau of Labor Statistics' Census of Fatal Occupational Injuries count for work-related unintentional injuries beginning with 1992 data. Because of the lower Work class total resulting from this change, adjustments had to be made to the Home and Public classes. Long-term historical comparisons for these three classes should be made with caution. Also, beginning with 1999 data, deaths are now classified according to the 10th revision of the *International Classification of Diseases*. Caution should be used in comparing data classified under the 10th revision with prior revisions. See the Technical Appendix for more information about both changes.

Deaths	**64,600**
Disabling Injuries	**18,100,000**
Death Rate per 100,000 Population	**21.8**
Costs	**$238.6 billion**

HOME AND COMMUNITY DEATHS AND DEATH RATES, UNITED STATES, 1995–2005

LEADING CAUSES OF UNINTENTIONAL-INJURY DEATHS IN HOME AND COMMUNITY, UNITED STATES, 2005

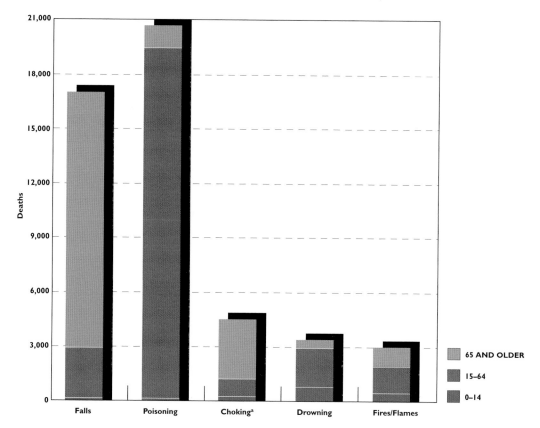

ᵃInhalation and ingestion of food or other object that obstructs breathing.

CAUSES OF UNINTENTIONAL-INJURY DEATHS IN HOME AND COMMUNITY, UNITED STATES, 2005

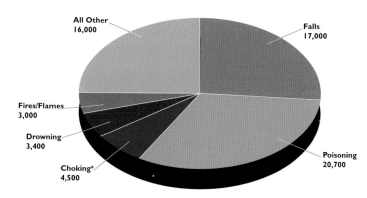

ᵃInhalation and ingestion of food or other object that obstructs breathing.

Between 1912 and 2005, public unintentional-injury deaths per 100,000 population were reduced 67% from 30 to 9.3 (after adjusting for the 1948 change in classification). In 1912, an estimated 28,000 to 30,000 persons died from public nonmotor-vehicle injuries. In 2005, with a population tripled, and travel and recreational activity greatly increased, 27,600 persons died of public unintentional injuries and 9,200,000 suffered disabling injuries. The public class excludes deaths and injuries involving motor vehicles and persons at work or at home.

The number of public unintentional-injury deaths was up 15% from the revised 2004 figure of 24,000. The death rate per 100,000 population increased from 8.2 to 9.3, or 13%.

With an estimated 9,200,000 disabling unintentional injuries occurring in public places and a population of more than 296 million people, on average about one person in 32 experienced such an injury.

The Council adopted the Bureau of Labor Statistics' Census of Fatal Occupational Injuries count for work-related unintentional injuries beginning with 1992 data. This affected long-term historical comparisons for the Work, Home, and Public classes. Beginning with 1999 data, deaths are classified according to the 10th revision of the *International Classification of Diseases*. Caution should be used in comparing current data with data classified under prior revisions. See the Technical Appendix for more information.

Deaths **27,600**
Disabling Injuries **9,200,000**
Death Rate per 100,000 Population **9.3**
Costs .... **$96.3 billion**

PUBLIC DEATHS AND DEATH RATES, UNITED STATES, 1995–2005

PRINCIPAL TYPES OF PUBLIC UNINTENTIONAL-INJURY DEATHS, UNITED STATES, 1985–2005

Year	Total Public[a]	Falls	Drowning	Poisoning	Suffocation by Ingestion	Fires/ Burns	Firearms	Mechanical Suffocation	Air Transport	Water Transport	Rail Transport[b]
1985	18,800	4,100	3,300	(c)	(c)	500	600	(c)	1,000	900	400
1986	18,700	3,900	3,600	(c)	(c)	500	600	(c)	800	900	400
1987	18,400	4,000	3,200	(c)	(c)	500	600	(c)	900	800	400
1988	18,400	4,100	3,100	(c)	(c)	500	600	(c)	700	800	400
1989	18,200	4,200	3,000	(c)	(c)	500	600	(c)	800	700	400
1990	17,400	4,300	2,800	(c)	(c)	400	500	(c)	700	800	400
1991	17,600	4,500	2,800	(c)	(c)	400	600	(c)	700	700	500
1992	19,000	4,400	2,500	(c)	(c)	200	400	(c)	700	700	600
1993	19,700	4,600	2,800	(c)	(c)	200	400	(c)	600	700	600
1994	19,600	4,700	2,400	(c)	(c)	200	400	(c)	600	600	600
1995	20,100	5,000	2,800	(c)	(c)	200	300	(c)	600	700	500
1996	21,000	5,300	2,500	(c)	(c)	200	300	(c)	700	600	500
1997	21,700	5,600	2,600	(c)	(c)	200	300	(c)	500	600	400
1998	22,600	6,000	2,900	(c)	(c)	200	300	(c)	500	600	500
1999[d]	22,200	4,800	2,600	2,800	2,000	200	300	500	500	600	400
2000	22,700	5,500	2,400	2,900	2,200	(c)	(c)	300	500	500	400
2001	21,800	5,600	2,400	2,700	2,100	(c)	(c)	300	700	500	400
2002	22,500	5,900	2,500	3,600	2,200	(c)	(c)	300	500	500	400
2003[e]	23,200	6,300	2,400	3,400	2,200	(c)	(c)	300	600	500	400
2004[e]	24,000	6,200	2,500	3,800	2,400	(c)	(c)	300	600	600	500
2005[f]	27,600	6,600	2,500	4,500	2,800	(c)	(c)	400	500	600	500

Source: National Safety Council estimates based on data from the National Center for Health Statistics and state vital statistics departments. The Council adopted the Bureau of Labor Statistics' Census of Fatal Occupational Injuries count for work-related unintentional injuries retroactive to 1992 data. Because of the lower Work class total resulting from this change, several thousand unintentional-injury deaths that had been classified by the Council as work-related, had to be reassigned to the Home and Public classes. For this reason long-term historical comparisons for these three classes should be made with caution. See the Technical Appendix for an explanation of the methodological changes.
[a] *Includes some deaths not shown separately.*
[b] *Includes subways and elevateds.*
[c] *Estimates not available.*
[d] *In 1999, a revision was made in the International Classification of Diseases. See the Technical Appendix for comparability with earlier years.*
[e] *Revised.*
[f] *Preliminary.*

PRINCIPAL TYPES OF PUBLIC UNINTENTIONAL-INJURY DEATHS, UNITED STATES, 2005

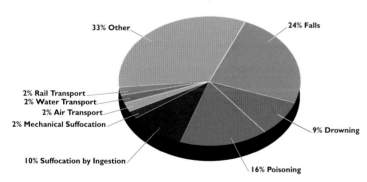

- 33% Other
- 24% Falls
- 9% Drowning
- 16% Poisoning
- 10% Suffocation by Ingestion
- 2% Mechanical Suffocation
- 2% Air Transport
- 2% Water Transport
- 2% Rail Transport

TYPE OF EVENT AND AGE OF VICTIM

All Public
Includes deaths in public places or places used in a public way and not involving motor vehicles. Most sports, recreation, and transportation deaths are included. Excludes deaths in the course of employment.

	Total	Change from 2004	Death Rate[a]
Deaths	27,600	+15%	9.3

Falls
Includes deaths from falls from one level to another or on the same level in public places. Excludes deaths from falls in moving vehicles.

	Total	Change from 2004	Death Rate[a]
Deaths	6,600	+6%	2.2

Poisoning
Includes deaths from drugs, medicines, other solid and liquid substances, and gases and vapors. Excludes poisonings from spoiled foods, salmonella, etc., which are classified as disease deaths.

	Total	Change from 2004	Death Rate[a]
Deaths	4,500	+18%	1.5

Choking
Includes deaths from unintentional ingestion or inhalation of food or other objects resulting in the obstruction of respiratory passages.

	Total	Change from 2004	Death Rate[a]
Deaths	2,800	+17%	0.9

Drowning
Includes drownings of person swimming or playing in water, or falling into water, except on home premises or at work. Excludes drownings involving boats, which are in water transportation.

	Total	Change from 2004	Death Rate[a]
Deaths	2,500	0%	0.8

See footnotes on page 125.

TYPE OF EVENT AND AGE OF VICTIM

Water Transport

Includes deaths in water transport accidents from falls, burns, etc., as well as drownings. Excludes crews and persons traveling in the course of employment.

	Total	Change from 2004	Death Rate[a]
Deaths	600	0%	0.2

Age	0–4	5–14	15–24	25–44	45–64	65–74	75+
Deaths	10	40	110	180	190	30	40

Air Transport

Includes deaths in private flying, passengers in commercial aviation, and deaths of military personnel in the U.S. Excludes crews and persons traveling in the course of employment.

	Total	Change from 2004	Death Rate[a]
Deaths	500	−17%	0.2

Age	0–4	5–14	15–24	25–44	45–64	65–74	75+
Deaths	10	20	30	120	200	80	40

Railroad

Includes deaths arising from railroad vehicles in motion (except involving motor vehicles), subway and elevated trains, and persons boarding or alighting from standing trains. Excludes crews and persons traveling in the course of employment.

	Total	Change from 2004	Death Rate[a]
Deaths	500	0%	0.2

Age	0–4	5–14	15–24	25–44	45–64	65–74	75+
Deaths	10	20	90	220	110	10	40

Mechanical Suffocation

Includes deaths from hanging and strangulation, and suffocation in enclosed or confined spaces, cave-ins, or by bed clothes, plastic bags, or similar materials.

	Total	Change from 2004	Death Rate[a]
Deaths	400	+33%	0.1

Age	0–4	5–14	15–24	25–44	45–64	65–74	75+
Deaths	20	30	20	130	100	30	70

All Other Public

Most important types included are: excessive natural heat or cold, firearms, fires and flames, and machinery.

	Total	Change from 2004	Death Rate[a]
Deaths	9,200	+30%	3.1

[a]Deaths per 100,000 population.
[b]Deaths per 100,000 population in each age group.
[c]Death rate less than 0.05.

Age	0–4	5–14	15–24	25–44	45–64	65–74	75+
Deaths	20	80	700	1,650	1,850	900	4,000

HOME, 2005

Between 1912 and 2005, unintentional-home-injury deaths per 100,000 population were reduced 49% from 28 to 12.5 (after adjusting for the 1948 classification change). In 1912, when there were 21 million households, an estimated 26,000 to 28,000 persons were killed by unintentional home injuries. In 2005, with more than 113 million households and the population tripled, home deaths numbered 37,000.

The injury total of 8,900,000 means that 1 person in 33 in the United States was disabled one full day or more by unintentional injuries received in the home in 2005. Disabling injuries are more numerous in the home than in the workplace and in motor-vehicle crashes combined.

The National Health Interview Survey indicates that about 15,268,000 episodes of medically-attended home injuries occurred in 2004 (the latest year available). This means that about 1 person in 19 incurred a home injury requiring medical attention. About 46% of all medically attended injuries occurred at home.

The Council adopted the Bureau of Labor Statistics' Census of Fatal Occupational Injuries count for work-related unintentional injuries beginning with 1992 data. This affected long-term historical comparisons for the Work, Home, and Public classes. Beginning with 1999 data, deaths are classified according to the 10th revision of the International Classification of Diseases. Caution should be used in comparing current data with data classified under prior revisions. See the Technical Appendix for more information.

Deaths **37,000**
Disabling Injuries **8,900,000**
Death Rate per 100,000 Population **12.5**
Costs .... **$142.3 billion**

HOME DEATHS AND DEATH RATES, UNITED STATES, 1995–2005

HOME, 2005 (CONT.)

PRINCIPAL TYPES OF HOME UNINTENTIONAL-INJURY DEATHS, UNITED STATES, 1985–2005

Year	Total Home	Falls	Fires/ Burns[a]	Suffocation by Ingestion	Mechanical Suffocation	Drowning	Poisoning	Natural Heat/Cold	Firearms	Other
1985	21,600	6,500	4,000	2,400	600	[b]	3,900	[b]	900	3,300
1986	21,700	6,100	4,000	2,500	600	[b]	4,300	[b]	800	3,400
1987	21,400	6,300	3,900	2,500	600	[b]	4,100	[b]	800	3,200
1988	22,700	6,600	4,100	2,600	600	[b]	4,800	[b]	800	3,200
1989	22,500	6,600	3,900	2,500	600	[b]	5,000	[b]	800	3,100
1990	21,500	6,700	3,400	2,300	600	[b]	4,500	[b]	800	3,200
1991	22,100	6,900	3,400	2,200	700	[b]	5,000	[b]	800	3,100
1992	24,000	7,700	3,700	1,500	700	900	5,200	[b]	1,000	3,300
1993	26,100	7,900	3,700	1,700	700	900	6,500	[b]	1,100	3,600
1994	26,300	8,100	3,700	1,600	800	900	6,800	[b]	900	3,500
1995	27,200	8,400	3,500	1,500	800	900	7,000	[b]	900	4,200
1996	27,500	9,000	3,500	1,500	800	900	7,300	[b]	800	3,700
1997	27,700	9,100	3,200	1,500	800	900	7,800	[b]	700	3,500
1998	29,000	9,500	2,900	1,800	800	1,000	8,400	[b]	600	4,000
1999[c]	30,500	7,600	3,000	1,900	1,100	900	9,300	700	600	5,400
2000	29,200	7,100	2,700	2,100	1,000	1,000	9,800	400	500	4,600
2001	33,200	8,600	3,000	2,000	1,100	900	11,300	400	600	5,300
2002	36,200	9,700	2,800	1,900	1,100	900	13,900	400	500	5,000
2003[d]	38,600	10,300	2,900	2,100	1,000	800	15,900	400	500	4,700
2004[d]	40,000	10,500	3,100	2,100	1,100	1,000	16,000	500	500	5,200
2005[e]	37,000	10,400	2,600	1,700	900	900	16,200	400	500	3,400

Source: National Safety Council estimates based on data from National Center for Health Statistics and state vital statistics departments. The Council adopted the Bureau of Labor Statistics' Census of Fatal Occupational Injuries count for work-related unintentional injuries retroactive to 1992 data. Because of the lower Work class total resulting from this change, several thousand unintentional-injury deaths that had been classified by the Council as work-related, had to be reassigned to the Home and Public classes. For this reason long-term historical comparisons for these three classes should be made with caution. See the Technical Appendix for an explanation of the methodological changes.
[a] Includes deaths resulting from conflagration, regardless of nature of injury.
[b] Included in Other.
[c] In 1999, a revision was made in the International Classification of Diseases. See the Technical Appendix for comparability with earlier years.
[d] Revised.
[e] Preliminary.

PRINCIPAL TYPES OF HOME UNINTENTIONAL-INJURY DEATHS, UNITED STATES, 2005

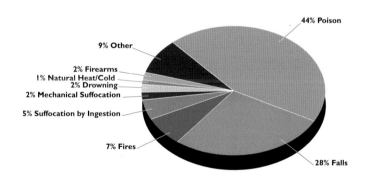

44% Poison
9% Other
2% Firearms
1% Natural Heat/Cold
2% Drowning
2% Mechanical Suffocation
5% Suffocation by Ingestion
7% Fires
28% Falls

DEATHS DUE TO UNINTENTIONAL HOME INJURIES, 2005

TYPE OF EVENT AND AGE OF VICTIM

All Home

Includes deaths in the home and on home premises to occupants, guests, and trespassers. Also includes hired household workers but excludes other persons working on home premises.

	Total	Change from 2004	Death Rate[a]
Deaths	37,000	−8%	12.5

Poisoning

Includes deaths from drugs, medicines, other solid and liquid substances, and gases and vapors. Excludes poisonings from spoiled foods, salmonella, etc., which are classified as disease deaths.

	Total	Change from 2004	Death Rate[a]
Deaths	16,200	+1%	5.5

Falls

Includes deaths from falls from one level to another or on the same level in the home or on home premises.

	Total	Change from 2004	Death Rate[a]
Deaths	10,400	−1%	3.5

Fires, Flames, and Smoke

Includes deaths from fires, burns, and injuries in conflagrations in the home — such as asphyxiation, falls, and struck by falling objects. Excludes burns from hot objects or liquids.

	Total	Change from 2004	Death Rate[a]
Deaths	2,600	−16%	0.9

Choking

Includes deaths from unintentional ingestion or inhalation of objects or food resulting in the obstruction of respiratory passages.

	Total	Change from 2004	Death Rate[a]
Deaths	1,700	−19%	0.6

See footnotes on page 137.

TYPE OF EVENT AND AGE OF VICTIM

Mechanical Suffocation

Includes deaths from smothering by bed clothes, thin plastic materials, etc.; suffocation by cave-ins or confinement in closed spaces; and mechanical strangulation and hanging.

	Total	Change from 2004	Death Rate[a]
Deaths	900	−18%	0.3

Drowning

Includes drownings of persons in or on home premises — such as in swimming pools and bathtubs. Excludes drowning in floods and other cataclysms.

	Total	Change from 2004	Death Rate[a]
Deaths	900	−10%	0.3

Natural Heat or Cold

Includes deaths resulting from exposure to excessive natural heat and cold (e.g., extreme weather conditions).

	Total	Change from 2004	Death Rate[a]
Deaths	400	−20%	0.1

Firearms

Includes firearms injuries in or on home premises — such as while cleaning or playing with guns. Excludes deaths from explosive materials.

	Total	Change from 2004	Death Rate[a]
Deaths	500	0%	0.2

All Other Home

Most important types included are: struck by or against objects, machinery, and electric current.

	Total	Change from 2004	Death Rate[a]
Deaths	3,400	−35%	1.1

[a] Deaths per 100,000 population.
[b] Deaths per 100,000 population in each age group.
[c] Death rate less than 0.05.

SPORTS AND RECREATION INJURIES

In the U.S. in 2005, basketball injuries resulted in over half a million emergency department visits.

The table below shows estimates of injuries treated in hospital emergency departments and participants associated with various sports and recreational activities. Differences between the two sources in methods, coverage, classification systems, and definitions can affect comparisons among sports. Because this list of sports is not complete, because the frequency and duration of participation is not known, and because the number of participants varies greatly, no inference should be made concerning the relative hazard of these sports or rank with respect to risk of injury. In particular, it is *not* appropriate to calculate injury rates from these data.

SPORTS PARTICIPATION AND INJURIES, UNITED STATES, 2005

Sport or Activity	Participants	Injuries	Percent of Injuries by Age				
			0–4	5–14	15–24	25–64	65 & Over
Archery	6,800,000	3,568	3.8	20.2	23.9	45.8	6.4
Baseball	14,600,000	155,898	3.3	49.5	27.8	19.1	0.2
Basketball	29,900,000	512,213	0.4	34.9	45.1	19.4	0.2
Bicycle riding[a]	43,100,000	485,669	5.5	48.4	16.3	27.1	2.7
Billiards, pool	37,300,000	5,878	5.8	24.2	25.0	40.1	4.9
Bowling	45,400,000	22,155	6.2	16.3	18.9	50.1	8.5
Boxing	(b)	12,238	0.2	12.3	52.4	35.0	0.0
Cheerleading	3,300,000	24,462	0.3	44.7	53.9	1.1	0.0
Exercise	(b)	180,050[c]	2.9	16.1	19.7	51.3	9.9
Fishing	43,300,000	63,026	2.6	19.4	14.4	54.7	8.9
Football	17,800,000[d,e]	418,260	0.3	48.0	42.0	9.7	0.1
Golf	24,700,000	34,382[f]	5.7	24.3	8.0	41.8	20.1
Gymnastics	(b)	27,821[g]	3.9	71.2	19.4	5.5	0.1
Hockey, street, roller & field	(b)	7,322[h]	0.0	35.1	54.9	9.7	0.2
Horseback riding	(b)	73,576	1.2	20.2	18.8	57.2	2.4
Horseshoe pitching	(b)	2,473	4.2	24.3	20.6	45.4	5.5
Ice hockey	2,400,000	18,584	1.1	34.9	46.5	17.4	0.1
Ice skating	(b)	19,388[i]	0.6	51.3	20.2	26.3	1.6
Martial arts	4,700,000[d]	25,263	0.6	25.3	28.4	45.6	0.1
Mountain biking	9,200,000	9,043	0.0	6.3	25.2	68.3	0.2
Mountain climbing	(b)	4,078	0.5	20.2	42.0	36.9	0.4
Racquetball, squash & paddleball	(b)	7,783	0.1	1.9	22.3	70.9	4.7
Roller skating	(b)	61,938[j]	1.2	58.6	15.1	23.9	1.2
Rugby	(b)	10,691	0.1	1.0	76.0	22.9	0.0
Scuba diving	(b)	1,401	4.9	6.0	12.5	70.1	6.5
Skateboarding	12,000,000	112,544	1.1	53.1	37.7	7.9	0.1
Snowboarding	6,000,000	57,113	0.4	30.7	49.9	18.9	0.1
Snowmobiling	(b)	12,586	0.7	5.3	29.4	63.8	0.8
Soccer	14,100,000	174,686	0.5	44.1	39.5	15.7	0.2
Softball	14,100,000	106,884	0.3	24.9	32.6	41.2	1.0
Swimming	58,000,000	165,725[k]	8.5	45.2	18.1	26.2	2.0
Tennis	11,100,000	19,487	0.9	14.8	22.2	47.0	14.7
Track & field	(b)	17,306	0.0	42.0	54.0	4.1	0.0
Volleyball	13,200,000	52,091	0.1	29.1	42.0	28.2	0.5
Water skiing	6,700,000	7,495	0.0	14.1	29.8	55.9	0.2
Weight lifting	35,500,000	65,716	4.8	12.1	36.0	45.4	1.6
Wrestling	(b)	33,734	0.1	36.9	58.9	4.1	0.0

Source: Participants — National Sporting Goods Association; figures include those seven years of age or older who participated more than once per year except for bicycle riding and swimming, which include those who participated six or more times per year. Injuries — Consumer Product Safety Commission; figures include only injuries treated in hospital emergency departments.
a Excludes mountain biking.
b Data not available
c Includes exercise equipment (40,583 injuries) and exercise activity (139,467 injuries).
d Data for 2004.
e Includes 9,600,000 in touch football and 8,200,000 in tackle football.
f Excludes golf carts (12,978 injuries).
g Excludes trampolines (108,029 injuries).
h Includes field hockey (4,681 injuries) and street hockey (2,641 injuries). Excludes 34,000 injuries in hockey, unspecified.
i Excludes 9,970 injuries in skating, unspecified.
j Includes roller skating (35,003 injuries) and in-line skating (26,935 injuries).
k Includes injuries associated with swimming, swimming pools, pool slides, diving or diving boards, and swimming pool equipment.

Cheerleading

A recent study examined data on cheerleading-related injuries to children 5 to 18 years of age that were treated in hospital emergency departments (EDs) from the National Electronic Injury Surveillance System (NEISS) of the Consumer Product Safety Commission for the 13-year period from 1990–2002. An estimated 208,800 children (95% confidence interval — CI: 166,620–250,980) were treated during this period and the number of injuries increased by 110% from 10,900 in 1990 to 22,900 in 2002, averaging 16,100 (95% CI: 12,848–19,352) per year. Peak periods for cheerleading-related injuries were from September to November (44% of injuries) and December to February (26% of injuries), thus coinciding with the football and basketball seasons, respectively.

The body parts injured were the lower extremity (37.2%), upper extremity (26.4%), head/neck (18.8%), and trunk (16.8%). Upper extremity injuries were more common among those aged 5 to 11 compared with 12- to 18-year-olds, while lower-extremity injuries were more common among those in the older age group. Sprains and strains (52.4%) dominated the injury diagnoses, followed by soft tissue injuries (18.4%) and fractures/dislocations (16.4%). Fractures or dislocations were more common in the 5- to 11-year-old age group compared to 12- to 18-year-olds, while sprains or strains were more common in the older age group. The majority (98.7%) of patients were treated and released from the ED.

The 110% increase in the number of cheerleading-related injuries during the study period was accompanied by an estimated 18% increase in the number of cheerleading participants 6 years of age or older. The authors state that the greater increase in injuries relative to participants may be attributed partly to the increased difficulty of cheerleading skills being attempted in recent years, with most injuries occurring during gymnastics maneuvers and partner stunts.

Source: Shields, B. J. & Smith, G.A. (2006). Cheerleading-related injuries to children 5 to 18 years of age: United States, 1990–2002. Pediatrics, 117(1), 122–129.

ESTIMATED NUMBER OF CHILDREN 5 TO 18 YEARS OF AGE WITH CHEERLEADING INJURIES, 1990–2002

Snowboarding

Snowboarding has become one of the key growth areas in alpine sports, with snowboarders constituting between one-third and one-half of participants at most alpine resorts. The growth in the popularity of snowboarding has been accompanied by an increasing level of interest in snowboarding injuries. A recent review article summarized the results of 10 studies conducted in six different countries between 1991 and 2002.

The sport is predominantly youth-oriented, with two-thirds of participants under the age of 25. Beginner or novice snowboarders constitute 40–60% of those injured, compared with 18–34% in skiing. The majority of snowboarding injuries are related to human error and, compared with skiers, snowboarders are injured three times more frequently from jumping. Collisions with objects or other slope users account for only about 10% of snowboard injuries, which is less frequent than that in skiers. Studies have demonstrated a 2- to 3-fold greater risk of upper to lower limb injuries, with approximately two-thirds of all injuries involving the upper limb and upper body. This result is again the opposite of that typically seen in alpine skiing injuries.

The most common body part injured in snowboarders is the wrist, accounting for 22% of all snowboarding injuries. Wrist fractures and sprains were more common in snowboarding novices, in women, and in the younger age groups, while intermediate and more experienced snowboarders, especially men, were more likely to experience hand, elbow, and shoulder injuries. Some studies have reported that snowboarders who wear protective wrist guards are significantly less likely to sustain wrist injuries than those who do not, with the design of the protection device also an important factor.

Source: Bladin, C., McCrory, P. & Pogorzelski, A. (2004). Snowboarding injuries—Current trends and future directions. Sports Medicine, 34(2), 133–139.

WEATHER

Hurricanes caused 77% of weather-related deaths in 2005.

A variety of weather events resulted in 1,922 deaths in the 50 United States and District of Columbia in 2005. Hurricanes Dennis (July), Katrina (August), Rita (September), and Wilma (October) accounted for more than three fourths of the fatalities.

Temperature extremes resulted in 9% of the deaths. Most of these occurred in the summer months.

Except for the hurricanes, the data on weather-related deaths was compiled by the National Climatic Data Center (NCDC), which is part of the National Oceanic and Atmospheric Administration. NCDC data may differ from data based on death certificates that appears elsewhere in *Injury Facts*. Hurricane data came from infoplease.com and may be incomplete.

WEATHER-RELATED DEATHS, UNITED STATES, 2005

Event	Total	Jan	Feb	Mar	Apr	May	Jun	Jul	Aug	Sep	Oct	Nov	Dec
Total	**1,922**	**68**	**5**	**13**	**10**	**19**	**37**	**114**	**1,355**	**183**	**50**	**35**	**33**
Hurricane/Tropical Storm	1,479	0	0	0	0	0	0	2	1,323	119	35	0	0
Temperature Extremes	182	15	1	0	0	12	10	75	10	51	0	0	8
Thunderstorm/High Winds	47	15	1	0	5	1	3	9	1	2	1	0	9
Snow/Ice	45	20	1	6	1	3	0	0	0	0	1	2	11
Flood	40	9	1	3	2	1	5	3	8	0	7	0	1
Ocean/Lake Surf	40	3	0	3	0	1	8	11	2	8	1	3	0
Lightning	38	0	1	0	2	1	10	12	7	2	3	0	0
Tornado	38	4	0	1	0	0	0	0	4	1	0	28	0
Precipitation	6	2	0	0	0	0	1	2	0	0	1	0	0
Wild/Forest Fire	6	0	0	0	0	0	0	0	0	0	0	2	4
Hail	1	0	0	0	0	0	0	0	0	0	1	0	0
Drought	0	0	0	0	0	0	0	0	0	0	0	0	0
Dust Storm	0	0	0	0	0	0	0	0	0	0	0	0	0
Fog	0	0	0	0	0	0	0	0	0	0	0	0	0
Funnel Cloud/Waterspout	0	0	0	0	0	0	0	0	0	0	0	0	0

Source: National Safety Council analysis of National Climatic Data Center data except for hurricanes Katrina, Rita, and Wilma which are from infoplease.com.

WEATHER-RELATED FATALITIES BY MONTH, UNITED STATES, 2005

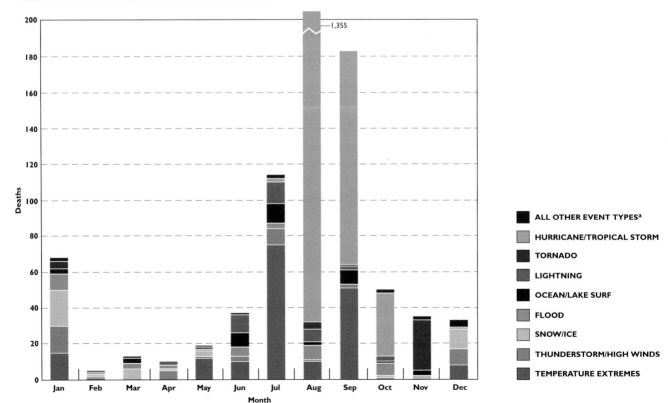

a Includes precipitation, wild/forest fire, and hail.

FIREARMS

Unintentional firearms-related deaths down 4% in 2003.

Firearm-related deaths from unintentional, intentional, and undetermined causes totaled 30,136 in 2003, a decrease of less than 0.5% from 2002. Suicides accounted for 56.1% of firearms deaths, 39.6% were homicides, and 2.4% were unintentional deaths. Males dominate all categories of firearms deaths and accounted for 86.7% of the total.

The numbers of homicide deaths by firearms increased for the third year. Unintentional deaths decreased for

the second year, while suicide deaths decreased in 2003 after increasing in 2002 from 16,869 to 17,108.

Hospital emergency department surveillance data indicate an estimated 18,941 nonfatal unintentional firearm-related injuries in 2003. For assault there were an estimated 42,505 nonfatal injuries and 3,687 intentionally self-inflicted nonfatal injuries.

Source: National Safety Council analysis of National Center for Health Statistics mortality data and National Center for Injury Prevention and Control injury surveillance data using WISQARS™ (http://www.cdc.gov/ncipc/wisqars/).

DEATHS INVOLVING FIREARMS BY AGE AND SEX, UNITED STATES, 2003

Type & Sex	All Ages	Under 5 Years	5–14 Years	15–19 Years	20–24 Years	25–44 Years	45–64 Years	65–74 Years	75 & Over
Total Firearms Deaths	**30,136**	**56**	**324**	**2,469**	**4,377**	**11,306**	**7,354**	**1,912**	**2,338**
Male	26,124	35	256	2,231	3,955	9,694	6,139	1,694	2,120
Female	4,012	21	68	238	422	1,612	1,215	218	218
Unintentional	**730**	**7**	**49**	**95**	**105**	**238**	**154**	**39**	**43**
Male	656	7	46	88	94	215	137	30	39
Female	74	0	3	7	11	23	17	9	4
Suicide	**16,907**	**—**	**74**	**736**	**1,339**	**5,308**	**5,596**	**1,700**	**2,154**
Male	14,827	—	63	659	1,220	4,569	4,769	1,538	2,009
Female	2,080	—	11	77	119	739	827	162	145
Homicide	**11,920**	**48**	**187**	**1,587**	**2,823**	**5,481**	**1,504**	**161**	**129**
Male	10,126	27	134	1,436	2,541	4,660	1,152	115	61
Female	1,794	21	53	151	282	821	352	46	68
Legal Intervention	**347**	**0**	**2**	**20**	**72**	**198**	**49**	**4**	**2**
Male	329	0	1	19	69	191	43	4	2
Female	18	0	1	1	3	7	6	0	0
Undetermined[a]	**232**	**1**	**12**	**31**	**38**	**81**	**51**	**8**	**10**
Male	186	1	12	29	31	59	38	7	9
Female	46	0	0	2	7	22	13	1	1

Source: National Safety Council tabulation of National Center for Health Statistics mortality data.
Note: Dashes (—) indicate category not applicable.
[a]Undetermined means the intentionality of the deaths (unintentional, homicide, suicide) was not determined.

FIREARMS DEATHS BY INTENTIONALITY AND YEAR, UNITED STATES, 1994–2003

TRANSPORTATION MODE COMPARISONS

Passenger transportation incidents account for three out of ten unintentional-injury deaths. But the risk of death to the passenger, expressed on a per mile basis, varies greatly by transportation mode. Highway travel by personal vehicle presents the greatest risk; air, rail, and bus travel have much lower death rates. The tables below show the latest information on passenger transportation deaths and death rates.

The statistics for automobiles, vans, sport utility vehicles (SUVs), pickups, and other light trucks shown in the tables below represent all passenger vehicle usage, both intercity and local. The bus data also include

intercity and local (transit) bus travel. Railroad includes both intercity (Amtrak) and local commuting travel. Scheduled airlines includes both large airlines and commuter airlines but excludes on-demand air taxis and charter operations. In comparing the four modes, drivers of automobiles (except taxis), vans, SUVs, and pickup trucks are considered passengers. Bus drivers and airline or railroad crews are not considered passengers.

Other comparisons are possible based on passenger-trips, vehicle-miles, or vehicle-trips, but passenger-miles is the most commonly used basis for comparing the safety of various modes of travel.

TRANSPORTATION ACCIDENT DEATH RATES, 2002–2004

Mode of Transportation	2004			2002–2004 Average Death Rate
	Passenger Deaths	Passenger Miles (billions)	Deaths per 100,000,000 Passenger Miles	
Passenger automobiles[a]	19,183	2,710.9	0.71	0.74
Vans, SUVs, pickup trucks[b]	12,678	1,663.0	0.76	0.77
Buses[c]	27	59.8	0.05	0.05
Transit buses	1	21.6	0.005	0.03
Intercity buses	19	38.2	0.05	0.03
Railroad passenger trains[d]	3	15.5	0.02	0.03
Scheduled airlines[e]	13	556.7	0.002	0.002

Source: Highway passenger deaths — Fatality Analysis Reporting System data. Railroad passenger deaths — Federal Railroad Administration. Airline passenger deaths — National Transportation Safety Board. Passenger miles for transit buses — American Public Transit Association. All other figures — National Safety Council estimates.
[a]Includes taxi passengers. Drivers of passenger automobiles are considered passengers.
[b]Includes 2-axle, 4-tire vehicles under 10,000 lbs GVWR other than automobiles.
[c]Figures exclude school buses but include "other" and "unknown" bus types.
[d]Includes Amtrak and commuter rail service.
[e]Includes large airlines and scheduled commuter airlines; excludes charter, cargo, and on-demand service and suicide/sabotage.

PASSENGER DEATHS AND DEATH RATES, UNITED STATES, 1995–2004

Year	Passenger Automobiles		Vans, SUVs, Pickup Trucks		Buses		Railroad Passenger Trains		Scheduled Airlines	
	Deaths	Rate[a]	Deaths	Rate[a]	Deaths	Rate[a]	Deaths	Rate[a]	Deaths	Rate[a]
1995	22,288	0.97	—	—	16	0.03	0	0.00	159	0.04
1996	22,359	0.96	—	—	10	0.02	12	0.09	329	0.08
1997	21,920	0.92	—	—	4	0.01	6	0.05	42	0.01
1998	21,099	0.86	—	—	26	0.05	4	0.03	0	0.00
1999	20,763	0.83	10,666	0.72	39	0.07	14	0.10	17	0.003
2000	20,444	0.80	11,435	0.76	3	0.01	4	0.03	87	0.02
2001	20,221	0.78	11,690	0.76	11	0.02	3	0.02	279	0.06
2002	20,408	0.77	12,186	0.77	36	0.06	7	0.05	0	0.00
2003	19,718	0.74	12,551	0.78	31	0.05	3	0.02	24	0.005
2004	19,183	0.71	12,678	0.76	27	0.05	3	0.02	13	0.002
10-year average	20,840	0.83	—	—	20	0.04	6	0.04	95	0.02

Source: See table above. Note: Dashes (—) indicate data not available.
[a]Deaths per 100,000,000 passenger miles.

PASSENGER DEATH RATES, UNITED STATES, 2002–2004

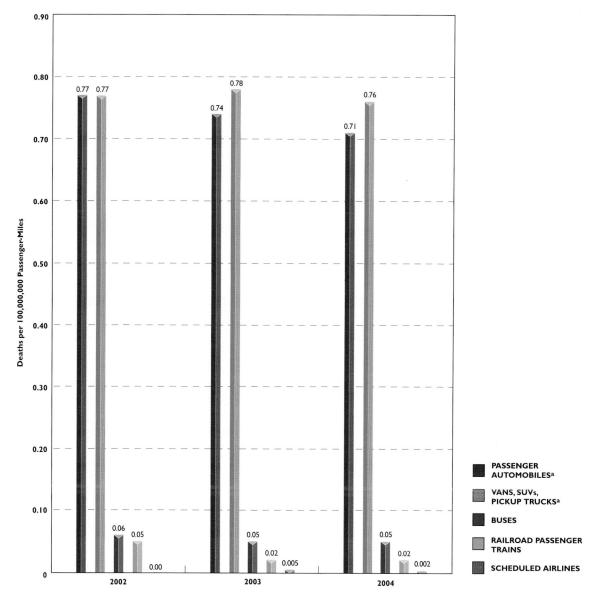

Drivers of these vehicles are considered passengers.

AVIATION

In 2005, there were 18 aircraft accidents that resulted in 713 fatalities to passengers according to preliminary full-year data reported by the International Civil Aviation Organization (ICAO). Compared to 2004, the 2005 data illustrate a noticeable deterioration in passenger safety — reported accidents increased by two-fold and fatalities by 3.5-fold. The 713 deaths resulted in a preliminary fatality rate of 0.02 per 100 million passenger-kilometers — a two-fold increase in risk compared to the prior year.

WORLDWIDE SCHEDULED AIR SERVICE ACCIDENTS, DEATHS, AND DEATH RATES, 1990–2005

Year	Fatal Accidents[a]	Passenger Deaths	Death Rate[b]	Year	Fatal Accidents[a]	Passenger Deaths	Death Rate[b]
1990	27	544	0.03	1998	20	904	0.03
1991	29	638	0.03	1999	21	499	0.02
1992	28	1,070	0.06	2000	18	757	0.03
1993	33	864	0.04	2001	13	577	0.02
1994	27	1,170	0.05	2002	13	791	0.025
1995	25	711	0.03	2003	7	466	0.015
1996	24	1,146	0.05	2004	9	203	0.01
1997	25	921	0.04	2005[c]	18	713	0.02

Source: International Civil Aviation Organization. Figures include the USSR up to 1992 and the Commonwealth of Independent States thereafter.
[a] Involving a passenger fatality and an aircraft with maximum take-off mass >2,250 kg.
[b] Passenger deaths per 100 million passenger-kilometers.
[c] Preliminary data.

U.S. CIVIL AVIATION ACCIDENTS, DEATHS, AND DEATH RATES, 2001–2005

Year	Accidents Total	Accidents Fatal	Total Deaths[a]	Per 100,000 Flight-Hours Total	Per 100,000 Flight-Hours Fatal	Per Million Aircraft-Miles Total	Per Million Aircraft-Miles Fatal
Large Airlines[b]							
2001[c]	41	6	531	0.216	0.012	0.0053	0.0003
2002	35	0	0	0.209	0	0.0051	0
2003	51	2	22	0.302	0.012	0.0073	0.0003
2004	21	1	13	0.126	0.005	0.0030	0.0001
2005	32	3	22	0.171	0.016	0.0041	0.0004
Commuter Airlines[b]							
2001	7	2	13	2.330	0.666	0.1624	0.0464
2002	7	0	0	2.559	0	0.1681	0
2003	2	1	2	0.627	0.313	0.0422	0.0211
2004	4	0	0	1.324	0	0.0855	0
2005	6	0	0	2.000	0	0.1298	0
On-Demand Air Taxis[b]							
2001	72	18	60	2.40	0.60	—	—
2002	60	18	35	2.06	0.62	—	—
2003	74	18	42	2.53	0.61	—	—
2004	66	23	64	2.04	0.71	—	—
2005	66	11	18	2.02	0.34	—	—
General Aviation[b]							
2001[c]	1,727	325	562	6.78	1.27	—	—
2002[c]	1,715	345	581	6.69	1.33	—	—
2003[c]	1,739	352	632	6.75	1.36	—	—
2004[c]	1,617	314	558	6.49	1.26	—	—
2005[c]	1,669	321	562	6.83	1.31	—	—

Source: National Transportation Safety Board: 2005 preliminary, 2001–2004 revised; exposure data for rates from Federal Aviation Administration.
Note: Dash (—) indicates data not available.
[a] Includes passengers, crew members, and others such as persons on the ground.
[b] Civil aviation accident statistics collected by the National Transportation Safety Board are classified according to the Federal air regulations under which the flights were made. The classifications are (1) large airlines operating scheduled service under Title 14, Code of Federal Regulations, part 121 (14 CFR 121); (2) commuter carriers operating scheduled service under 14 CFR 135; (3) unscheduled, "on-demand" air taxis under 14 CFR 135; and (4) "general aviation," which includes accidents involving aircraft flown under rules other than 14 CFR 121 and 14 CFR 135. Not shown in the table is nonscheduled air carrier operations under 14 CFR 121 which experienced 7 accidents, but no fatalities in 2005. Since 1997, Large Airlines includes aircraft with 10 or more seats, formerly operated as commuter carriers under 14 CFR 135.
[c] Suicide/sabotage/terrorism and stolen/unauthorized cases are included in "accident" and fatality totals but excluded from rates — Large Airlines, 2001 (4 crashes/265 deaths); General Aviation, 2001 (3/1), 2002 (6/5), 2003 (2/1), 2004 (3/0), 2005 (2/1).

RAILROAD

Railroad deaths totaled 893 in 2005, comparable to the 2004 total of 895, but a 7% decrease from the 1996–2004 average of 963. In 2005, there was a 4% decrease in fatalities at highway-rail crossings over the prior year, but fatalities from other types of incidents increased by 2% from 526 in 2004 to 537 in 2005. The latter included 473 deaths, or 88%, to trespassers. Twenty-five employees were killed while on duty, the same as in 2004 but slightly lower than the 1996–2004 average of 26. Deaths to passengers on trains totaled 16, thus reaching a 10-year high, up from 3 deaths in 2004 and the nine-year average of 6.

For every railroad-related death, there are typically 10 nonfatal cases of reportable injuries and illnesses. In 2005, railroad accidents resulted in 9,066 cases of nonfatal conditions, compared to 9,071 in 2004 and the 1996–2004 average of 11,055. Eleven percent of the total was attributed to highway-rail crossing incidents, which declined by 9% over the 2004 total of 1,090 and by 22% over the 1996–2004 average of 1,261. Of the 5,586 nonfatal occupational injuries and illnesses reported in 2005, less than 2% were attributed to highway-rail crossing incidents.

DEATHS AND NONFATAL CASES IN RAILROAD ACCIDENTS AND INCIDENTS, UNITED STATES, 1996–2005

Year	Total	Highway-Rail Crossing Incident?		Occuring in Other Than Highway-Rail Crossing Incident		Employees On Duty At Highway-Rail Crossing?		Passengers on Trains[a] At Highway-Rail Crossing?	
		Yes	No	Trespassers	Others	Yes	No	Yes	No
Deaths									
1996	1,039	488	551	471	80	1	32	0	12
1997	1,063	461	602	533	69	0	37	0	6
1998	1,008	431	577	536	41	4	23	2	2
1999	932	402	530	479	51	2	29	11	3
2000	937	425	512	463	49	2	22	0	4
2001	971	421	550	511	39	1	21	0	3
2002	951	357	594	540	54	1	19	0	7
2003	868	334	534	501	33	1	18	1	2
2004	895	369	526	478	48	2	23	0	3
2005	893	356	537	473	64	2	23	0	16
Nonfatal conditions									
1996	12,558	1,610	10,948	474	10,474	79	9,120	24	489
1997	11,767	1,540	10,227	516	9,711	111	8,184	43	558
1998	11,459	1,303	10,156	513	9,643	122	8,276	19	516
1999	11,700	1,396	10,304	445	9,859	140	8,482	43	438
2000	11,643	1,219	10,424	414	10,010	100	8,323	10	648
2001	10,985	1,157	9,828	404	9,424	97	7,718	20	726
2002	11,103	999	10,104	395	9,709	110	6,534	26	851
2003	9,209	1,033	8,176	399	7,777	76	6,153	74	640
2004	9,071	1,090	7,981	404	7,577	116	5,866	21	646
2005	9,066	987	8,079	406	7,673	109	5,477	28	840

Source: Federal Railroad Administration.
[a] Passenger cases include all circumstances, including getting on/off standing trains, stumbling aboard trains, assaults, train accidents, crossing incidents, etc.

CASUALTIES AT PUBLIC AND PRIVATE HIGHWAY-RAIL CROSSINGS, UNITED STATES, 1996–2005

Year	Deaths				Nonfatal Conditions			
	Total	Motor-Vehicle Related	Pedestrians	Others	Total	Motor-Vehicle Related	Pedestrians	Others
1996	488	415	60	13	1,610	1,545	31	34
1997	461	419	38	4	1,540	1,494	33	13
1998	431	369	50	12	1,303	1,257	33	13
1999	402	345	45	12	1,396	1,338	35	23
2000	425	361	51	13	1,219	1,169	34	16
2001	421	345	67	9	1,157	1,110	31	16
2002	357	310	35	12	999	939	29	31
2003	334	281	50	3	1,033	998	28	7
2004	369	287	73	9	1,090	1,055	30	5
2005	356	280	58	18	987	941	36	10

Source: Federal Railroad Administration.

UNINTENTIONAL POISONINGS

Poisoning deaths up 11% from 2002 to 2003.

Deaths from unintentional poisoning numbered 19,457 in 2003, the latest year for which data are available. The death rate per 100,000 population was 6.7 — 9.2 for males and 4.2 for females. Total poisoning deaths increased 11% from 17,550 in 2002 and are 2.5 times the 1993 total. See pages 42–45 for long-term trends.

Almost half of the poisoning deaths (47%) were classified in the "narcotics and psychodysleptics (hallucinogens), not elsewhere classified," category, which includes many illegal drugs such as cocaine, heroin, cannabinol, and LSD.

Carbon monoxide poisoning is included in the category of "other gases and vapors." Deaths due to alcohol poisoning numbered 373 in 2003, but alcohol may also be present in combination with other drugs.

Additional information on human poisoning exposure cases, both fatal and nonfatal, may be found on page 140.

UNINTENTIONAL POISONING DEATHS BY TYPE, AGE, AND SEX, UNITED STATES, 2003

Type of Poison	All Ages	0–4 Years	5–14 Years	15–19 Years	20–24 Years	25–44 Years	45–64 Years	65 Years & Over
Both Sexes								
Total Poisoning Deaths	19,457	69	61	520	1,479	9,665	6,804	859
Deaths per 100,000 population	6.7	0.3	0.1	2.5	7.1	11.5	9.9	2.4
Nonopioid analgesics, antipyretics and antirheumatics (X40)a	210	4	1	4	9	82	80	30
Antiepileptic, sedative-hypnotic, antiparkinsonism and psychotropic drugs, n.e.c. (X41)	1,205	5	2	22	88	603	447	38
Narcotics and psychodysleptics (hallucinogens), n.e.c. (X42)	9,231	10	10	255	744	4,870	3,197	145
Other drugs acting on the autonomic nervous system (X43)	37	1	0	0	4	11	14	7
Other and unspecified drugs, medicaments and biological substances (X44)	7,611	22	14	190	566	3,699	2,669	451
Alcohol (X45)	373	0	0	21	15	157	165	15
Organic solvents and halogenated hydrocarbons and their vapors (X46)	60	1	2	3	5	32	16	1
Other gases and vapors (X47)	630	24	30	18	46	183	181	148
Pesticides (X48)	3	1	0	0	0	0	1	1
Other and unspecified chemical and noxious substances (X49)	97	1	2	7	2	28	34	23
Males								
Total Poisoning Deaths	13,176	36	31	398	1,164	6,680	4,439	428
Deaths per 100,000 population	9.2	0.4	0.1	3.8	10.9	15.8	13.3	2.9
Nonopioid analgesics, antipyretics and antirheumatics (X40)	89	3	0	2	5	35	35	9
Antiepileptic, sedative-hypnotic, antiparkinsonism and psychotropic drugs, n.e.c. (X41)	754	3	1	15	57	397	258	23
Narcotics and psychodysleptics (hallucinogens), n.e.c. (X42)	6,825	7	4	194	603	3,590	2,335	92
Other drugs acting on the autonomic nervous system (X43)	20	1	0	0	4	5	6	4
Other and unspecified drugs, medicaments and biological substances (X44)	4,609	9	8	144	441	2,332	1,488	187
Alcohol (X45)	298	0	0	18	11	130	130	9
Organic solvents and halogenated hydrocarbons and their vapors (X46)	51	0	1	3	5	25	16	1
Other gases and vapors (X47)	463	12	16	15	36	147	144	93
Pesticides (X48)	3	1	0	0	0	0	1	1
Other and unspecified chemical and noxious substances (X49)	64	0	1	7	2	19	26	9
Females								
Total Poisoning Deaths	6,281	33	30	122	315	2,985	2,365	431
Deaths per 100,000 population	4.2	0.3	0.2	1.2	3.1	7.1	6.7	2.1
Nonopioid analgesics, antipyretics and antirheumatics (X40)	121	1	1	2	4	47	45	21
Antiepileptic, sedative-hypnotic, antiparkinsonism and psychotropic drugs, n.e.c. (X41)	451	2	1	7	31	206	189	15
Narcotics and psychodysleptics (hallucinogens), n.e.c. (X42)	2,406	3	6	61	141	1,280	862	53
Other drugs acting on the autonomic nervous system (X43)	17	0	0	0	0	6	8	3
Other and unspecified drugs, medicaments and biological substances (X44)	3,002	13	6	46	125	1,367	1,181	264
Alcohol (X45)	75	0	0	3	4	27	35	6
Organic solvents and halogenated hydrocarbons and their vapors (X46)	9	1	1	0	0	7	0	0
Other gases and vapors (X47)	167	12	14	3	10	36	37	55
Pesticides (X48)	0	0	0	0	0	0	0	0
Other and unspecified chemical and noxious substances (X49)	33	1	1	0	0	9	8	14

Source: National Safety Council tabulations of National Center for Health Statistics mortality data.
Note: n.e.c. means not elsewhere classified.
a Numbers following titles refer to external cause of injury and poisoning classifications in ICD-10.

UNINTENTIONAL POISONING DEATHS, UNITED STATES, 1994–2003

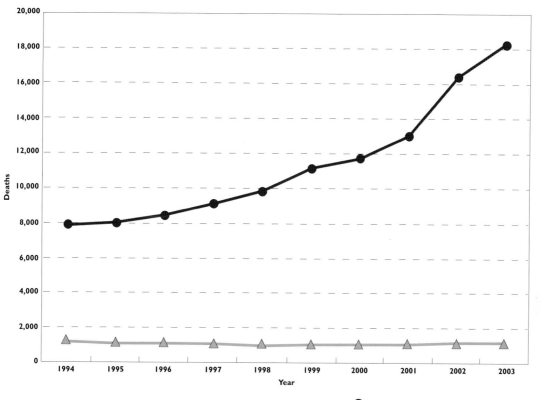

Note: Classification system changed in 1999 (see the Technical Appendix).

● DRUGS, MEDICAMENTS, BIOLOGICALS (X40–X44)

▲ OTHER SUBSTANCES (X45–X49)

POISONING EXPOSURES

Total poisoning exposures up 2% from 2003 to 2004.

In 2004, over 2.4 million human poisoning exposure cases, both fatal and nonfatal, were reported to 62 poison control centers, which served the entire U.S. population. The total was an increase of 1.8% compared to 2003 and is equivalent to about 8.3 reported exposures per 1,000 population, according to the American Association of Poison Control Centers. Nearly 93% of the exposures occurred at a residence, while 2% occurred in the workplace, and less than 0.5% occurred in each of food services and health care facilities. Peak call volumes at poison control centers were from 4 to 11 p.m., with 90% of all calls logged between 8 a.m. and midnight. The average number of calls handled per day by all centers was 6,663, with higher volumes observed in the warmer months. On average, poison control centers handled one poison exposure every 13 seconds.

More than half (51.3%) of the poisoning exposures involved children under 6 years old, with nearly a quarter of these exposures involving cosmetics and personal care products or cleaning substances (see table). A male predominance is found among poison exposure victims less than 13 years of age, with the sex distribution reversed in teenagers and adults. Children under six years of age comprised just 2.3% of the poisoning fatalities, while persons 20 to 49 years of age accounted for over 56%. A single substance was implicated in over 91% of reports, and about 3% of patients were exposed to more than two possibly

poisonous drugs or products. In contrast, nearly 51% of fatal cases involved two or more drugs or products. About 92% of human exposures were acute, compared with 56% of poison-related fatal exposures. Chronic exposures comprised 1.8% of all poison exposure reports, and acute-on-chronic exposures comprised 5.5%.

Over 84% of poison exposures were unintentional, 12.4% were intentional, 2.5% were due to adverse reactions, and "Other" and "Unknown" reasons accounted for less than 1% each. Unintentional therapeutic errors accounted for 9.1% of exposures, while nonpharmaceutical product misuse comprised another 3.9%. Suspected suicidal intent was present in 8.0% of cases. Unintentional poison exposures outnumbered intentional exposures in all age groups, while for the 1,183 human fatalities reported, 87.8% of adolescent (13–19 years of age) deaths and 80.2% of adult (greater than 19 years of age) deaths were intentional. Ingestion was the route of exposure for about 77% and 75%, respectively, of all exposure cases and fatal exposure cases. The substances most frequently involved in human poisoning exposures were analgesics (11.5% of exposures), cleaning substances (9.4%), cosmetics and personal care products (9.2%), and sedatives/hypnotics/antipsychotics (5.3%).

Source: Watson, W. A., Litovitz, T. L., Rodgers Jr., G. C., Klein-Schwartz, Reid, N., Youniss, J., Flanagan, A., & Wruk, K.M. (2005). 2004 Annual Report of the American Association of Poison Control Centers Toxic Exposure Surveillance System. The American Journal of Emergency Medicine, 23(5), 589–666.

SUBSTANCES MOST FREQUENTLY INVOLVED IN PEDIATRIC[a] POISON EXPOSURES, UNITED STATES, 2004

Substance[b]	No. of Exposures	Percent[c]
Cosmetics and personal care products	168,021	13.4
Cleaning substances	124,962	10.0
Analgesics	98,237	7.9
Topicals	92,482	7.4
Foreign bodies	91,10	7.3
Cough and cold preparations	67,494	5.4
Plants	55,078	4.4
Pesticides	52,174	4.2
Vitamins	48,989	3.9
Antihistamines	34,40	2.8
Antimicrobials	33,528	2.7
Gastrointestinal preparations	30,289	2.4
Arts/crafts/office supplies	29,798	2.4
Electrolytes and minerals	24,886	2.0
Hormones and hormone antagonists	22,877	1.8

[a] Children younger than 6 years.
[b] Despite a high frequency of involvement, these substances are not necessarily the most toxic, but rather may be the most readily accessible.
[c] Percentages are based on the total number of exposures in children younger than 6 years (1,250,536) rather than the total number of substances.

INJURIES ASSOCIATED WITH CONSUMER PRODUCTS

Over 2 million injury-related emergency department visits each year are associated with stairs, steps, floors, and flooring materials

The following list of items found in and around the home was selected from the U.S. Consumer Product Safety Commission's National Electronic Injury Surveillance System (NEISS) for 2005. The NEISS estimates are calculated from a statistically representative sample of hospitals in the United States. Injury totals represent estimates of the number of hospital emergency department-treated cases nationwide associated with various products. However, product involvement may or may not be the cause of the injury.

CONSUMER PRODUCT–RELATED INJURIES TREATED IN HOSPITAL EMERGENCY DEPARTMENTS, 2005
(excluding most sports or sports equipment; see also page 130)

Description	Injuries
Home Workshop Equipment	
Saws (hand or power)	95,448
Hammers	34,105
Tools, not specified	31,132
Household Packaging and Containers	
Household containers and packaging	207,680
Bottles and jars	73,916
Bags	38,829
Paper products	23,749
Housewares	
Knives	429,021
Tableware and flatware (excl. knives)	97,559
Drinking glasses	74,018
Waste containers, trash baskets, etc.	33,718
Scissors	31,801
Cookware, bowls, and canisters	28,432
Manual cleaning equipment (excl. buckets)	21,373
Other kitchen gadgets	21,144
Home Furnishing, Fixtures, and Accessories	
Beds	505,826
Chairs	302,328
Tables, n.e.c.[a]	298,949
Household cabinets, racks, and shelves	245,555
Bathtubs and showers	214,542
Ladders	178,792
Sofas, couches, davenports, divans, etc.	144,301
Rugs and carpets	119,572
Other furniture[b]	107,472
Toilets	62,313
Misc. decorating items	51,033
Stools	47,933
Benches	27,570
Mirrors or mirror glass	22,668
Sinks	21,619
Home Structures and Construction Materials	
Floors or flooring materials	1,114,816
Stairs or steps	1,104,071
Ceilings and walls	308,518
Other doors[c]	307,713
Nails, screws, tacks or bolts	156,846
Porches, balconies, open-side floors	129,653
Windows	128,000
Fences or fence posts	109,610
House repair and construction materials	95,360
Door sills or frames	44,321
Counters or countertops	40,859
Handrails, railings, or banisters	39,247
Poles	38,732
Glass doors	28,803

Description	Injuries
General Household Appliances	
Refrigerators	32,131
Ranges or ovens, not specified	28,080
Heating, Cooling, and Ventilating Equipment	
Pipes (excluding smoking pipes)	29,841
Home Communication and Entertainment Equipment	
Televisions	51,091
Personal-Use Items	
Footwear	115,944
Wheelchairs	103,055
Crutches, canes, walkers	81,205
Jewelry	73,853
Daywear	45,330
First aid equipment	42,999
Desk supplies	39,000
Razors and shavers	34,884
Coins	28,626
Other clothing[d]	26,365
Hair grooming equipment and accessories	21,698
Luggage	21,615
Yard and Garden Equipment	
Lawn mowers	84,316
Pruning, trimming, and edging equipment	38,133
Chainsaws	26,939
Other unpowered garden tools[e]	24,409
Recreation Equipment	
Bicycles	494,712
Skateboards	112,544
Trampolines	108,029
Toys, n.e.c.	94,827
Monkey bars or other playground climbing	80,312
Swimming pools	79,823
Minibikes or trailbikes	71,349
Swings or swing sets	60,725
Dancing activity, apparel, or equipment	44,191
Slides or sliding boards	42,904
Scooters (unpowered)	38,946
Aquariums and other pet supplies	35,539
Sleds	31,798
Other playground equipment[f]	26,834
Gas, air, or spring operated guns	21,056
Miscellaneous Products	
Carts	45,268
Hot water	41,331

Source: U.S. Consumer Product Safety Commission, National Electronic Injury Surveillance System, Product Summary Report, All Products, CY2005.
Note: Products are listed above if the estimate was greater than 21,000 cases.
n.e.c. = not elsewhere classified.
[a] Excludes baby changing and television tables or stands.

[b] Excludes cabinets, racks shelves, desks, bureaus, chests, buffets, etc.
[c] Excludes glass doors and garage doors.
[d] Excludes costumes, masks, daywear, footwear, nightwear, and outerwear.
[e] Includes cultivators, hoes, pitchforks, rakes, shovels, spades, and trowels.
[f] Excludes monkey bars, seesaws, slides, and swings.

FIRES

The estimated annual average[a] number of structure fires for the period 1999–2002 was 517,130. These fire events resulted in annual averages of 3,142 civilian deaths, 17,729 civilian injuries, and $8.6 billion in direct property damage over the same period. While comprising just 30% of all fire incidents, structure fires accounted for 85% of civilian deaths, 86% of civilian injuries, and 86% of the direct property damage.

Over three-quarters of the fires, 97% of the civilian deaths, 89% of the civilian injuries, and about 65% of the direct property damage occurred in residential occupancy structures, including homes and other residential structures such as rooming or boarding houses, residential hotels, hotels or motels, dormitories, fraternities, sororities, or barracks, etc. More than half of the fires, over three-quarters of the civilian deaths, about 60% of the civilian injuries, and nearly 50% of the direct property damage occurred in one- or two-family dwellings, while about 18% of fires, 16% of civilian deaths, 26% of civilian injuries, and about 13% of direct property damage occurred in apartments or multi-family dwellings. By comparison, only about 3% of fires, civilian deaths, civilian injuries, and direct

property damage, respectively, occurred in other residential structures. Seventy-four percent of home fire deaths occurred in properties without working smoke alarms.

Cooking equipment was the leading cause of home structure fires and civilian fire injuries during the period 1999–2002 (see chart). The leading cause of civilian fire deaths was smoking materials, while intentionally set fires caused the largest percentage of direct property damage. Centrally installed, maintained, and supervised systems in apartment buildings, such as heating and electrical distribution equipment, cause a smaller share of the fires in apartments than they do in one- and two-family dwellings. Causes of fires that involve actions on the part of the occupants, such as cooking, rank high in both kinds of properties. Note that when a type of equipment is shown as a cause, it means the equipment was involved in the ignition and does not mean that the equipment was defective or malfunctioned — in many cases, properly operating equipment is used improperly.

[a] Excluding the events of September 11, 2001.
Source: Ahrens, M. (2006, March). U.S. fires in selected occupancies. Quincy, MA: National Fire Protection Association.

PERCENT OF HOME STRUCTURE FIRES, CIVILIAN DEATHS, CIVILIAN INJURIES, AND DIRECT PROPERTY DAMAGE BY LEADING CAUSES, 1999–2002 ANNUAL AVERAGES

PEDALCYCLES

The estimated number of deaths from pedalcycle-motor-vehicle collisions increased from about 750 in 1940 to 1,200 in 1980, then declined to about 1,000 in 2005. Nonfatal disabling injuries were estimated to number 51,000 in 2005.

In 2003, 572 pedalcyclists died in motor-vehicle crashes and 190 in other accidents according to National Center for Health Statistics mortality data. Males accounted for more than 88% of all pedalcycle deaths, over seven times the female fatalities.

Emergency-room-treated injuries associated with bicycles and bicycle accessories were estimated to total 524,455 in 2004 and 485,669 in 2005, according to

the U.S. Consumer Product Safety Commission (see also page 130). The CPSC reported that bike helmet use was 50% in 1998. About 38% of adults and 69% of children under 16 reported wearing bike helmets regularly. The Bicycle Helmet Safety Institute estimates that helmets reduce the risk of all head injuries by up to 85% and reduce the risk of brain injuries by as much as 88%. In 2006, 20 states, the District of Columbia, and at least 149 localities had bicycle helmet laws according to the Bicycle Helmet Safety Institute.

Source: National Safety Council estimates and tabulations of National Center for Health Statistics mortality data. Rodgers, G.B., & Tinsworth, D. (1999). Bike Helmets. Consumer Product Safety Review, (4), 2-4. Data from Bicycle Helmet Safety Institute retrieved 11/14/06 from www.bhsi.org.

PEDALCYCLE DEATHS AND DEATH RATES BY SEX AND AGE GROUP, UNITED STATES, 2003

Source: National Safety Council based on National Center for Health Statistics data.

PEDALCYCLE FATALITIES BY MONTH, UNITED STATES, 2003

DROWNING

Drowning was the sixth leading cause of unintentional-injury death in 2003 according to data from the National Center for Health Statistics. It was the leading cause of accidental death for 2 year olds and the second leading cause for children 3, 6, 7, and 10–15 years old.

Of the 2,343 drownings where the location was specified, 1,225 (52%) occurred in natural bodies of water such as rivers, lakes, ponds, streams, and oceans; 515 (22%) occurred in swimming pools; and 332 (14%) occurred in bath tubs. Drowning while in a

natural body of water was the most common location for all age groups except the youngest. For children under 5 years old, the most common location was while in a swimming pool.

More than four out of five (83%) bathtub drownings happened at home. Fifty three percent of drownings while in a swimming pool occurred at home, but 78% of pool drownings following a fall into a pool occurred at home. Overall, about 23% of all drownings happened at home.

DROWNING DEATHS BY LOCATION AND AGE GROUP, UNITED STATES, 2003

Location	Total	0–4 Years	5–14 Years	15–24 Years	25–44 Years	45–64 Years	65–74 Years	75 & Over
Total	3,306	514	268	567	818	662	202	275
Bath tub	332	68	18	18	67	63	38	60
While in bath tub	304	63	17	18	61	58	33	54
Following fall into bath tub	28	5	1	0	6	5	5	6
Swimming pool	515	225	60	39	68	54	33	36
While in swimming pool	430	178	56	38	64	41	25	28
Following fall into pool	85	47	4	1	4	13	8	8
Natural body of water	1,225	58	91	287	370	276	55	88
While in natural water	989	40	76	263	308	201	37	64
Following fall into water	236	18	15	24	62	75	18	24
Other specified drowning	271	44	23	56	58	47	16	27
Unspecified drowning	963	119	76	167	255	222	60	64

Source: National Safety Council analysis of National Center for Health Statistics mortality data.

DROWNING DEATHS BY LOCATION, UNITED STATES, 2003

FALLS

Between 1999 and 2003, the number of fall-related deaths among persons 65 and older has risen 36% while the number of deaths increased by only 15% among those under 65 years old. The fall death rate for people 65 and older rose 31% during the same period. These increases continue long-term trends that began in the mid 1980s.

Between 1999 and 2004, visits to hospital emergency departments for fall-related injuries varied between 7,034,000 (2002) and 8,482,000 (2004) with an average of 7,810,000 per year.

Nonfatal falls involving older adults. Older women are disproportionately affected by nonfatal falls compared to older men. Of the estimated 1.64 million adults aged 65 and older who were treated in hospital emergency departments in 2001, 1.16 million or 70.5% were women. Fractures were 2.2 times more likely among women compared to men and hospitalization was 1.8 times more likely. Women were also much more likely to suffer leg/foot injuries (2.3 times), arm/hand injuries (2.0 times), and lower trunk injuries (2.0 times).[a]

Outdoor falls. In a case-control study of outdoor falls among adults aged 45 and older, researchers found that falls occurred outdoors more often than indoors. Study subjects were at high risk for outdoor falls if they reported more leisure-time physical activity. Poorer health was a risk factor for indoor falls.

Outdoor falls were associated with environmental factors such as uneven surfaces and tripping or slipping on objects. Falls usually occurred on sidewalks, curbs, and streets. Walking was the activity in almost half (47.3%) of the falls.

Because physical activity is being promoted to improve health among all ages and especially among older adults, researchers concluded that improvements in outdoor environments are necessary to avoid an increase in outdoor falls.[b]

Risk factors. Certain factors increase the risk of falling for older adults. Some are personal risk factors and others are environmental. Personal risk factors include lower-body weakness, problems with gait and balance, use of psychoactive medications, and visual impairment. These may be mitigated by exercise, medication management, identification and treatment for symptoms of chronic diseases such as Parkinson's Disease, stroke, and arthritis, and other approaches. Environmental factors may include tripping hazards, lack of stair railings or grab bars, unstable furniture, poor lighting, and inappropriate footwear. Research has shown that interventions that used clinical assessment and risk factor reduction lowered the risk of falling by 18% and reduced the average number of falls by 43%.[c]

[a] Stevens, J.A., & Sogolow, E.D. (2005). Gender differences for non-fatal unintentional fall related injuries among older adults. Injury Prevention, 11(2), 115–119.
[b] Li, W., Keegan, T.H.M., Sternfeld, B., Sidney, S., Quesenberry, C.P., & Kelsey, J.L. (2006). Outdoor falls among middle-aged and older adults: A neglected public health problem. American Journal of Public Health, 96(7), 1192–1200.
[c] Stevens, J.A. (2005). Falls among older adults—risk factors and prevention strategies. Journal of Safety Research, 36(4), 409–411.

FALL DEATHS AND DEATH RATES, UNITED STATES, 1999–2003

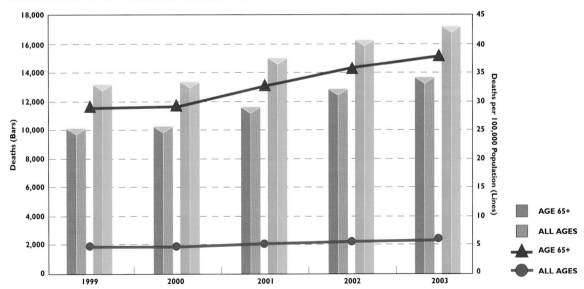

YOUTH RISK BEHAVIOR SURVEILLANCE — NATIONAL DATA

Unintentional injuries are the leading cause of mortality and motor-vehicle crashes are the leading cause of injury-related mortality for teens in the United States. Nearly three-quarters of all deaths among persons aged 15–19 years are due to unintentional injuries (50%), homicide (14%), and suicide (11%)[a]. Developed by the Center for Disease Control and Prevention (CDC), the Youth Risk Behavior Surveillance System (YRBSS) includes national, state, and local school-based surveys of students in grades 9 through 12 and is intended to monitor health behaviors, including seatbelt use, bicycle and motorcycle helmet use, alcohol and other drug use, smoking, sexual behaviors, dietary behaviors, and physical exercise.

The 2005 national Youth Risk Behavior Survey was completed by 13,953 students from 159 schools nationwide, with the student response rate of 86% (78% school response rate). Ten percent of students reported rarely or never wearing a seatbelt while riding in a car driven by someone else, and the reported seatbelt usage rates were lower for males compared to females. Twelve percent of males reported driving after drinking alcohol, compared with 8% of females. In 2005, about 68% of students had ridden a bicycle during the 12 months preceding the survey. Of those, 83% (80% females, 86% males) had rarely or never worn a helmet. Twenty-eight percent of students had ridden a motorcycle during the 12 months preceding the survey. Of these students, 37% (33% females, 38% males) had rarely or never worn a helmet. As illustrated in the tables below, the prevalence of these behaviors varies across race and ethnic groups.

RISK BEHAVIORS AMONG HIGH-SCHOOL STUDENTS BY SEX AND RACE, UNITED STATES, 2005

Race and Ethnicity	Rarely or never wore a seatbelt[b], % (CI)[c]			Rode with a driver who had been drinking[d], % (CI)			Drove when drinking[d], % (CI)		
	Female	Male	Both Sexes	Female	Male	Both Sexes	Female	Male	Both Sexes
Black, non-Hispanic	9.4 (2.9)	17.7 (4.7)	13.4 (3.4)	24.0 (2.6)	24.3 (2.5)	24.1 (2.1)	3.5 (1.7)	6.5 (1.9)	4.9 (1.3)
Hispanic	8.7 (2.3)	12.5 (2.4)	10.6 (2.1)	34.7 (2.7)	37.4 (4.5)	36.1 (3.3)	6.4 (1.2)	14.6 (3.4)	10.5 (1.8)
White, non-Hispanic	7.2 (1.9)	11.5 (2.7)	9.4 (2.2)	30.4 (3.3)	26.2 (2.5)	28.3 (2.6)	10.1 (1.4)	12.4 (1.5)	11.3 (1.2)
Total	**7.8 (1.5)**	**12.5 (2.2)**	**10.2 (1.8)**	**29.6 (2.4)**	**27.2 (2.0)**	**28.5 (1.9)**	**8.1 (1.0)**	**11.7 (1.4)**	**9.9 (1.0)**

Race and Ethnicity	Rarely or never wore a bicycle helmet[e], % (CI)			Rarely or never wore a motorcycle helmet[f], % (CI)		
	Female	Male	Both Sexes	Female	Male	Both Sexes
Black, non-Hispanic	90.1 (3.6)	93.5 (2.0)	92.0 (1.8)	40.7 (11.7)	48.0 (8.7)	44.8 (8.1)
Hispanic	83.4 (4.5)	88.6 (3.0)	86.5 (3.2)	48.3 (7.2)	46.1 (7.3)	47.1 (5.5)
White, non-Hispanic	77.9 (4.8)	84.4 (3.3)	81.5 (3.8)	30.2 (7.6)	35.6 (7.7)	33.7 (6.9)
Total	**79.9 (4.0)**	**86.1 (2.8)**	**83.4 (3.2)**	**33.2 (5.9)**	**38.4 (6.5)**	**36.5 (5.7)**

Source: Centers for Disease Control and Prevention. Youth Risk Behavior Surveillance — United States, 2005. Surveillance Summaries, June 9, 2006, Morbidity and Mortality Weekly Report, 55(SS-5).
[a] Centers for Disease Control and Prevention. Web-based Injury Statistics Query and Reporting System (WISQARS).
[b] When riding in a car or other vehicle driven by someone else.
[c] 95% confidence interval (CI). Confidence interval shows the level of uncertainty of a percent estimate and defines the range in which the true value is likely to be found. The lower boundary is calculated by subtracting the CI value figure from the percent estimate and the upper boundary is calculated by adding the CI value to the estimate.
[d] One or more times during the 30 days prior to the survey.
[e] Among the 68% of students nationwide who had ridden a bicycle during the 12 months prior to the survey.
[f] Among the 28% of students nationwide who had ridden a motorcycle during the 12 months prior to the survey.

YOUTH RISK BEHAVIOR
SURVEILLANCE — STATE DATA

Forty state surveys were completed for the 2005 YRBSS cycle. The percentage of students who had rarely or never worn a bicycle helmet ranged from 56% (Vermont) to 95% (South Dakota), and the percentage of students who had driven a car or other vehicle one or more times when they had been drinking alcohol ranged from 4% (Utah) to 22% (North Dakota). Other injury-related risk behaviors showed less striking differences across states.

RISK BEHAVIORS AMONG HIGH-SCHOOL STUDENTS BY STATE, UNITED STATES, 2005

State	Rarely or never wore a seatbelt[a] Percent (CI)[d]	Rode with a driver who had been drinking[b] Percent (CI)	Drove when drinking[b] Percent (CI)	Rarely or never wore a bicycle helmet[c] Percent (CI)
Alabama	14.2 (3.8)	28.8 (2.8)	11.1 (1.9)	88.1 (3.3)
Arizona	13.9 (2.2)	34.3 (2.2)	12.4 (1.8)	87.3 (2.9)
Arkansas	17.8 (3.2)	27.8 (3.1)	12.9 (3.0)	92.7 (2.3)
Colorado	7.6 (2.3)	26.9 (4.5)	11.0 (3.7)	70.7 (7.0)
Connecticut	11.4 (2.3)	29.7 (2.4)	11.0 (1.8)	76.2 (5.4)
Delaware	7.5 (1.1)	26.7 (2.0)	9.3 (1.5)	84.2 (2.3)
Florida	12.5 (1.6)	27.2 (1.8)	10.2 (1.1)	87.7 (1.3)
Georgia	9.6 (3.8)	26.7 (3.2)	8.8 (2.9)	85.6 (6.4)
Hawaii	4.8 (1.2)	33.0 (2.8)	7.9 (1.6)	85.7 (2.7)
Idaho	9.3 (1.8)	27.7 (4.1)	12.9 (3.1)	82.3 (3.0)
Indiana	8.2 (1.5)	24.6 (3.5)	11.2 (2.7)	92.3 (2.4)
Iowa	7.5 (1.7)	30.6 (4.5)	16.1 (3.9)	91.0 (3.1)
Kansas	14.7 (2.8)	29.2 (3.3)	16.5 (3.5)	86.7 (3.7)
Kentucky	18.1 (1.7)	22.0 (1.7)	8.5 (1.4)	92.9 (1.1)
Maine	14.4 (3.1)	25.2 (3.6)	11.2 (2.6)	70.5 (6.3)
Maryland	6.1 (1.3)	25.0 (3.9)	7.2 (2.4)	81.7 (6.1)
Massachusetts	15.4 (2.3)	27.2 (1.6)	10.5 (1.7)	(e)
Michigan	6.3 (1.4)	24.9 (2.8)	8.5 (1.5)	89.8 (3.6)
Missouri	12.2 (2.0)	25.0 (2.9)	11.4 (2.1)	88.7 (2.4)
Montana	13.9 (1.7)	34.4 (2.5)	18.5 (2.4)	82.3 (2.0)
Nebraska	15.9 (2.4)	35.6 (2.2)	17.3 (2.1)	91.7 (1.3)
Nevada	(e)	26.4 (2.8)	10.4 (2.0)	(e)
New Hampshire	13.0 (2.7)	21.6 (2.3)	9.9 (2.2)	(e)
New Jersey	8.4 (2.3)	27.5 (3.9)	9.6 (2.5)	86.3 (4.0)
New Mexico	8.4 (1.9)	31.5 (4.0)	12.0 (1.3)	(e)
New York	10.6 (1.5)	20.2 (2.1)	5.8 (1.1)	80.6 (3.0)
North Carolina	8.3 (1.6)	25.3 (3.2)	9.4 (2.3)	86.4 (2.8)
North Dakota	17.4 (3.1)	37.4 (4.0)	22.0 (3.2)	(e)
Ohio	16.5 (2.7)	21.3 (3.4)	8.6 (2.1)	(e)
Oklahoma	9.5 (2.3)	25.8 (2.4)	12.3 (2.0)	93.2 (2.2)
Rhode Island	12.5 (2.8)	28.8 (2.6)	11.1 (1.4)	82.9 (4.3)
South Carolina	17.8 (2.6)	30.0 (2.9)	11.5 (2.8)	91.6 (4.2)
South Dakota	19.6 (3.9)	32.0 (4.3)	17.2 (3.0)	94.6 (1.3)
Tennessee	13.2 (1.8)	25.1 (3.1)	10.9 (2.0)	89.0 (3.0)
Texas	6.2 (1.4)	37.0 (3.0)	15.4 (2.7)	89.6 (3.8)
Utah	5.9 (1.6)	13.4 (2.9)	4.1 (1.3)	76.8 (4.3)
Vermont	8.5 (2.4)	22.9 (3.2)	8.9 (1.3)	55.9 (9.0)
West Virginia	15.2 (2.2)	24.8 (2.7)	10.6 (2.0)	84.0 (4.4)
Wisconsin	13.1 (2.1)	31.2 (2.8)	13.6 (1.6)	88.9 (2.7)
Wyoming	15.7 (1.9)	29.7 (2.4)	15.3 (1.9)	83.1 (2.5)
Median	**8.7**	**27.2**	**11.0**	**86.5**
Range	**3.4–14.1**	**13.4–37.4**	**4.1–22.0**	**55.9–94.6**

Source: Centers for Disease Control and Prevention. Youth Risk Behavior Surveillance — United States, 2005. *Surveillance Summaries, June 9, 2006, Morbidity and Mortality Weekly Report, 55(SS-5).*
[a]*When riding in a car or other vehicle driven by someone else.*
[b]*One or more times during the 30 days prior to the survey.*
[c]*Among the 68% of students nationwide who had ridden a bicycle during the 12 months prior to the survey.*
[d]*95% confidence interval. Confidence interval shows the level of uncertainty of a percent estimate and defines the range in which the true value is likely to be found. The lower boundary is calculated by subtracting the CI value figure from the percent estimate and the upper boundary is calculated by adding the CI value to the estimate.*
[e]*Data not available.*

INJURY FACTS®

NATIONAL SAFETY COUNCIL

STATE DATA

Motor-vehicle crashes are the leading cause of U-I deaths in 48 states.

This section on state-level data includes data for occupational and motor-vehicle injuries as well as general injury mortality.

Death rates for unintentional injuries (U-I) can vary greatly from one type of injury to the next and from state to state. The graph on the next page shows for each state the death rates (per 100,000 population) for total unintentional-injury deaths and the four leading types of unintentional-injury deaths nationally — motor-vehicle crashes, poisonings, falls, and choking (inhalation or ingestion of food or other object that obstructs breathing).

The map on page 152 shows graphically the overall unintentional-injury death rates by state. Rates by region were lowest in New England and highest in the east south central states.

The charts on pages 153 through 155 show: (a) total unintentional-injury deaths and where U-I rank as a cause of death in each state, and (b) the five leading causes of U-I deaths in each state.

Unintentional injuries as a whole are the fifth leading cause of death in the United States and in 27 states. U-I are the third leading cause of death in Alaska, Arizona, New Mexico, Wyoming, and the District of Columbia and the fourth leading cause in 12 states. U-I rank sixth in six states (Maryland, New Jersey, New York, North Dakota, Ohio, and Washington), and eighth in Massachusetts.

In 2003, motor-vehicle crashes were the leading cause of U-I deaths in 48 states. Falls were the leading cause in Rhode Island and Vermont. The leading cause in the District of Columbia was poisoning.

The second leading cause of U-I deaths was poisoning in 27 states and falls in 21 states. Motor-vehicle crashes were second in Rhode Island, Vermont, and the District of Columbia.

The most common third leading causes of U-I deaths were falls in 26 states and the District of Columbia, and poisoning in 19 states. Choking ranked third in two states (Massachusetts and Nebraska), drowning in Maryland, fire in Rhode Island, and air transport in Alaska.

Choking was the fourth leading cause of U-I deaths in 29 states, while the fourth ranking cause was drowning in 12 states, and fires, flames, and smoke in five states and the District of Columbia. Poisoning ranked fourth in Maryland, Massachusetts, and Nebraska, and air transport in Idaho.

Fires, burns, and smoke were the fifth leading U-I cause of death in 23 states. Drowning ranked fifth in 14 states, and choking was fifth in 11 states and the District of Columbia. The fifth ranking cause was air transport in Delaware, Utah, and Wyoming, water transport in Alaska and Oregon, natural heat or cold in Montana and North Dakota, mechanical suffocation in Rhode Island, and struck by or against an object or person in Vermont.

The table on pages 156 and 157 shows the number of U-I deaths by state for the 15 most common types of injury events. State populations are also shown to facilitate computation of detailed death rates.

The table on page 158 consists of a 4-year state-by-state comparison of unintentional-injury deaths and death rates for 1999 through 2002. Because of the change in mortality classification schemes from ICD-9 to ICD-10 in 1999, caution must be exercised in making comparisons of 1999 and later data with earlier years.

Page 159 shows fatal occupational injuries by state and counts of deaths for some of the principal types of events — transportation accidents, assaults and violent acts, contacts with objects and equipment, falls, exposure to harmful substances or environments, and fires and explosions.

Nonfatal occupational injury and illness incidence rates for most states are shown in the table on page 160 and graphically in the map on page 161. States not shown do not have state occupational safety and health plans.

Pages 162 and 163 show motor-vehicle-related deaths and death rates by state both in tables and maps. The maps show death rates based on population, vehicle miles traveled, and registered vehicles.

UNINTENTIONAL-INJURY DEATH RATES BY STATE, UNITED STATES, 2003

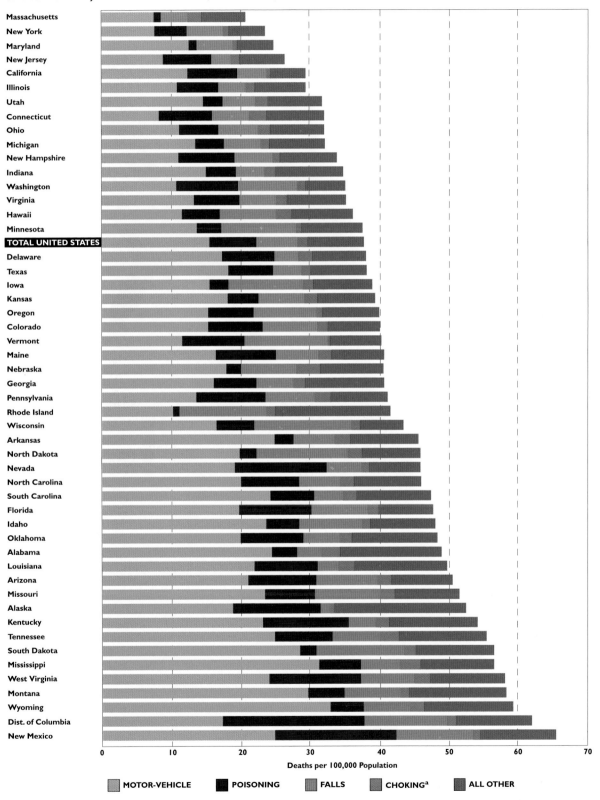

Deaths per 100,000 Population

■ MOTOR-VEHICLE ■ POISONING ■ FALLS ■ CHOKINGᵃ ■ ALL OTHER

ᵃSuffocation by ingestion or inhalation of food or other object.

UNINTENTIONAL-INJURY DEATH RATES BY STATE

UNINTENTIONAL-INJURY DEATHS PER 100,000 POPULATION BY STATE, 2003

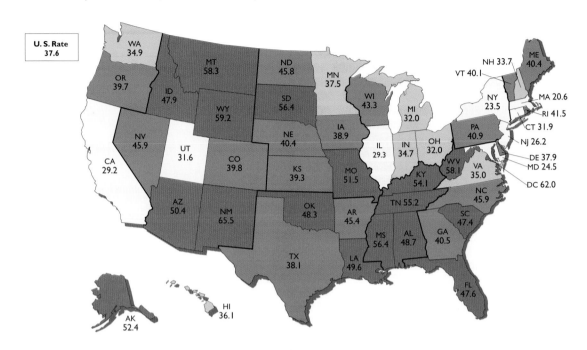

U. S. Rate
37.6

WA 34.9
OR 39.7
ID 47.9
MT 58.3
ND 45.8
MN 37.5
WY 59.2
SD 56.4
WI 43.3
MI 32.0
NV 45.9
UT 31.6
CO 39.8
NE 40.4
IA 38.9
IL 29.3
IN 34.7
OH 32.0
CA 29.2
AZ 50.4
NM 65.5
KS 39.3
MO 51.5
KY 54.1
WV 58.1
VA 35.0
OK 48.3
AR 45.4
TN 55.2
NC 45.9
SC 47.4
TX 38.1
MS 56.4
AL 48.7
GA 40.5
LA 49.6
FL 47.6
AK 52.4
HI 36.1

NH 33.7
VT 40.1
ME 40.4
NY 23.5
MA 20.6
RI 41.5
CT 31.9
PA 40.9
NJ 26.2
DE 37.9
MD 24.5
DC 62.0

REGIONAL RATES

NEW ENGLAND (CT, ME, MA, NH, RI, VT)	**28.8**
MIDDLE ATLANTIC (NJ, NY, PA)	**29.4**
EAST NORTH CENTRAL (IL, IN, MI, OH, WI)	**33.0**
WEST NORTH CENTRAL (IA, KS, MN, MO, NE, ND, SD)	**43.3**
SOUTH ATLANTIC (DE, DC, FL, GA, MD, NC, SC, VA, WV)	**42.5**
EAST SOUTH CENTRAL (AL, KY, MS, TN)	**53.5**
WEST SOUTH CENTRAL (AR, LA, OK, TX)	**41.4**
MOUNTAIN (AZ, CO, ID, MT, NV, NM, UT, WY)	**47.0**
PACIFIC (AK, CA, HI, OR, WA)	**31.2**

Source: National Center for Health Statistics, and U.S. Census Bureau.

BELOW 32.0 — 8 STATES

32.0 TO 37.6 — 8 STATES

37.7 TO 45.9 — 17 STATES

ABOVE 45.9 — 17 STATES
AND DISTRICT OF COLUMBIA

The following series of charts is a state-by-state ranking of the five leading causes of deaths due to unintentional injuries (U-I) based on 2003 data. The first line of each section gives the rank of unintentional-injury deaths among all causes of death, the total number of U-I deaths, and the rate of U-I deaths per 100,000 population in the state. The following lines list the five leading types of unintentional-injury deaths in the state along with the number and rate for each type.

TOTAL UNITED STATES

Rank	Cause	Deaths	Rate
5	All U-I	109,277	37.6
1	Motor-vehicle	44,757	15.4
2	Poisoning[a]	19,457	6.7
3	Falls	17,229	5.9
4	Choking[b]	4,272	1.5
5	Fires, flames, smoke	3,369	1.2

ALABAMA

Rank	Cause	Deaths	Rate
5	All U-I	2,194	48.7
1	Motor-vehicle	1,093	24.3
2	Poisoning[a]	161	3.6
3	Falls	160	3.6
4	Choking[b]	116	2.6
5	Fires, flames, smoke	109	2.4

ALASKA

Rank	Cause	Deaths	Rate
3	All U-I	340	52.4
1	Motor-vehicle	121	18.7
2	Poisoning[a]	82	12.6
3	Air transportation	33	5.1
4	Drowning	19	2.9
5	Water transportation	18	2.8

ARIZONA

Rank	Cause	Deaths	Rate
3	All U-I	2,812	50.4
1	Motor-vehicle	1,164	20.9
2	Poisoning[a]	548	9.8
3	Falls	499	8.9
4	Choking[b]	104	1.9
5	Drowning[c]	95	1.7

ARKANSAS

Rank	Cause	Deaths	Rate
5	All U-I	1,239	45.4
1	Motor-vehicle	672	24.7
2	Falls	164	6.0
3	Poisoning[a]	73	2.7
4	Choking[b]	59	2.2
5	Fires, flames, smoke	50	1.8
5	Drowning[c]	50	1.8

CALIFORNIA

Rank	Cause	Deaths	Rate
5	All U-I	10,348	29.2
1	Motor-vehicle	4,374	12.3
2	Poisoning[a]	2,518	7.1
3	Falls	1,491	4.2
4	Drowning[c]	377	1.1
5	Fires, flames, smoke	215	0.6

COLORADO

Rank	Cause	Deaths	Rate
5	All U-I	1,809	39.8
1	Motor-vehicle	690	15.2
2	Falls	358	7.9
3	Poisoning[a]	353	7.8
4	Choking[b]	69	1.5
5	Drowning[c]	42	0.9

CONNECTICUT

Rank	Cause	Deaths	Rate
5	All U-I	1,111	31.9
1	Motor-vehicle	285	8.2
2	Poisoning[a]	264	7.6
3	Falls	186	5.3
4	Choking[b]	87	2.5
5	Fires, flames, smoke	26	0.7

DELAWARE

Rank	Cause	Deaths	Rate
5	All U-I	310	37.9
1	Motor-vehicle	141	17.2
2	Poisoning[a]	61	7.5
3	Falls	28	3.4
4	Choking[b]	17	2.1
5	Drowning[c]	5	0.6
5	Air transportation	5	0.6

DISTRICT OF COLUMBIA

Rank	Cause	Deaths	Rate
3	All U-I	346	62.0
1	Poisoning[a]	114	20.4
2	Motor-vehicle	96	17.2
3	Falls	67	12.0
4	Fires, flames, smoke	10	1.8
5	Choking[b]	7	1.3

FLORIDA

Rank	Cause	Deaths	Rate
5	All U-I	8,081	47.6
1	Motor-vehicle	3,324	19.6
2	Poisoning[a]	1,763	10.4
3	Falls	1,400	8.2
4	Drowning[c]	435	2.6
5	Choking[b]	260	1.5

GEORGIA

Rank	Cause	Deaths	Rate
4	All U-I	3,542	40.5
1	Motor-vehicle	1,397	16.0
2	Poisoning[a]	535	6.1
3	Falls	467	5.3
4	Choking[b]	149	1.7
5	Fires, flames, smoke	145	1.7

HAWAII

Rank	Cause	Deaths	Rate
4	All U-I	451	36.1
1	Motor-vehicle	144	11.5
2	Falls	101	8.1
3	Poisoning[a]	68	5.4
4	Drowning[c]	49	3.9
5	Choking[b]	28	2.2

IDAHO

Rank	Cause	Deaths	Rate
4	All U-I	655	47.9
1	Motor-vehicle	321	23.5
2	Falls	124	9.1
3	Poisoning[a]	64	4.7
4	Air transportation	22	1.6
5	Drowning[c]	17	1.2
5	Choking[b]	17	1.2

ILLINOIS

Rank	Cause	Deaths	Rate
5	All U-I	3,704	29.3
1	Motor-vehicle	1,369	10.8
2	Poisoning[a]	749	5.9
3	Falls	497	3.9
4	Choking[b]	169	1.3
5	Fires, flames, smoke	134	1.1

INDIANA

Rank	Cause	Deaths	Rate
5	All U-I	2,150	34.7
1	Motor-vehicle	925	14.9
2	Poisoning[a]	264	4.3
3	Falls	257	4.1
4	Choking[b]	101	1.6
5	Fires, flames, smoke	86	1.4

IOWA

Rank	Cause	Deaths	Rate
5	All U-I	1,143	38.9
1	Motor-vehicle	454	15.4
2	Falls	316	10.7
3	Poisoning[a]	78	2.7
4	Choking[b]	45	1.5
5	Fires, flames, smoke	33	1.1

KANSAS

Rank	Cause	Deaths	Rate
5	All U-I	1,070	39.3
1	Motor-vehicle	490	18.0
2	Falls	180	6.6
3	Poisoning[a]	121	4.4
4	Choking[b]	53	1.9
5	Fires, flames, smoke	34	1.2

See footnotes on page 155.

UNINTENTIONAL-INJURY DEATHS
BY STATE (CONT.)

KENTUCKY

Rank	Cause	Deaths	Rate
5	All U-I	2,228	54.1
I	Motor-vehicle	946	23.0
2	Poisoning[a]	505	12.3
3	Falls	166	4.0
4	Choking[b]	78	1.9
5	Fires, flames, smoke	73	1.8

LOUISIANA

Rank	Cause	Deaths	Rate
4	All U-I	2,229	49.6
I	Motor-vehicle	980	21.8
2	Poisoning[a]	409	9.1
3	Falls	134	3.0
4	Choking[b]	105	2.3
5	Fires, flames, smoke	86	1.9

MAINE

Rank	Cause	Deaths	Rate
5	All U-I	529	40.4
I	Motor-vehicle	213	16.3
2	Poisoning[a]	112	8.6
3	Falls	81	6.2
4	Choking[b]	23	1.8
5	Drowning[c]	20	1.5

MARYLAND

Rank	Cause	Deaths	Rate
6	All U-I	1,353	24.5
I	Motor-vehicle	687	12.5
2	Falls	289	5.2
3	Drowning[c]	68	1.2
4	Poisoning[a]	58	1.1
5	Fires, flames, smoke	49	0.9

MASSACHUSETTS

Rank	Cause	Deaths	Rate
8	All U-I	1,325	20.6
I	Motor-vehicle	483	7.5
2	Falls	249	3.9
3	Choking[b]	125	1.9
4	Poisoning[a]	65	1.0
5	Fires, flames, smoke	56	0.9

MICHIGAN

Rank	Cause	Deaths	Rate
5	All U-I	3,224	32.0
I	Motor-vehicle	1,346	13.4
2	Falls	539	5.3
3	Poisoning[a]	415	4.1
4	Fires and flames	135	1.3
5	Choking[b]	117	1.2

MINNESOTA

Rank	Cause	Deaths	Rate
4	All U-I	1,898	37.5
I	Motor-vehicle	689	13.6
2	Falls	541	10.7
3	Poisoning[a]	179	3.5
4	Drowning[c]	46	0.9
5	Choking[b]	43	0.8

MISSISSIPPI

Rank	Cause	Deaths	Rate
4	All U-I	1,624	56.4
I	Motor-vehicle	895	31.1
2	Poisoning[a]	172	6.0
3	Falls	164	5.7
4	Choking[b]	86	3.0
5	Fires, flames, smoke	74	2.6

MISSOURI

Rank	Cause	Deaths	Rate
5	All U-I	2,943	51.5
I	Motor-vehicle	1,332	23.3
2	Falls	540	9.4
3	Poisoning[a]	411	7.2
4	Choking[b]	120	2.1
5	Fires, flames, smoke	85	1.5

MONTANA

Rank	Cause	Deaths	Rate
5	All U-I	535	58.3
I	Motor-vehicle	271	29.5
2	Falls	74	8.1
3	Poisoning[a]	48	5.2
4	Drowning[c]	17	1.9
5	Natural heat, cold	15	1.6

NEBRASKA

Rank	Cause	Deaths	Rate
5	All U-I	703	40.4
I	Motor-vehicle	310	17.8
2	Falls	138	7.9
3	Choking[b]	61	3.5
4	Poisoning[a]	36	2.1
5	Drowning[c]	19	1.1

NEVADA

Rank	Cause	Deaths	Rate
5	All U-I	1,028	45.9
I	Motor-vehicle	426	19.0
2	Poisoning[a]	297	13.2
3	Falls	114	5.1
4	Drowning[c]	26	1.2
5	Choking[b]	24	1.1

NEW HAMPSHIRE

Rank	Cause	Deaths	Rate
5	All U-I	434	33.7
I	Motor-vehicle	142	11.0
2	Poisoning[a]	103	8.0
3	Falls	71	5.5
4	Drowning[c]	17	1.3
5	Choking[b]	13	1.0

NEW JERSEY

Rank	Cause	Deaths	Rate
6	All U-I	2,263	26.2
I	Motor-vehicle	758	8.8
2	Poisoning[a]	595	6.9
3	Falls	244	2.8
4	Choking[b]	108	1.2
5	Fires, flames, smoke	60	0.7

NEW MEXICO

Rank	Cause	Deaths	Rate
3	All U-I	1,231	65.5
I	Motor-vehicle	464	24.7
2	Poisoning[a]	329	17.5
3	Falls	213	11.3
4	Drowning[c]	34	1.8
5	Fires, flames, smoke	23	1.2

NEW YORK

Rank	Cause	Deaths	Rate
6	All U-I	4,518	23.5
I	Motor-vehicle	1,465	7.6
2	Falls	1,001	5.2
3	Poisoning[a]	894	4.6
4	Fires, flames, smoke	206	1.1
5	Choking[b]	162	0.8

NORTH CAROLINA

Rank	Cause	Deaths	Rate
5	All U-I	3,866	45.9
I	Motor-vehicle	1,677	19.9
2	Poisoning[a]	696	8.3
3	Falls	493	5.9
4	Choking[b]	171	2.0
5	Fires, flames, smoke	126	1.5

NORTH DAKOTA

Rank	Cause	Deaths	Rate
6	All U-I	290	45.8
I	Motor-vehicle	125	19.7
2	Falls	83	13.1
3	Poisoning[a]	15	2.4
4	Choking[b]	13	2.1
5	Natural heat, cold	7	1.1

See footnotes on page 155.

OHIO

Rank	Cause	Deaths	Rate
6	All U-I	3,654	32.0
1	Motor-vehicle	1,270	11.1
2	Falls	651	5.7
3	Poisoning[a]	644	5.6
4	Choking[b]	198	1.7
5	Fires, flames, smoke	132	1.2

PENNSYLVANIA

Rank	Cause	Deaths	Rate
5	All U-I	5,061	40.9
1	Motor-vehicle	1,665	13.5
2	Poisoning[a]	1,223	9.9
3	Falls	876	7.1
4	Choking[b]	282	2.3
5	Fires, flames, smoke	184	1.5

SOUTH DAKOTA

Rank	Cause	Deaths	Rate
4	All U-I	431	56.4
1	Motor-vehicle	216	28.3
2	Falls	97	12.7
3	Poisoning[a]	18	2.4
4	Choking[b]	13	1.7
5	Fires, flames, smoke	10	1.3

UTAH

Rank	Cause	Deaths	Rate
4	All U-I	751	31.6
1	Motor-vehicle	346	14.5
2	Falls	112	4.7
3	Poisoning[a]	66	2.8
4	Choking[b]	42	1.8
5	Air transportation	23	1.0

WASHINGTON

Rank	Cause	Deaths	Rate
6	All U-I	2,137	34.9
1	Motor-vehicle	657	10.7
2	Poisoning[a]	538	8.8
3	Falls	523	8.5
4	Drowning[c]	79	1.3
5	Choking[b]	71	1.2

WYOMING

Rank	Cause	Deaths	Rate
3	All U-I	297	59.2
1	Motor-vehicle	164	32.7
2	Falls	34	6.8
3	Poisoning[a]	24	4.8
4	Choking[b]	10	2.0
5	Drowning[c]	6	1.2
5	Air transportation	6	1.2

OKLAHOMA

Rank	Cause	Deaths	Rate
5	All U-I	1,693	48.3
1	Motor-vehicle	694	19.8
2	Poisoning[a]	317	9.0
3	Falls	187	5.3
4	Fires, flames, smoke	69	2.0
5	Drowning[c]	63	1.8

RHODE ISLAND

Rank	Cause	Deaths	Rate
5	All U-I	446	41.5
1	Falls	133	12.4
2	Motor-vehicle	110	10.2
3	Fires, flames, smoke	105	9.8
4	Choking[b]	14	1.3
5	Mechanical suffocation	12	1.1
5	Drowning[c]	12	1.1

TENNESSEE

Rank	Cause	Deaths	Rate
4	All U-I	3,227	55.2
1	Motor-vehicle	1,442	24.7
2	Poisoning[a]	484	8.3
3	Falls	401	6.9
4	Fires, flames, smoke	165	2.8
5	Choking[b]	155	2.7

VERMONT

Rank	Cause	Deaths	Rate
5	All U-I	248	40.1
1	Falls	74	12.0
2	Motor-vehicle	71	11.5
3	Poisoning[a]	55	8.9
4	Fires, flames, smoke	10	1.6
5	Drowning[c]	5	0.8
5	Struck by, against	5	0.8

WEST VIRGINIA

Rank	Cause	Deaths	Rate
5	All U-I	1,051	58.1
1	Motor-vehicle	433	23.9
2	Poisoning[a]	239	13.2
3	Falls	141	7.8
4	Choking[b]	41	2.3
5	Drowning[c]	31	1.7

OREGON

Rank	Cause	Deaths	Rate
5	All U-I	1,416	39.7
1	Motor-vehicle	540	15.2
2	Falls	323	9.1
3	Poisoning[a]	232	6.5
4	Drowning[c]	43	1.2
5	Fires, flames, smoke	29	0.8
5	Water transportation	29	0.8

SOUTH CAROLINA

Rank	Cause	Deaths	Rate
4	All U-I	1,966	47.4
1	Motor-vehicle	999	24.1
2	Poisoning[a]	263	6.3
3	Falls	171	4.1
4	Choking[b]	84	2.0
4	Fires, flames, smoke	84	2.0

TEXAS

Rank	Cause	Deaths	Rate
4	All U-I	8,417	38.1
1	Motor-vehicle	4,009	18.1
2	Poisoning[a]	1,413	6.4
3	Falls	915	4.1
4	Drowning[c]	306	1.4
5	Choking[b]	289	1.3

VIRGINIA

Rank	Cause	Deaths	Rate
5	All U-I	2,584	35.0
1	Motor-vehicle	976	13.2
2	Poisoning[a]	479	6.5
3	Falls	386	5.2
4	Choking[b]	115	1.6
5	Drowning[c]	89	1.2

WISCONSIN

Rank	Cause	Deaths	Rate
4	All U-I	2,372	43.3
1	Motor-vehicle	896	16.4
2	Falls	767	14.0
3	Poisoning[a]	297	5.4
4	Choking[b]	66	1.2
5	Drowning[c]	62	1.1

Source: National Safety Council tabulations of National Center for Health Statistics mortality data.
[a] Solid, liquid, gas, and vapor poisoning.
[b] Inhalation or ingestion of food or other objects.
[c] Excludes transport drownings.

UNINTENTIONAL-INJURY DEATHS BY STATE AND EVENT

UNINTENTIONAL-INJURY DEATHS BY STATE AND TYPE OF EVENT, UNITED STATES, 2003

State	Population (000)	Total[a]	Motor-vehicle[b]	Poisoning	Falls	Choking[c]	Fires Flames, and Smoke	Drowning[d]	Mechanical Suffocation
Total U.S.	290,850	109,277	44,757	19,457	17,229	4,272	3,369	3,306	1,307
Alabama	4,502	2,194	1,093	161	160	116	109	55	18
Alaska	649	340	121	82	9	4	6	19	7
Arizona	5,578	2,812	1,164	548	499	104	47	95	31
Arkansas	2,726	1,239	672	73	164	59	50	50	15
California	35,457	10,348	4,374	2,518	1,491	207	215	377	87
Colorado	4,548	1,809	690	353	358	69	20	42	30
Connecticut	3,486	1,111	285	264	186	87	26	24	12
Delaware	818	310	141	61	28	17	2	5	4
Dist. of Columbia	558	346	96	114	67	7	10	5	2
Florida	16,993	8,081	3,324	1,763	1,400	260	132	435	104
Georgia	8,747	3,542	1,397	535	467	149	145	106	39
Hawaii	1,248	451	144	68	101	28	4	49	3
Idaho	1,368	655	321	64	124	17	9	17	10
Illinois	12,650	3,704	1,369	749	497	169	134	66	67
Indiana	6,196	2,150	925	264	257	101	86	50	50
Iowa	2,941	1,143	454	78	316	45	33	20	13
Kansas	2,724	1,070	490	121	180	53	34	25	14
Kentucky	4,117	2,228	946	505	166	78	73	41	42
Louisiana	4,490	2,229	980	409	134	105	86	78	41
Maine	1,308	529	213	112	81	23	14	20	3
Maryland	5,512	1,353	687	58	289	31	49	68	18
Massachusetts	6,418	1,325	483	65	249	125	56	36	20
Michigan	10,078	3,224	1,346	415	539	117	135	92	74
Minnesota	5,062	1,898	689	179	541	43	38	46	34
Mississippi	2,881	1,624	895	172	164	86	74	50	15
Missouri	5,719	2,943	1,332	411	540	120	85	51	42
Montana	918	535	271	48	74	12	9	17	12
Nebraska	1,738	703	310	36	138	61	16	19	7
Nevada	2,242	1,028	426	297	114	24	18	26	14
New Hampshire	1,288	434	142	103	71	13	10	17	4
New Jersey	8,640	2,263	758	595	244	108	60	54	18
New Mexico	1,879	1,231	464	329	213	19	23	34	12
New York	19,228	4,518	1,465	894	1,001	162	206	77	44
North Carolina	8,422	3,866	1,677	696	493	171	126	91	29
North Dakota	633	290	125	15	83	13	5	6	0
Ohio	11,432	3,654	1,270	644	651	198	132	73	61
Oklahoma	3,505	1,693	694	317	187	59	69	63	11
Oregon	3,563	1,416	540	232	323	28	29	43	14
Pennsylvania	12,365	5,061	1,665	1,223	876	282	184	73	36
Rhode Island	1,076	446	110	10	133	14	105	12	12
South Carolina	4,147	1,966	999	263	171	84	84	81	23
South Dakota	765	431	216	18	97	13	10	7	7
Tennessee	5,842	3,227	1,442	484	401	155	165	96	41
Texas	22,099	8,417	4,009	1,413	915	289	233	306	73
Utah	2,379	751	346	66	112	42	14	17	6
Vermont	619	248	71	55	74	2	10	5	1
Virginia	7,383	2,584	976	479	386	115	80	89	26
Washington	6,131	2,137	657	538	523	71	35	79	20
West Virginia	1,810	1,051	433	239	141	41	23	31	8
Wisconsin	5,472	2,372	896	297	767	66	51	62	29
Wyoming	502	297	164	24	34	10	0	6	4

See source and footnotes on page 157.

UNINTENTIONAL-INJURY DEATHS BY STATE AND TYPE OF EVENT, UNITED STATES, 2003, Cont.

State	Natural Heat or Cold	Struck By/Against Object	Firearms	Machinery	Electric Current	Water Transport	Air Transport	Rail Transport	All Other Accidents
Total U.S.	893	809	730	640	376	573	742	426	10,391
Alabama	8	14	40	15	7	14	13	4	367
Alaska	6	1	3	3	0	18	33	0	28
Arizona	67	17	12	8	5	7	38	7	163
Arkansas	10	10	18	12	2	3	6	3	92
California	64	52	68	53	22	39	87	63	631
Colorado	12	13	6	6	2	6	21	0	181
Connecticut	13	3	5	1	1	0	2	1	201
Delaware	1	1	1	1	1	0	5	3	39
Dist. of Columbia	2	1	2	0	1	1	0	0	38
Florida	24	52	26	25	33	66	53	23	361
Georgia	20	39	11	26	4	20	26	24	534
Hawaii	1	3	1	0	0	2	11	0	36
Idaho	6	8	2	7	1	8	22	2	37
Illinois	25	32	21	18	14	9	10	26	498
Indiana	16	8	16	22	6	4	10	8	327
Iowa	8	13	4	24	5	3	11	4	112
Kansas	7	7	7	9	5	5	6	5	102
Kentucky	20	17	30	14	5	3	17	8	263
Louisiana	6	18	50	11	13	44	9	11	234
Maine	5	7	3	4	2	3	6	1	32
Maryland	16	8	3	5	6	4	3	8	100
Massachusetts	14	7	1	8	2	3	18	7	231
Michigan	37	33	9	18	13	18	9	8	361
Minnesota	19	17	6	13	1	13	19	3	237
Mississippi	17	14	20	3	7	15	7	2	83
Missouri	33	19	20	27	19	17	3	9	215
Montana	15	3	5	1	1	5	3	2	57
Nebraska	3	6	4	6	4	2	1	4	86
Nevada	12	9	4	1	4	3	18	2	56
New Hampshire	5	3	3	3	2	3	1	1	53
New Jersey	27	14	10	8	7	6	2	13	339
New Mexico	14	10	17	5	2	0	8	5	76
New York	44	28	22	16	12	22	22	34	469
North Carolina	22	33	32	19	13	12	30	14	408
North Dakota	7	4	2	6	1	0	0	4	19
Ohio	22	22	21	19	21	9	17	9	485
Oklahoma	24	9	14	13	4	5	8	8	208
Oregon	13	14	4	8	7	29	18	6	108
Pennsylvania	56	29	21	36	19	10	13	16	522
Rhode Island	9	2	0	2	3	4	1	0	29
South Carolina	10	17	24	9	10	19	13	5	154
South Dakota	4	6	8	4	1	4	4	0	32
Tennessee	15	34	47	20	6	8	19	11	283
Texas	65	69	58	57	54	42	48	30	756
Utah	5	7	6	6	2	0	23	2	97
Vermont	4	5	2	3	0	1	0	0	15
Virginia	26	19	9	24	12	12	12	3	316
Washington	11	11	6	15	3	23	16	8	121
West Virginia	5	16	11	12	4	6	3	6	72
Wisconsin	13	20	10	12	7	19	11	12	100
Wyoming	5	5	5	2	0	4	6	1	27

Source: National Safety Council tabulations of National Center for Health Statistics mortality data.
[a] Deaths are by place of occurrence and exclude nonresident aliens. See also page 152.
[b] See page 162 for motor-vehicle deaths by place of residence.
[c] Suffocation by inhalation or ingestion of food or other object.
[d] Excludes water transport drownings.

UNINTENTIONAL-INJURY TRENDS BY STATE

Nationwide, from 2000 to 2003, unintentional-injury (U-I) deaths increased 12% over the four years and the death rate increased 6%. By state, the greatest decrease in U-I deaths occurred in Connecticut (–3%) and the greatest increase occurred in Rhode Island (+76%). The death rate also decreased the most in Connecticut (–9%) and increased the most Rhode Island (+63%).

The table below shows the trend in unintentional-injury deaths and death rates by state over the most recent four years for which data are available.

UNINTENTIONAL-INJURY DEATHS BY STATE, UNITED STATES, 2000–2003

State	Deaths[a]				Deaths per 100,000 Population			
	2003[b]	2002	2001	2000	2003[b]	2002	2001	2000
Total U.S.	109,277	106,742	101,537	97,900	37.6	37.1	35.6	35.6
Alabama	2,194	2,205	2,210	2,099	48.7	49.2	49.5	47.0
Alaska	340	350	357	342	52.4	54.6	56.4	52.2
Arizona	2,812	2,666	2,549	2,432	50.4	49.0	48.1	50.6
Arkansas	1,239	1,273	1,243	1,237	45.4	47.0	46.2	46.9
California	10,348	10,028	8,010	8,510	29.2	28.7	23.2	26.1
Colorado	1,809	1,837	1,798	1,702	39.8	40.8	40.6	40.7
Connecticut	1,111	1,161	1,049	1,150	31.9	33.6	30.6	34.9
Delaware	310	312	297	279	37.9	38.7	37.3	36.2
Dist. of Columbia	346	283	324	303	62.0	50.1	56.6	57.8
Florida	8,081	7,572	7,093	6,337	47.6	45.4	43.4	41.5
Georgia	3,542	3,389	3,449	3,099	40.5	39.7	41.1	39.3
Hawaii	451	424	388	387	36.1	34.3	31.7	30.7
Idaho	655	586	572	531	47.9	43.6	43.3	39.3
Illinois	3,704	3,974	3,825	3,815	29.3	31.6	30.6	31.6
Indiana	2,150	2,099	2,154	2,086	34.7	34.1	35.2	34.4
Iowa	1,143	1,095	1,033	1,031	38.9	37.3	35.2	35.5
Kansas	1,070	1,103	1,095	993	39.3	40.7	40.5	37.1
Kentucky	2,228	2,045	1,948	1,841	54.1	50.0	47.9	46.0
Louisiana	2,229	2,102	2,033	1,988	49.6	47.0	45.5	44.8
Maine	529	509	486	410	40.4	39.2	37.8	32.5
Maryland	1,353	1,290	1,248	1,135	24.5	23.7	23.2	21.5
Massachusetts	1,325	1,358	1,465	1,322	20.6	21.2	22.9	21.3
Michigan	3,224	3,212	3,218	3,127	32.0	32.0	32.2	32.2
Minnesota	1,898	1,918	1,805	1,695	37.5	38.2	36.2	35.0
Mississippi	1,624	1,636	1,518	1,637	56.4	57.1	53.1	58.0
Missouri	2,943	2,761	2,584	2,584	51.5	48.6	45.8	46.5
Montana	535	555	490	500	58.3	60.9	54.1	52.5
Nebraska	703	756	614	658	40.4	43.8	35.7	38.5
Nevada	1,028	930	790	811	45.9	42.9	37.7	43.2
New Hampshire	434	402	373	326	33.7	31.5	29.6	26.6
New Jersey	2,263	2,466	2,296	2,165	26.2	28.8	27.0	26.4
New Mexico	1,231	1,142	1,065	1,029	65.5	61.6	58.2	55.2
New York	4,518	4,552	4,896	4,118	23.5	23.8	25.7	22.6
North Carolina	3,866	3,705	3,469	3,596	45.9	44.6	42.3	46.1
North Dakota	290	264	261	253	45.8	41.7	41.0	38.1
Ohio	3,654	4,047	3,774	3,427	32.0	35.5	33.1	30.2
Oklahoma	1,693	1,537	1,663	1,546	48.3	44.1	48.0	45.7
Oregon	1,416	1,393	1,328	1,255	39.7	39.5	38.2	36.9
Pennsylvania	5,061	4,749	4,595	4,615	40.9	38.5	37.4	37.7
Rhode Island	446	292	281	254	41.5	27.3	26.5	25.4
South Carolina	1,966	1,979	1,978	1,998	47.4	48.2	48.7	51.7
South Dakota	431	385	404	341	56.4	50.6	53.3	43.8
Tennessee	3,227	2,976	2,999	2,993	55.2	51.4	52.2	52.8
Texas	8,417	8,237	7,920	7,418	38.1	37.9	36.8	36.8
Utah	751	775	681	727	31.6	33.4	29.9	32.9
Vermont	248	238	226	238	40.1	38.6	36.9	38.5
Virginia	2,584	2,463	2,360	2,337	35.0	33.9	32.8	33.3
Washington	2,137	2,161	2,031	1,971	34.9	35.6	33.9	33.6
West Virginia	1,051	989	872	843	58.1	54.8	48.4	45.7
Wisconsin	2,372	2,246	2,094	2,141	43.3	41.3	38.7	40.1
Wyoming	297	315	326	268	59.2	63.1	66.0	50.9

Source: National Safety Council estimates based on data from National Center for Health Statistics and U.S. Bureau of the Census. See Technical Appendix for comparability.
[a] Deaths for each state are by place of occurrence and exclude nonresident aliens.
[b] Latest official figures.

FATAL OCCUPATIONAL INJURIES BY STATE

In general, the states with the largest number of persons employed have the largest number of work-related fatalities. The four largest states — California, Florida, New York, and Texas — accounted for more than one fourth of the total fatalities in the United States. Each state's industry mix, geographical features, age of population, and other characteristics of the workforce must be considered when evaluating state fatality profiles.

FATAL OCCUPATIONAL INJURIES BY STATE AND EVENT OR EXPOSURE, UNITED STATES, 2004–2005

State	2004 Total[a]	2005							
		Total[b]	Transpor- tation[c]	Contact with Objects & Equipment	Assaults & Violent Acts[d]	Falls	Exposure to Harmful Substances or Environments	Fires & Explosions	All Other
Total	5,764	5,702	2,480	1,001	787	767	496	158	13
Alabama	133	128	55	23	19	21	8	—	—
Alaska	42	29	21	—	—	3	—	—	—
Arizona	84	99	42	17	16	9	11	—	—
Arkansas	70	80	53	9	5	8	3	—	—
California	467	453	165	76	87	59	51	14	—
Colorado	117	125	76	17	8	9	11	3	—
Connecticut	54	46	12	10	14	8	—	—	—
Delaware	10	10	—	—	—	3	—	—	—
Dist. of Columbia	11	12	—	—	4	4	—	—	—
Florida	422	404	186	39	47	72	50	8	—
Georgia	232	200	81	31	32	39	13	3	—
Hawaii	25	15	6	—	—	3	4	—	—
Idaho	38	35	15	12	—	5	—	—	—
Illinois	208	194	74	34	30	24	26	6	—
Indiana	153	157	72	25	15	23	14	8	—
Iowa	82	88	44	26	3	8	—	4	—
Kansas	80	81	40	16	12	4	5	—	—
Kentucky	143	122	54	30	16	16	5	—	—
Louisiana	121	106	53	18	11	10	13	—	—
Maine	16	15	5	5	—	3	—	—	—
Maryland	81	95	31	16	23	19	4	—	—
Massachusetts	72	75	23	15	12	14	7	4	—
Michigan	127	110	40	20	16	19	10	5	—
Minnesota	80	87	34	26	12	11	3	—	—
Mississippi	88	111	49	20	19	17	6	—	—
Missouri	165	183	91	42	20	12	12	6	—
Montana	39	50	19	14	8	7	—	—	—
Nebraska	46	36	18	10	4	3	—	—	—
Nevada	61	57	26	7	7	10	6	—	—
New Hampshire	15	18	9	5	—	3	—	—	—
New Jersey	129	111	51	16	17	15	6	5	—
New Mexico	57	44	23	4	9	4	—	—	—
New York	254	239	87	40	49	33	23	7	—
North Carolina	183	165	62	31	22	30	15	5	—
North Dakota	24	22	9	5	—	5	3	—	—
Ohio	202	168	71	34	23	18	18	4	—
Oklahoma	91	95	57	10	9	10	5	4	—
Oregon	60	65	31	15	5	11	—	—	—
Pennsylvania	230	223	107	30	41	33	10	—	—
Rhode Island	7	6	—	—	—	—	—	—	—
South Carolina	113	133	61	21	18	13	17	—	—
South Dakota	24	28	16	7	—	3	—	—	—
Tennessee	145	139	70	29	18	14	5	3	—
Texas	440	495	200	80	67	54	63	31	—
Utah	50	54	29	12	—	5	4	—	—
Vermont	7	7	—	4	—	—	—	—	—
Virginia	171	186	69	35	22	33	21	6	—
Washington	98	83	40	20	6	8	8	—	—
West Virginia	58	46	23	7	5	3	7	—	—
Wisconsin	94	125	48	22	20	25	6	3	—
Wyoming	43	46	25	11	3	—	—	—	—

Source: U.S. Department of Labor, Bureau of Labor Statistics.
Note: Dashes (—) indicate no data or data that do not meet publication criteria.
[a]Data for 2004 revised.
[b]Data for 2005 preliminary and total includes two deaths for which state of occurrence could not be determined.
[c]Includes highway, nonhighway, air, water, and rail fatalities, and fatalities resulting from being struck by a vehicle or mobile equipment.
[d]Includes violence by persons, self-inflicted injury, and attacks by animals.

NONFATAL OCCUPATIONAL INCIDENCE RATES BY STATE

NONFATAL OCCUPATIONAL INJURY AND ILLNESS INCIDENCE RATES[a] BY STATE, PRIVATE INDUSTRY, 2004

State	Total Recordable Cases	Cases with Days away from Work[b]	Cases with Job Transfer or Restriction	Other Recordable Cases
Private Industry[c]	**4.8**	**1.4**	**1.1**	**2.3**
Alabama	5.1	1.2	1.2	2.8
Alaska	5.1	2.6	0.4	2.1
Arizona	4.5	1.2	1.0	2.3
Arkansas	4.7	1.2	1.1	2.3
California	4.9	1.5	1.4	2.0
Colorado	—	—	—	—
Connecticut	4.8	1.6	1.0	2.2
Delaware	3.7	1.5	0.6	1.6
Dist. of Columbia	2.3	0.7	0.2	1.3
Florida	4.9	1.3	1.3	2.2
Georgia	3.9	1.1	0.9	1.9
Hawaii	4.9	2.6	0.4	2.0
Idaho	—	—	—	—
Illinois	4.4	1.4	1.0	2.1
Indiana	6.3	1.3	1.7	3.2
Iowa	6.4	1.5	1.6	3.3
Kansas	5.5	1.1	1.2	3.1
Kentucky	6.1	1.8	1.5	2.8
Louisiana	3.4	1.0	0.6	1.8
Maine	6.9	1.7	2.2	3.0
Maryland	4.2	1.7	0.6	1.9
Massachusetts	4.3	1.7	0.6	1.9
Michigan	5.6	1.2	1.6	2.8
Minnesota	5.3	1.4	1.2	2.7
Mississippi	—	—	—	—
Missouri	5.3	1.3	1.4	2.6
Montana	7.2	2.3	1.0	4.0
Nebraska	5.3	1.4	1.1	2.9
Nevada	5.5	1.5	1.5	2.5
New Hampshire	—	—	—	—
New Jersey	3.8	1.4	0.6	1.7
New Mexico	4.8	1.4	0.9	2.5
New York	3.0	1.5	0.2	1.3
North Carolina	4.1	1.0	1.0	2.0
North Dakota	—	—	—	—
Ohio	—	—	—	—
Oklahoma	5.6	1.7	1.2	2.8
Oregon	5.8	1.9	1.2	2.7
Pennsylvania	—	—	—	—
Rhode Island	5.2	2.1	0.8	2.4
South Carolina	4.1	1.2	0.9	2.0
South Dakota	—	—	—	—
Tennessee	5.3	1.3	1.5	2.5
Texas	3.7	1.1	1.0	1.6
Utah	5.7	1.2	1.1	3.4
Vermont	5.8	1.6	0.9	3.3
Virginia	3.8	1.2	0.9	1.7
Washington	6.9	2.1	1.0	3.8
West Virginia	6.1	2.9	0.5	2.6
Wisconsin	6.4	1.8	1.3	3.2
Wyoming	5.3	2.3	0.5	2.5

Source: Bureau of Labor Statistics, U.S. Department of Labor.
Note: Because of rounding, components may not add to totals. Dashes (—) indicate data not available.
[a]Incidence rates represent the number of injuries and illnesses per 100 full-time workers using 200,000 hours as the equivalent.
[b]Days-away-from-work cases include those that result in days away from work with or without job transfer or restriction.
[c]Data cover all 50 states.

NONFATAL OCCUPATIONAL INJURY AND ILLNESS INCIDENCE RATES BY STATE, PRIVATE INDUSTRY, 2004

**U.S. Private
Industry
4.8**

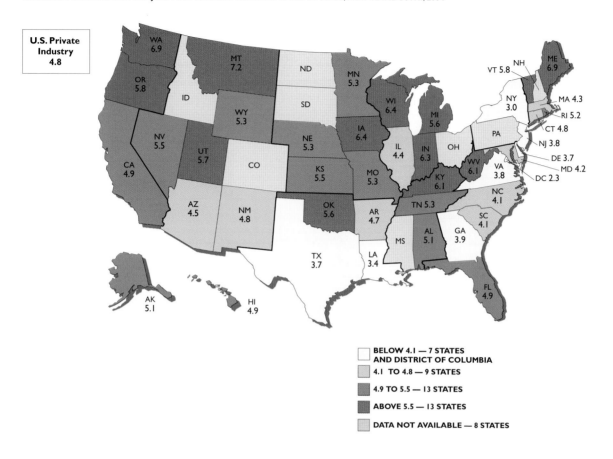

WA 6.9
MT 7.2
ND
MN 5.3
VT 5.8
NH
ME 6.9
OR 5.8
ID
SD
WI 6.4
NY 3.0
MA 4.3
WY 5.3
MI 5.6
RI 5.2
CT 4.8
NV 5.5
UT 5.7
NE 5.3
IA 6.4
PA
NJ 3.8
CA 4.9
CO
KS 5.5
IL 4.4
IN 6.3
OH
WV 6.1
DE 3.7
MD 4.2
VA 3.8
DC 2.3
MO 5.3
KY 6.1
AZ 4.5
NM 4.8
OK 5.6
AR 4.7
TN 5.3
NC 4.1
SC 4.1
TX 3.7
LA 3.4
MS
AL 5.1
GA 3.9
AK 5.1
HI 4.9
FL 4.9

BELOW 4.1 — 7 STATES
AND DISTRICT OF COLUMBIA

4.1 TO 4.8 — 9 STATES

4.9 TO 5.5 — 13 STATES

ABOVE 5.5 — 13 STATES

DATA NOT AVAILABLE — 8 STATES

MOTOR-VEHICLE DEATHS BY STATE

MOTOR-VEHICLE DEATHS BY STATE, UNITED STATES, 2002–2005

State	Motor-Vehicle Traffic Deaths (Place of Accident)				Total Motor-Vehicle Deaths[a] (Place of Residence)			
	Number		Mileage Rate[b]		Number		Population Rate[b]	
	2005	2004	2005	2004	2003[c]	2002	2003	2002
Total U.S.[a]	45,800	45,300	1.5	1.5	44,757	45,380	15.4	15.8
Alabama	1,144	1,155	1.9	1.9	1,069	1,115	23.7	24.9
Alaska	72	101	1.4	2.0	119	112	18.3	17.5
Arizona	1,179	1,150	2.1	2.1	1,097	1,105	19.7	20.3
Arkansas	647	704	2.0	2.3	720	693	26.4	25.6
California	4,304	4,082	1.3	1.2	4,465	4,248	12.6	12.1
Colorado	606	640	1.3	1.5	707	781	15.5	17.4
Connecticut	292	306	0.9	1.0	283	348	8.1	10.1
Delaware	133	140	1.4	1.5	131	121	16.0	15.0
Dist. of Columbia	49	45	1.3	1.1	64	58	11.5	10.3
Florida	3,558	3,257	1.8	1.7	3,248	3,196	19.1	19.2
Georgia	1,740	1,641	1.5	1.5	1,432	1,526	16.4	17.9
Hawaii	140	142	1.4	1.5	142	121	11.4	9.8
Idaho	275	260	1.9	1.8	283	296	20.7	22.0
Illinois	1,365	1,356	1.2	1.3	1,510	1,579	11.9	12.5
Indiana	938	947	1.3	1.3	948	963	15.3	15.6
Iowa	450	390	1.4	1.2	458	426	15.6	14.5
Kansas	428	458	1.5	1.6	494	563	18.1	20.8
Kentucky	985	964	2.1	2.0	940	923	22.8	22.6
Louisiana	—	922	—	2.1	961	959	21.4	21.4
Maine	169	196	1.1	1.3	201	215	15.4	16.6
Maryland	614	643	1.1	1.2	709	718	12.9	13.2
Massachusetts	439	476	0.8	0.9	529	565	8.2	8.8
Michigan	1,129	1,159	1.1	1.1	1,390	1,386	13.8	13.8
Minnesota	561	567	1.0	1.0	703	744	13.9	14.8
Mississippi	931	900	2.4	2.4	898	879	31.2	30.7
Missouri	1,239	1,130	1.8	1.6	1,225	1,213	21.4	21.4
Montana	251	229	2.2	2.1	258	255	28.1	28.0
Nebraska	276	254	1.4	1.3	307	337	17.7	19.5
Nevada	427	398	2.2	2.0	371	386	16.5	17.8
New Hampshire	164	170	1.2	1.3	130	125	10.1	9.8
New Jersey	701	731	1.0	1.0	786	786	9.1	9.2
New Mexico	488	522	2.0	2.3	435	423	23.1	22.8
New York	1,428	1,503	1.0	1.1	1,573	1,695	8.2	8.9
North Carolina	1,534	1,574	1.6	1.7	1,662	1,690	19.7	20.3
North Dakota	121	100	1.6	1.3	121	111	19.1	17.5
Ohio	1,321	1,286	1.2	1.2	1,348	1,602	11.8	14.0
Oklahoma	800	774	1.7	1.7	721	766	20.6	22.0
Oregon	487	456	1.4	1.3	543	462	15.2	13.1
Pennsylvania	1,616	—	1.5	—	1,652	1,739	13.4	14.1
Rhode Island	87	83	1.0	1.0	103	95	9.6	8.9
South Carolina	1,094	1,046	2.2	2.1	946	1,024	22.8	24.9
South Dakota	185	197	2.1	2.3	210	186	27.5	24.5
Tennessee	1,270	1,317	1.8	1.9	1,308	1,250	22.4	21.6
Texas	3,439	3,654	1.5	1.6	4,022	4,024	18.2	18.5
Utah	282	296	1.1	1.2	307	329	12.9	14.2
Vermont	—	—	—	—	74	78	12.0	12.7
Virginia	942	922	1.2	1.2	1,009	963	13.7	13.2
Washington	647	563	1.2	1.0	719	760	11.7	12.5
West Virginia	373	410	1.8	2.0	402	414	22.2	22.9
Wisconsin	801	784	1.3	1.3	888	870	16.2	16.0
Wyoming	170	164	1.8	1.8	136	157	27.1	31.5

Source: Motor-Vehicle Traffic Deaths are provisional counts from state traffic authorities; Total Motor-Vehicle Deaths are from the National Center for Health Statistics (see also page 156).
Note: Dashes (—) indicate data not reported.
[a]Includes both traffic and nontraffic motor-vehicle deaths. See definitions of motor-vehicle traffic and nontraffic accidents on page 183.
[b]The mileage death rate is deaths per 100,000,000 vehicle miles; the population death rate is deaths per 100,000 population. Death rates are National Safety Council estimates.
[c]Latest year available. See Technical Appendix for comparability.

MILEAGE DEATH RATES, 2005
MOTOR-VEHICLE TRAFFIC DEATHS PER 100,000,000 VEHICLE MILES

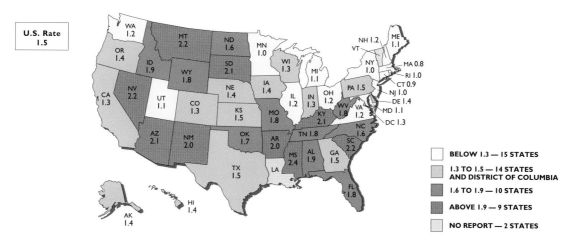

REGISTRATION DEATH RATES, 2005
MOTOR-VEHICLE TRAFFIC DEATHS PER 10,000 MOTOR VEHICLES

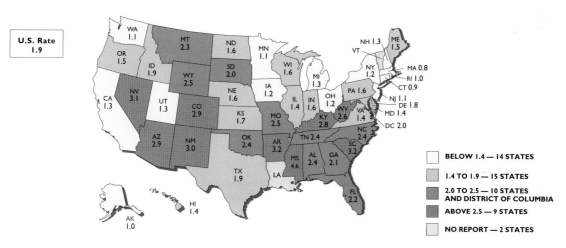

POPULATION DEATH RATES, 2005
MOTOR-VEHICLE TRAFFIC DEATHS PER 100,000 POPULATION

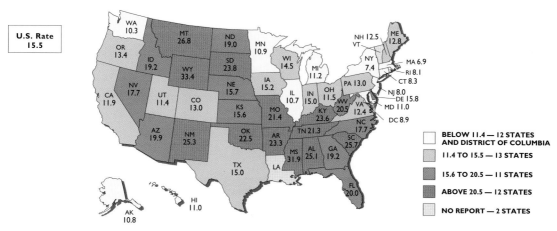

Source: Rates estimated by National Safety Council based on data from state traffic authorities, National Center for Health Statistics, Federal Highway Administration, and the U.S. Census Bureau.

INJURY FACTS®

NATIONAL SAFETY COUNCIL

INTERNATIONAL UNINTENTIONAL-INJURY DEATHS AND DEATH RATES

The term "Accidents and Adverse Effects" used in the International Classification of Diseases system (ICD) refers to all causes of unintentional injury deaths, including transportation accidents, unintentional poisonings, falls, fires, burns, natural and environmental factors, drowning, suffocation, medical and surgical complications and misadventures, and other causes such as those involving machinery, firearms, or electric current. The data presented in the table below are identified by codes V01–X59, Y85–Y86 of the tenth ICD revision (except were noted).

The tables on pages 166 through 169 show the numbers of injury deaths and the death rates per 100,000 population (not adjusted for differences among countries in the age distribution of the population) for 40 countries for which injury mortality data and national population estimates were obtained.

UNINTENTIONAL INJURY DEATHS AND DEATH RATES BY AGE GROUP, LATEST YEAR AVAILABLE

Country	Year	Deaths		Deaths per 100,000 Population						
		Total	% Male	All Ages	0 to 4	5 to 14	15 to 24	25 to 44	45 to 64	65+
Australia	2002	4,964	63.2	25.3	9.6	4.1	24.1	21.9	18.1	79.0
Austria	2004	2,479	63.8	30.3	3.0	3.0	24.5	16.4	25.0	98.7
Azerbaijan[a]	2002	1,869	76.1	22.9	15.7	8.5	19.5	28.6	33.0	37.2
Belarus[a]	2003	16,513	78.6	167.2	32.9	12.7	80.3	198.1	282.0	188.3
Canada	2002	9,050	56.9	28.8	6.9	5.2	22.6	20.0	22.5	102.7
Croatia	2004	1,846	63.3	41.6	11.9	5.9	29.4	24.9	33.6	124.6
Czech Republic	2004	4,749	59.2	46.5	7.8	3.8	26.7	27.4	40.5	163.1
Denmark	2001	2,118	54.4	39.6	3.6	3.8	20.5	20.0	23.1	166.7
Estonia	2003	1,239	77.0	91.5	33.5	6.4	45.1	82.4	160.7	122.9
Finland	2004	3,063	64.6	58.6	8.5	8.4	22.6	33.2	71.0	163.6
France	2002	27,674	54.5	46.4	7.8	3.9	28.2	22.6	28.7	175.7
Georgia	2001	626	76.0	13.8	3.7	3.2	7.2	17.3	16.8	23.9
Germany	2004	18,617	56.7	22.6	4.7	2.3	18.0	11.6	15.2	69.3
Hong Kong, China	2002	856	70.1	12.6	3.4	1.6	5.6	8.2	11.9	51.0
Hungary	2003	6,269	58.3	61.9	8.0	5.4	18.9	31.2	59.4	217.6
Israel	2003	1,274	66.2	19.0	7.0	3.6	15.8	15.7	15.1	81.3
Japan	2003	39,980	61.6	31.7	6.7	3.1	11.9	10.2	22.1	108.3
Kuwait	2002	531	82.9	22.5	11.2	11.4	32.0	21.1	26.5	110.5
Kyrgyzstan	2004	2,351	77.0	47.7	43.3	11.5	24.0	64.5	108.6	79.5
Latvia	2004	2,158	72.4	93.3	25.0	13.3	42.7	89.7	161.0	115.3
Lithuania	2004	3,071	77.2	89.4	26.0	8.2	43.0	88.0	154.1	127.5
Luxembourg	2004	158	55.7	34.9	3.6	1.7	25.0	25.3	21.9	129.1
Malta	2004	94	54.3	23.4	9.8	0.0	17.1	11.8	11.1	107.9
Moldova, Republic of	2004	2,445	76.0	67.8	45.3	15.8	31.4	59.4	123.2	125.5
Netherlands	2004	3,352	53.1	20.6	4.2	2.8	11.6	8.5	11.5	94.1
Norway	2003	1,898	58.6	41.6	5.1	3.6	22.3	26.0	28.1	160.7
Poland	2003	15,692	71.7	41.1	7.9	7.1	25.8	35.9	50.9	99.3
Portugal	2003	3,927	70.1	37.5	9.0	7.5	31.5	28.8	32.9	92.0
Romania	2004	9,768	75.9	45.1	34.1	13.3	25.0	38.4	64.4	76.2
Russian Federation[a]	2004	327,123	77.7	227.5	40.8	25.9	133.7	276.4	345.5	250.8
Serbia and Montenegro	2002	1,566	73.2	19.3	5.7	6.9	13.6	14.9	20.4	41.4
Slovakia	2002	1,906	79.0	35.4	9.7	6.9	27.7	31.4	53.0	64.4
Slovenia	2003	875	66.7	43.8	4.5	2.9	28.1	22.9	43.6	141.7
South Korea	2002	17,638	68.3	36.6	19.5	8.7	17.1	23.8	51.8	164.3
Spain	2003	12,141	70.9	28.9	7.2	4.4	28.4	25.0	23.7	64.3
Sweden	2002	2,995	60.5	33.6	2.0	2.2	14.7	13.6	22.5	127.7
Switzerland[a]	2002	3,653	60.7	49.9	6.2	3.6	31.3	32.7	44.9	154.6
Thailand	2002	24,087	79.0	38.5	23.3	19.8	52.5	40.1	41.4	46.1
United Kingdom	2002	12,130	55.4	20.5	4.1	2.5	14.9	12.7	13.0	70.8
United States	2002	106,742	64.9	37.0	13.2	6.6	38.0	34.5	34.5	94.7

Source: National Safety Council tabulations of World Health Organization data.
[a]*Data include deaths due to all external causes, including self-harm and assault.*

INTERNATIONAL MOTOR-VEHICLE DEATHS AND DEATH RATES

The International Classification of Diseases system (ICD) identifies motor-vehicle traffic accidents by selected four-character categories for codes V02-V04, V09, V12–V14, V19–V79, and V80–V89 of the tenth ICD revision. A motor vehicle is a mechanically or electrically powered device used in the transportation of persons or property on a land highway. A motor-vehicle traffic accident involves a motor vehicle in transport (i.e., in motion or on a roadway) on a public highway.

MOTOR-VEHICLE DEATHS AND DEATH RATES BY AGE GROUP, LATEST YEAR AVAILABLE

Country	Year	Deaths		Deaths per 100,000 Population						
		Total	% Male	All Ages	0 to 4	5 to 14	15 to 24	25 to 44	45 to 64	65+
Australia	2002	1,765	73.4	9.0	2.2	2.3	17.2	10.4	7.1	10.9
Austria	2004	451	74.1	5.5	0.5	1.0	8.9	5.8	4.6	8.5
Azerbaijan[a]	2002	389	80.7	4.8	0.7	1.7	3.0	6.6	7.4	9.0
Belarus[a]	2003	2,241	76.1	22.7	2.4	3.6	23.7	28.2	28.3	23.4
Canada	2002	2,953	68.9	9.4	2.0	3.4	16.1	8.9	8.9	13.7
Croatia	2004	448	79.2	10.1	5.2	2.6	16.9	10.9	8.6	12.2
Czech Republic	2004	834	72.9	8.2	0.7	1.5	12.5	9.0	7.9	10.4
Denmark	2001	412	72.6	7.7	1.2	2.7	15.0	7.1	6.4	12.5
Estonia	2003	158	79.7	11.7	3.2	2.5	14.5	15.3	11.9	11.5
Finland	2004	382	67.8	7.3	2.1	1.4	13.7	5.7	6.2	13.3
France	2002	7,038	73.9	11.8	2.3	2.2	22.6	13.6	9.6	14.2
Georgia	2001	186	80.1	4.1	0.5	0.7	2.9	5.9	5.4	4.7
Germany	2004	4,865	72.6	5.9	1.2	1.2	13.1	5.9	4.7	6.7
Hong Kong, China	2002	190	70.5	2.8	0.4	0.8	2.9	1.6	2.5	9.9
Hungary	2003	1,465	76.3	14.5	1.3	2.4	12.8	17.5	17.3	18.4
Israel	2003	321	77.6	4.8	1.5	1.0	7.9	6.6	5.2	4.2
Japan	2003	9,987	68.6	7.9	1.5	1.5	8.8	5.0	7.1	17.4
Kuwait	2002	338	84.9	14.3	2.0	7.2	25.5	13.4	15.2	65.8
Kyrgyzstan	2004	479	74.7	9.7	1.4	3.4	6.6	16.4	16.8	13.3
Latvia	2004	478	72.6	20.7	0.0	2.4	27.4	24.5	23.1	21.4
Lithuania	2004	737	78.3	21.5	3.2	2.5	27.9	25.1	25.2	23.8
Luxembourg	2004	54	72.2	11.9	0.0	0.0	21.1	15.5	7.3	20.2
Malta	2004	14	85.7	3.5	0.0	0.0	8.5	3.6	2.8	3.8
Moldova	2004	509	77.8	14.1	3.9	4.6	15.7	16.3	18.4	13.8
Netherlands	2004	783	70.9	4.8	0.8	1.4	9.4	4.2	3.6	9.2
Norway	2003	303	74.9	6.6	2.7	2.1	11.3	7.6	4.5	10.2
Poland	2003	5,115	77.1	13.4	2.3	3.5	15.0	15.5	14.9	17.7
Portugal	2003	1,724	79.5	16.5	3.4	3.6	24.5	17.8	15.5	21.3
Romania	2004	2,299	76.0	10.6	2.6	4.8	8.8	10.8	12.8	15.6
Russian Federation[a]	2004	41,802	72.8	29.1	4.4	6.8	32.9	36.8	29.8	32.4
Serbia and Montenegro	2002	429	78.8	5.3	1.1	1.5	5.7	4.7	6.4	7.9
Slovakia	2002	668	76.8	12.4	2.2	4.2	16.8	13.1	12.8	17.2
Slovenia	2003	270	79.6	13.5	2.2	1.5	20.9	11.6	14.3	20.9
South Korea	2002	8,837	71.7	18.4	8.5	4.9	13.2	14.1	27.2	59.0
Spain	2003	5,594	77.2	13.3	2.8	2.6	20.9	14.5	12.0	16.2
Sweden	2002	502	74.3	5.6	0.7	1.2	10.8	5.8	5.1	7.4
Switzerland[a]	2002	500	74.4	6.8	2.7	1.3	13.1	6.7	5.9	9.4
Thailand	2002	10,872	81.4	17.4	3.4	4.9	30.9	20.0	17.4	13.4
United Kingdom	2002	3,236	74.7	5.5	1.0	1.3	10.7	6.3	4.1	6.8
United States	2002	45,380	68.5	15.7	3.7	3.9	28.2	16.7	14.5	21.6

Source: National Safety Council tabulations of World Health Organization data.
[a] Data include deaths due to all transportation-related causes, ICD-10 codes V01–V99

INTERNATIONAL FALL-RELATED DEATHS AND DEATH RATES

"Accidental falls" are identified by codes W00–W19 in the tenth revision of the International Classification of Diseases system.

FALL-RELATED DEATHS AND DEATH RATES BY AGE GROUP, LATEST YEAR AVAILABLE

Country	Year	Deaths		Deaths per 100,000 Population						
		Total	% Male	All Ages	0 to 4	5 to 14	15 to 24	25 to 44	45 to 64	65+
Australia	2002	627	52.0	3.2	0.3	0.2	0.7	1.0	1.9	18.3
Austria	2004	1,016	51.5	12.4	0.5	0.2	1.5	1.9	7.9	61.1
Azerbaijan	2002	31	67.7	0.4	0.0	0.2	0.2	0.3	0.7	1.7
Belarus	2003	1,181	77.1	12.0	2.2	1.0	3.5	12.3	20.8	18.9
Canada	2002	1,769	52.2	5.6	0.3	0.1	0.7	1.0	2.9	35.2
Croatia	2004	745	41.2	16.8	1.4	0.2	0.5	1.3	8.5	84.4
Czech Republic	2004	2,032	40.3	19.9	0.2	0.2	2.0	2.5	8.5	118.1
Denmark	2001	319	53.0	6.0	0.0	0.2	0.2	1.0	3.5	31.9
Estonia	2003	152	65.8	11.2	0.0	0.0	3.9	6.2	16.1	30.8
Finland	2004	1,131	52.9	21.6	0.0	0.5	1.1	3.4	14.5	105.0
France	2002	5,391	48.6	9.0	0.4	0.2	0.5	1.5	5.3	44.5
Georgia	2001	22	68.2	0.5	0.0	0.0	0.3	0.4	0.4	1.6
Germany	2004	7,913	43.4	9.6	0.5	0.2	0.4	1.1	4.2	44.3
Hong Kong, China	2002	157	68.8	2.3	0.7	0.1	0.2	0.8	2.4	12.4
Hungary	2003	3,116	44.4	30.8	0.2	0.3	0.6	3.2	18.1	161.3
Israel	2003	100	70.0	1.5	0.3	0.1	0.7	0.7	1.1	9.4
Japan	2003	6,722	59.8	5.3	0.5	0.2	0.7	1.1	3.2	21.0
Kuwait	2002	42	92.9	1.8	1.5	0.5	1.4	1.8	3.6	5.3
Kyrgyzstan	2004	139	85.6	2.8	3.6	0.9	1.2	3.7	5.1	6.3
Latvia	2004	274	62.8	11.8	3.0	1.2	2.0	8.1	15.1	32.0
Lithuania	2004	434	77.2	12.6	1.9	0.0	1.3	8.2	23.3	30.1
Luxembourg	2004	29	51.7	6.4	0.0	0.0	0.0	0.7	5.5	34.2
Malta	2004	53	39.6	13.2	0.0	0.0	1.7	0.9	3.7	88.9
Moldova	2004	210	78.6	5.8	2.2	0.2	2.1	3.4	12.6	14.9
Netherlands	2004	1,103	46.1	6.8	0.4	0.3	0.3	0.9	3.0	40.4
Norway	2003	843	44.4	18.5	0.0	0.2	1.3	1.0	4.6	114.4
Poland	2003	3,662	48.3	9.6	0.7	0.3	1.4	2.4	6.7	53.8
Portugal	2003	858	52.1	8.2	0.5	0.5	0.7	1.7	5.1	37.2
Romania	2004	1,497	79.3	6.9	1.7	0.5	1.4	4.7	12.0	15.5
Russian Federation	2004	13,718	75.2	9.5	1.9	0.9	4.0	9.2	14.6	17.7
Serbia and Montenegro	2002	187	53.5	2.3	0.3	0.1	0.3	0.9	1.5	9.6
Slovakia	2002	376	78.7	7.0	0.0	0.3	1.8	4.0	11.7	23.2
Slovenia	2003	365	51.8	18.3	0.0	0.5	2.2	3.0	12.6	92.2
South Korea	2002	3,145	60.9	6.5	3.2	0.6	0.6	2.8	8.7	44.8
Spain	2003	1,624	56.8	3.9	0.6	0.2	0.8	1.3	2.6	16.0
Sweden	2002	588	57.5	6.6	0.0	0.0	0.1	0.6	3.5	32.0
Switzerland	2002	1,086	42.2	14.8	0.3	0.5	1.1	1.6	4.3	83.7
Thailand	2002	849	75.7	1.4	0.4	0.2	0.5	1.2	2.6	4.4
United Kingdom	2002	3,237	48.1	5.5	0.2	0.1	0.6	1.1	3.5	26.4
United States	2002	16,257	52.1	5.6	0.3	0.1	0.6	1.1	3.2	36.1

Source: National Safety Council tabulations of World Health Organization data.

INTERNATIONAL DROWNING DEATHS AND DEATH RATES

The World Health Organization has identified unintentional drowning as a major, but often unrecognized, public health problem. The global mortality rate is estimated at 6.8 cases per 100,000 population, which makes drowning the second leading cause of injury-related death worldwide, following motor-vehicle crashes.[a]

The International Classification of Diseases system (ICD) identifies drowning by codes W65–W74, which include cases of unintentional drowning and submersion while in or following a fall in a bathtub, swimming pool, or natural body of water. Other specified and unspecified cases of drowning and submersion are also included.

[a]van Beeck, E.F., Branche, C.M., Szpilman, D., Modell, J.H., & Bierens, J.J. (2005). A new definition of drowning: towards documentation and prevention of a global public health problem. *Bulletin of the World Health Organization, 83(11): 853–856.*

UNINTENTIONAL DROWNING DEATHS AND DEATH RATES BY AGE GROUP, LATEST YEAR AVAILABLE

Country	Year	Deaths		Deaths per 100,000 Population						
		Total	% Male	All Ages	0 to 4	5 to 14	15 to 24	25 to 44	45 to 64	65+
Australia	2002	237	71.7	1.21	3.86	0.48	0.89	1.11	1.08	1.45
Austria	2004	76	82.9	0.93	0.50	0.22	0.90	0.44	1.46	1.71
Azerbaijan	2002	238	74.8	2.90	3.50	1.90	3.70	3.50	2.70	1.10
Belarus	2003	1,047	80.8	10.60	4.20	3.60	8.60	14.80	12.10	9.90
Canada	2002	316	79.1	1.01	1.68	0.42	1.33	0.84	1.04	1.30
Croatia	2004	73	83.6	1.64	1.43	0.79	0.84	1.22	2.59	2.17
Czech Republic	2004	166	71.7	1.63	1.30	0.83	0.79	1.45	2.16	2.45
Denmark	2001	49	85.7	0.92	0.89	0.45	1.00	0.76	1.08	1.26
Estonia	2003	105	89.5	7.76	4.78	1.27	3.88	9.10	13.10	6.44
Finland	2004	143	77.6	2.74	1.41	0.95	0.77	1.60	4.39	5.11
France	2002	1,020	71.7	1.71	1.90	0.38	0.84	1.15	2.19	3.62
Georgia	2001	45	91.1	0.99	0.00	0.85	0.72	0.97	0.95	1.87
Germany	2004	401	71.8	0.49	0.95	0.18	0.26	0.37	0.46	0.91
Hong Kong, China	2002	35	74.3	0.52	0.37	0.36	0.34	0.28	0.71	1.29
Hungary	2003	206	80.6	2.03	0.63	1.40	1.75	2.14	2.61	1.98
Israel	2003	35	74.3	0.52	0.44	0.17	0.99	0.56	0.41	0.60
Japan	2003	5,716	54.3	4.53	0.78	0.72	0.78	0.86	2.94	17.09
Kuwait	2002	20	90.0	0.85	2.44	0.00	1.13	0.46	0.32	13.15
Kyrgyzstan	2004	281	75.4	5.70	12.57	2.47	3.36	7.16	6.29	6.65
Latvia	2004	185	76.2	8.00	6.00	7.23	3.91	9.82	12.17	3.44
Lithuania	2004	307	82.1	8.94	8.87	2.05	5.32	10.34	11.89	11.21
Luxembourg	2004	4	75.0	0.88	0.00	0.00	1.92	0.00	1.82	1.56
Malta	2004	2	50.0	0.50	4.91	0.00	0.00	0.91	0.00	0.00
Moldova	2004	241	79.7	6.69	6.63	4.83	3.14	7.49	8.65	9.56
Netherlands	2004	96	74.0	0.59	1.48	0.35	0.36	0.23	0.76	1.06
Norway	2003	70	85.7	1.53	0.34	0.48	0.91	1.36	1.71	3.56
Poland	2003	1,082	82.1	2.83	1.63	1.51	2.73	3.10	3.63	2.61
Portugal	2003	167	74.9	1.59	1.26	0.82	1.62	1.29	1.70	2.55
Romania	2004	1,050	76.5	4.84	4.24	3.32	3.95	3.82	6.74	6.10
Russian Federation	2004	14,756	83.3	10.30	4.70	5.90	8.20	13.10	12.60	7.90
Serbia and Montenegro	2002	94	76.6	1.16	0.27	1.96	1.36	0.91	0.97	1.41
Slovakia	2002	183	73.8	3.40	2.62	1.70	1.89	2.19	5.28	7.14
Slovenia	2003	34	79.4	1.70	0.00	0.00	1.44	0.99	2.67	3.37
South Korea	2002	948	75.4	1.97	1.79	2.11	1.42	1.38	2.18	5.24
Spain	2003	562	82.2	1.34	1.36	0.54	0.95	1.10	1.43	2.41
Sweden	2002	134	79.9	1.50	1.09	0.43	0.58	0.66	2.30	3.20
Switzerland	2002	65	75.4	0.90	0.80	0.50	0.50	0.60	0.90	2.10
Thailand	2002	4,218	74.3	6.74	14.01	10.01	3.84	4.84	6.91	8.45
United Kingdom	2002	224	70.1	0.38	0.59	0.16	0.35	0.35	0.39	0.53
United States	2002	3,447	80.1	1.20	2.64	0.78	1.55	1.13	0.88	1.22

Source: National Safety Council tabulations of World Health Organization data.

OCCUPATIONAL DEATHS

Counts and rates of fatal work-related injuries are shown on this page and the next. Comparisons between countries should be made with caution and take into account the differences in sources, coverage, and kinds of cases included.

OCCUPATIONAL DEATHS BY COUNTRY, 2001–2005

Country	Deaths					Source of Data	Maximum Period[a]	Coverage		
	2001	2002	2003	2004	2005			Worker Types[b]	% of Total Employment[c]	Activities Excluded
Injuries Only — Compensated Cases										
France	730	686	661	626	—	IR	varies	E	75	P
Tunisia	172	160	184	155	—	IR	—	E	39	P
Injuries Only — Reported Cases										
Austria	122	130	103	532	—	IR	none	E, SE	71	none
Azerbaijan	27	59	52	72	54	LR	—	E	—	—
Belarus	234	228	214	248	235	C	same year	E	—	none
Czech Republic	231	206	199	190	164	AR	none	E, SE	95	AF, Pol
Hungary	124	163	133	160	125	LR	90 days	E, SE	98	none
Japan	1,790	1,658	1,628	1,620	1,514	LR	—	E	—	none
Latvia	72	56	41	61	56	S	none	E	—	none
Moldova, Rep. of	39	41	43	38	49	C	none	E	52	none
Norway	37	39	49	38	48	LR	none	E	100	none
Poland	554	515	515	490	470	LR	6 months	E, SE	76	Agr
Puerto Rico	53	38	29	55	—	C	—	E, SE	97	—
Singapore	52	64	55	51	44	LR	none	E	33	none
Slovakia	100	87	94	79	76	C	none	IE	98	none
Spain	1,030	805	722	695	693	IR	—	—	—	—
Sweden	56	60	56	57	—	IR	none	E, SE	97	none
Taiwan, China	543	507	401	366	382	LR	—	—	—	—
Ukraine	1,325	1,227	1,128	1,068	989	LR	4 months	E	71	AF
United Kingdom	210	191	174	179	—	LR	1 year	E, SE	92	SF, AT
United States	5,915	5,534	5,575	5,764	—	C	none	E, SE	100	none
Injuries and Commuting Accidents — Compensated Cases										
Croatia	42	44	47	38	62	IR	immediate	E, SE	84	none
El Salvador	259	191	206	—	—	IR	none	IE	24	none
Germany	1,107	1,071	—	—	—	IR	none	E, SE	100	none
Italy	1,077	934	976	930	839	IR	none	I	76	none
Injuries and Commuting Accidents — Reported Cases										
Hong Kong, China	176	210	171	187	—	LR	none	E	77	none
Lithuania	86	83	118	94	112	LR	none	E, SE	64	AF
Romania	456	441	418	409	475	LR	same year	E, SE	61	AF, P
Russian Federation	4,370	3,920	3,540	3,290	3,090	S	none	E	5	Low
Slovenia	34	32	40	21	—	LR	1 month	I	85	none
Injuries and Diseases — Compensated Cases										
Australia[d]	196	176	151	119	—	IR	3 years	E	83	AF
Canada	919	934	963	928	—	IR	none	E, SE	85	AF
Finland	43	37	43	44	—	IR	1 year	E	85	none
Switzerland	72	53	46	67	—	IR	same year	IE	88	none
Injuries and Diseases — Reported Cases										
Sri Lanka	27	36	42	42	52	LR	1 year	E	35	M, E, TSC, C
Turkey	1,008	878	811	843	—	IR	—	IE	25	none
Injuries, Diseases, and Commuting Accidents — Compensated Cases										
Costa Rica	74	60	55	50	60	IR	none	I	56	none
Estonia	36	35	31	34	24	IR	1 year	I	100	AF, Pol
Israel	100	91	88	88	—	IR	same year	E, SE	100	none
South Korea[e]	1,298	1,271	1,408	1,417	1,288	IR	—	I	45	none
Syrian Arab Republic	185	383	174	205	612	LR	—	I	46	none
Thailand	597	650	787	861	1,444	IR	—	I	16	none
Injuries, Diseases, and Commuting Accidents — Reported Cases										
Bahrain	10	14	21	13	29	IR	none	E, SE	100	none
Bulgaria	138	115	114	130	—	AR	—	E, SE	35	none
Jordan	35	49	70	52	63	IR	none	E	—	AF
Mexico	1,502	1,361	1,427	1,364	1,367	IR	none	IE	32	none
New Zealand	75	81	84	82	91	IR	1 year	E, SE	100	none

Source: International Labour Office. (2006). Yearly Data of Total and Economically Active Population, Employment, Unemployment, Hours of Work, Wages, Labour Cost, Consumer Price Indices, Occupational Injuries, Strikes and Lockouts: 1969–2005. Data available at http://laborsta.ilo.org
Note: Dash (—) indicates data not available.
[a]Maximum period between accident and death for death to be counted.

[b]Types of workers included in the data.
[c]Workers covered by the statistics as a percentage of total employment; latest year available.
[d]Excluding Victoria and Australian Capital Territory.
[e]Establishments with 10 or more workers.

Source of Data	Worker Types	Economic Activities		
AR = Administrative reports	E = Employees	AF = Armed forces	D = Domestic services	PA = Public administration
C = Census	I = Insured persons	Agr = Agriculture	E = Electricity, gas, and water	Pol = Police
IR = Insurance records	IE = Insured employees	ASO = Air, sea, offshore accidents	Low = Activities with low rates of injuries	SF = Sea fishing
LR = Labor inspectorate records	SE = Self-employed	AT = Air transport	M = Manufacturing	TSC = Transport, storage, and communications
S = Survey		C = Construction	P = Public sector	

The International Labour Organization (ILO) estimates that work-related accidents cause about 351,500 deaths worldwide every year. Worker safety in Asian and Latin American countries, exposure to hazardous substances, construction work, and the safety and health of younger and older workers have been identified as top-priority areas in need of attention.

Source: International Labour Organization. (2005). World Day for Safety and Health at Work 2005: A Background Paper. Available at http://www.ilo.org/public/english/bureau/inf /download/sh_background.pdf

OCCUPATIONAL DEATH RATES BY COUNTRY, 2001–2005

Country	Coverage[a]	2001	2002	2003	2004	2005
Deaths per 100,000 Employed Persons						
Injuries Only						
Azerbaijan	RC	3.0	6.0	6.0	8.0	6.0
Belarus	RC	5.8	5.9	5.6	6.4	6.1
Hungary	RC	3.21	4.21	3.39	4.1	3.2
Moldova, Rep. of	RC	5.0	5.3	5.6	4.9	6.4
Norway	RC	1.6	1.7	2.1	1.7	2.1
Poland	RC	5.1	4.9	4.9	4.7	4.4
Sweden	RC	1.4	1.4	1.3	1.4	—
Ukraine	RC	10.5	10.0	9.4	8.9	8.4
United Kingdom	RC	0.8	0.74	0.7	0.7	—
United States	RC	4.0	4.0	4.0	4.0	—
Injuries and Commuting Accidents						
Croatia	CC	3.22	3.31	3.4	2.7	4.3
Germany	CC	2.95	2.92	—	—	—
Cyprus	RC	—	7.0	3.2	5.4	5.0
Hong Kong, China	RC	7.1	8.6	7.2	7.7	—
Lithuania	RC	8.9	8.1	11.3	9.0	10.4
Romania	RC	7.0	7.0	7.0	7.0	8.0
Russian Federation	RC	15.0	13.8	13.1	12.9	12.4
Injuries and Diseases						
Australia	CC	2.4	2.2	1.8	1.4	—
Canada	CC	6.1	6.1	6.1	5.8	—
Finland	CC	2.1	1.8	2.1	2.1	—
Malta	CC	4.28	2.82	8.2	8.1	—
Injuries and Commuting Accidents						
Israel	CC	4.2	3.83	3.6	3.3	—
Bahrain	RC	5.9	7.5	10.0	5.0	10.0
Deaths per 100,000 Workers Insured						
Injuries Only						
France	CC	4.2	3.8	3.7	3.5	—
Tunisia	CC	15.86	14.31	16.02	13.07	—
Austria	RC	4.5	4.74	3.86	19.53	—
Czech Republic	RC	5.2	4.6	4.5	4.3	3.7
Slovakia	RC	4.91	4.29	4.66	3.91	3.72
Spain	RC	8.0	6.06	5.27	4.89	4.68
Taiwan, China	RC	6.9	6.5	5.0	4.4	4.5
Injuries and Commuting Accidents						
Italy	CC	6.0	5.0	5.0	5.0	—
Slovenia	RC	4.3	4.0	5.1	2.6	—
Injuries and Diseases						
Switzerland	CC	2.0	1.5	1.3	1.9	—
Turkey	RC	20.6	16.8	14.4	13.6	—
Injuries, Diseases, and Commuting Accidents						
Costa Rica	CC	9.5	7.5	7.0	6.1	6.4
Estonia	CC	6.23	5.98	5.22	5.71	3.95
Thailand	CC	0.11	9.94	11.19	11.66	18.7
Bulgaria	RC	7.3	6.0	5.2	6.0	—
Mexico	RC	12.0	11.0	12.0	11.0	11.0
Deaths per 1,000,000 Hours Worked						
Injuries Only						
Japan	RC	0.01	0.01	0.01	—	0.01
Injuries and Diseases						
Sri Lanka	RC	0.007	0.008	0.01	0.007	0.009
Injuries, Diseases, and Commuting Accidents						
Jordan	RC	0.069	0.052	0.062	0.039	0.025
South Korea	CC	0.05	0.05	0.06	0.06	0.05

See source and limitations of data on page 170.
Note: Dash (—) indicates data not available
[a] *Includes reported cases (RC) and compensated cases (CC) of occupational fatalities*

INJURY FACTS®

NATIONAL SAFETY COUNCIL

This appendix gives a brief explanation of some of the sources and methods used by the National Safety Council (NSC) Statistics Department in preparing the estimates of deaths, injuries, and costs presented in this book. Because many of the estimates depend on death certificate data provided by the states or the National Center for Health Statistics (NCHS), it begins with a brief introduction to the certification and classification of deaths.

Certification and classification. The medical certification of death involves entering information on the death certificate about the disease or condition directly leading to death, antecedent causes, and other significant conditions. The death certificate is then registered with the appropriate authority and a code is assigned for the underlying cause of death. The underlying cause is defined as "(a) the disease or injury which initiated the train of morbid events leading directly to death, or (b) the circumstances of the accident or violence which produced the fatal injury" (World Health Organization [WHO], 1992). Deaths are classified and coded on the basis of a WHO standard, the *International Statistical Classification of Diseases and Related Health Problems*, commonly known as the International Classification of Diseases or ICD (WHO, 1992). For deaths due to injury and poisoning, the ICD provides a system of "external cause" codes to which the underlying cause of death is assigned. (See pages 18–19 of *Injury Facts*® for a condensed list of external cause codes.)

Comparability across ICD revisions. The ICD is revised periodically and these revisions can affect comparability from year to year. The sixth revision (1948) substantially expanded the list of external causes and provided for classifying the place of occurrence. Changes in the classification procedures for the sixth revision as well as the seventh (1958) and eighth (1968) revisions classified as diseases some deaths previously classified as injuries. The eighth revision also expanded and reorganized some external cause sections. The ninth revision (1979), provided more detail on the agency involved, the victim's activity, and the place of occurrence. The tenth revision, which was adopted in the United States effective with 1999 data, completely revised the transportation-related categories. Specific external cause categories affected by the revisions are noted in the historical tables.

The table at the end of this appendix (page 179) shows the ICD-9 codes, the ICD-10 codes, and a comparability ratio for each of the principal causes of unintentional-injury death. The comparability ratio represents the net effect of the new revision on statistics for the cause of death. The comparability ratio was obtained by classifying a sample of death certificates under both ICD-9 and ICD-10 and then dividing the number of deaths for a selected cause classified under ICD-10 by the number classified to the most nearly comparable ICD-9 cause. A comparability ratio of 1.00 indicates no net change due to the new classification scheme. A ratio less than 1.00 indicates fewer deaths assigned to a cause under ICD-10 than under ICD-9. A ratio greater than 1.00 indicates an increase in assignment of deaths to a cause under ICD-10 compared to ICD-9.

The broad category of "accidents" or "unintentional injuries" under ICD-9 included complications and misadventures of surgical and medical care (E870–E879) and adverse effects of drugs in therapeutic use (E930–E949). These categories are not included in "accidents" or "unintentional injuries" under ICD-10. In 1998, deaths in these two categories numbered 3,228 and 276, respectively.

Under ICD-9, the code range for falls (E880–E888) included a code for "fracture, cause unspecified" (E887). A similar code does not appear in ICD-10 (W00–W19), which probably accounts for the low comparability ratio (0.8409). In 1998, deaths in code E887 numbered 3,679.

Beginning with 1970 data, tabulations published by NCHS no longer include deaths of nonresident aliens. In 2003, there were 767 such accidental deaths, of which 347 were motor-vehicle related.

Fatality estimates. The Council uses four classes and three venues to categorize unintentional injuries. The four classes are Motor Vehicle, Work, Home, and Public. Each class represents an environment and an intervention route for injury prevention through a responsible authority such as a police department, an employer, a home owner, or public health department. The three venues are Transportation, Work, and Home & Community.

Motor vehicle. The Motor-Vehicle class can be identified by the underlying cause of death (see the table on page 179).

Work. The National Safety Council adopted the Bureau of Labor Statistics' Census of Fatal Occupational Injuries (CFOI) figure, beginning with the 1992 data year, as the authoritative count of unintentional work-related deaths. The CFOI system is described in detail in Toscano and Windau (1994).

The 2-Way Split. After subtracting the Motor-Vehicle and Work figures from the unintentional-injury total (ICD-10 codes V01–X59, Y85–Y86), the remainder belong to the Home and Public classes. The Home class can be identified by the "place of occurrence" subclassification (code .0) used with most nontransport deaths; the Public class is the remainder. Missing "place of occurrence" information, however, prevents the direct determination of the Home and Public class totals. Because of this, the Council allocates nonmotor-vehicle, nonwork deaths into the Home and Public classes based on the external cause, age group, and cases with specified "place of occurrence." This procedure, known as the 2-Way Split, uses the most recent death certificate data available from the NCHS and the CFOI data for the same calendar year. For each cause-code group and age group combination, the Motor-Vehicle and Work deaths are subtracted and the remainder, including those with "place of occurrence" unspecified, are allocated to Home and Public in the same proportion as those with "place of occurrence" specified.

The table on page 179 shows the ICD-10 cause-codes and CFOI event codes for the most common causes of unintentional-injury death. The CFOI event codes (BLS, 1992) do not match exactly with ICD cause codes, so there is some error in the allocation of deaths among the classes.

State reporting system. The Council operates a reporting system through which participating states send tabulations of unintentional-injury death data by age group, class, and type of event or industry. This is known as the Injury Mortality Tabulation reporting system. These data are used to make current year estimates based on the most recent 2-Way Split and CFOI data.

Linking up to current year. The benchmark data published by NCHS are usually two years old and the CFOI data are usually one year old. The link-relative technique is used to make current year estimates from these data using the state vital statistics data. This method assumes that the change in deaths from one year to the next in states reporting for both years reflects the change in deaths for the entire nation. The ratio is calculated and multiplied times the benchmark figure resulting in an estimate for the next year. It may be necessary to repeat the process, depending on the reference year of the benchmark. For example, the 2003 NCHS and CFOI data were used this year for a 2-Way Split and state data were used to make estimates for 2004 and 2005 Home and Public classes using the link-relative technique. CFOI data for 2004 and 2005 were also available so it was not necessary to make Work estimates.

Revisions of prior years. When the figures for a given year are published by NCHS, the 2-Way Split based on those figures and the CFOI become the final estimate of unintentional-injury deaths by class, age group, and type of event or industry. Subsequent years are revised by repeating the link-relative process described above. For example, in the current edition of *Injury Facts*®, the 2003 NCHS and CFOI data were used to produce final estimates using the 2-Way Split, the 2004 estimates were revised using more complete state data and 2004 CFOI figures, and the new 2005 estimates were made with the state data available in the late summer of 2006 together with 2005 CFOI data.

Nonfatal injury estimates. The Council uses the concept of "disabling injury" to define the kinds of injuries included in its estimates. See page 23 for the definition of disabling injury and the National Health Interview Survey (NHIS) injury definitions.

Injury to death ratios. There is no national injury surveillance system that provides disabling injury estimates on a current basis. The National Health Interview Survey, a household survey conducted by the NCHS (see page 23), produces national estimates using its own definition of injury (Schiller, Adams, & Coriaty Nelson, 2005). For this reason, the Council uses injury-to-death ratios to estimate nonfatal disabling injuries for the current year. Complete documentation of the procedure, effective with the 1993 edition, may be found in Landes, Ginsburg, Hoskin, and Miller (1990).

The resulting estimates are not direct measures of nonfatal injuries and should not be compared with prior years.

Population sources. All population figures used in computing rates are estimates taken from various reports published by the Bureau of the Census, U.S. Department of Commerce, on their Internet web site (www.census.gov). *Resident* population is used for computing rates.

Costs (pp. 4–7). The procedures for estimating the economic losses due to fatal and nonfatal unintentional injuries were extensively revised for the 1993 edition of *Accident Facts*®. New components were added, new benchmarks adopted, and a new discount rate assumed. All of these changes resulted in significantly higher cost estimates. For this reason, it must be re-emphasized that the cost estimates should not be compared to those in earlier editions of the book.

The Council's general philosophy underlying its cost estimates is that the figures represent income not received or expenses incurred because of fatal and nonfatal unintentional injuries. Stated this way, the Council's cost estimates are a measure of the economic impact of unintentional injuries and may be compared to other economic measures such as gross domestic product, per capita income, or personal consumption expenditures. (See page 91 and "lost quality of life" [p. 177] for a discussion of injury costs for cost-benefit analysis.)

The general approach followed was to identify a benchmark unit cost for each component, adjust the benchmark to the current year using an appropriate inflator, estimate the number of cases to which the component applied, and compute the product. Where possible, benchmarks were obtained for each class: Motor Vehicle, Work, Home, and Public.

Wage and productivity losses include the value of wages, fringe benefits, and household production for all classes, and travel delay for the Motor Vehicle class.

For fatalities, the present value of after-tax wages, fringe benefits, and household production was computed using the human capital method. The procedure incorporates data on life expectancy from the NCHS life tables, employment likelihood from the Bureau of Labor Statistics household survey, and mean earnings from the Bureau of the Census money income survey. The discount rate used was 4%, reduced from 6% used in earlier years. The present value obtained is highly sensitive to the discount rate; the lower the rate, the greater the present value.

For permanent partial disabilities, an average of 17% of earning power is lost (Berkowitz & Burton, 1987). The incidence of permanent disabilities, adjusted to remove intentional injuries, was computed from data on hospitalized cases from the National Hospital Discharge Survey (NHDS) and nonhospitalized cases from the National Health Interview Survey and National Council on Compensation Insurance data on probabilities of disability by nature of injury and part of body injured.

For temporary disabilities, an average daily wage, fringe benefit, and household production loss was calculated and this was multiplied by the number of days of restricted activity from the NHIS.

Travel delay costs were obtained from the Council's estimates of the number of fatal, injury, and property damage crashes and an average delay cost per crash from Miller et al. (1991).

Medical expenses, including ambulance and helicopter transport costs, were estimated for fatalities, hospitalized cases, and nonhospitalized cases in each class.

The incidence of hospitalized cases was derived from the NHDS data adjusted to eliminate intentional injuries. Average length of stay was benchmarked from Miller, Pindus, Douglass, and Rossman (1993b) and adjusted to estimate lifetime length of stay. The cost per hospital day was benchmarked to the National Medical Expenditure Survey (NMES).

Nonhospitalized cases were estimated by taking the difference between total NHIS injuries and hospitalized cases. Average cost per case was based on NMES data adjusted for inflation and lifetime costs.

Medical cost of fatalities was benchmarked to data from the National Council on Compensation Insurance

(1989) to which was added the cost of a premature funeral and coroner costs (Miller et al., 1991).

Cost per ambulance transport was benchmarked to NMES data and cost per helicopter transport was benchmarked to data in Miller et al. (1993a). The number of cases transported was based on data from Rice and MacKenzie (1989) and the National Electronic Injury Surveillance System.

Administrative expenses include the administrative cost of private and public insurance, which represents the cost of having insurance, and police and legal costs.

The administrative cost of motor-vehicle insurance was the difference between premiums earned (adjusted to remove fire, theft, and casualty premiums) and pure losses incurred, based on data from A. M. Best. Workers' compensation insurance administration was based on A. M. Best data for private carriers and regression estimates using Social Security Administration data for state funds and the self-insured. Administrative costs of public insurance (mainly Medicaid and Medicare) amount to about 4% of the medical expenses paid by public insurance, which were determined from Rice and MacKenzie (1989) and Hensler et al. (1991).

Average police costs for motor-vehicle crashes were taken from Miller et al. (1991) and multiplied by the Council's estimates of the number of fatal, injury and property damage crashes.

Legal expenses include court costs, and plaintiff's and defendant's time and expenses. Hensler et al. (1991) provided data on the proportion of injured persons who hire a lawyer, file a claim, and get compensation. Kakalik and Pace (1986) provided data on costs per case.

Fire losses were based on data published by the National Fire Protection Association in the *NFPA Journal*. The allocation into the classes was based on the property use for structure fires and other NFPA data for nonstructure fires.

Motor-vehicle damage costs were benchmarked to Blincoe and Faigin (1992) and multiplied by the Council's estimates of crash incidence.

Employer costs for work injuries is an estimate of the productivity costs incurred by employers. It assumes each fatality or permanent injury resulted in 4 person-months of disruption, serious injuries 1 person-month, and minor to moderate injuries 2 person-days. All injuries to nonworkers were assumed to involve 2 days of worker productivity loss. Average hourly earnings for supervisors and nonsupervisory workers were computed and then multiplied by the incidence and hours lost per case. Property damage and production delays (except motor-vehicle related) are not included in the estimates but can be substantial.

Lost quality of life is the difference between the value of a statistical fatality or statistical injury and the value of after-tax wages, fringe benefits, and household production. Because this does not represent real income not received or expenses incurred, it is not included in the total economic cost figure. If included, the resulting *comprehensive costs* can be used in cost-benefit analysis because the total costs then represent the maximum amount society should spend to prevent a statistical death or injury.

Work deaths and injuries (p. 48). The method for estimating total work-related deaths and injuries is discussed above. The breakdown of deaths by industry division for the current year is obtained from the CFOI and state Injury Mortality Tabulation figures using the link-relative technique (also discussed above).

The estimate of nonfatal disabling injuries by industry division is made by multiplying the estimate of employment for each industry division by the BLS estimate of the incidence rate of cases involving days away from work for each division (e.g., BLS, 2006) and then adjusting the results so that they add to the work-injury total previously established. The "private sector" average incidence rate is used for the government division, which is not covered in the BLS survey.

Employment. The employment estimates for 1992 to the present were changed for the 1998 edition. Estimates for these years in prior editions are not comparable. The total employment figure used by the Council represents the number of persons in the civilian labor force, aged 16 and older, who were wage or salary workers, self-employed, or unpaid family workers, plus active duty military personnel resident in the U.S. The total employment estimate is a combination of three figures — total civilian employment from the Current Population Survey (CPS) as published in *Employment and Earnings*, plus the difference between total resident population and total civilian population, which represents active duty military personnel.

Employment by industry is obtained from an unpublished Bureau of Labor Statistics table titled "Employed and experience unemployed persons by detailed industry and class of worker, Annual Average [year] (based on CPS)."

Time lost (p. 51) is the product of the number of cases and the average time lost per case. Deaths average 150 workdays lost in the current year and 5,850 in future years; permanent disabilities involve 75 and 565 days lost in current and future years, respectively; temporary disabilities involve 17 days lost in the current year only. Off-the-job injuries to workers are assumed to result in similar lost time.

Off-the-job (p. 52) deaths and injuries are estimated by assuming that employed persons incur injuries at the same rate as the entire population.

Motor-Vehicle (pp. 86–117). Estimates of miles traveled, registered vehicles and licensed drivers are published by the Federal Highway Administration in *Highway Statistics* and *Traffic Volume Trends*.

SELECTED UNINTENTIONAL-INJURY CODE GROUPINGS

Manner of Injury	ICD-9 Codes[a]	ICD-10 Codes[b]	Comparability Ratio[c]	OI & ICM[d] Event Codes
Unintentional Injuries	E800–E869, E880–E929[e]	V01–X59, Y85–Y86	1.0305 (1.0278–1.0333)[f]	00–60, 63–9999
Railway accident	E800–E807	V05, V15, V80.6, V81(.2–.9)	n/a	44
Motor-vehicle accident	E810–E825	V02–V04, V09.0, V09.2, V12–V14, V19.0–V19.2, V19.4–V19.6, V20–V79, V80.3–V80.5, V81.0–V81.1, V82.0–V82.1, V83–V86, V87.0–V87.8, V88.0–V88.8, V89.0, V89.2	0.9754 (0.9742–0.9766)	41, 42, 43 with source = 82, 83
Water transport accident	E830–E838	V90–V94	n/a	45
Air transport accident	E840–E845	V95–V97	n/a	46
Poisoning by solids and liquids	E850–58, E860–66	X40–X49	n/a	344
Poisoning by gases and vapors	E867–E869			341
Falls	E880–E888	W00–W19	0.8409 (0.8313–0.8505)	1
Fires and burns	E890–E899	X00–X09	0.9743 (0.9568–0.9918)	51
Drowning	E910	W65–W74	0.9965 (0.9716–1.0213)	381
Suffocation by ingestion or inhalation	E911–E912	W78–W80	n/a	382
Mechanical suffocation	E913	W75–W77, W81–W84	n/a	383, 384, 389
Firearms	E922	W32–W34	1.0579 (1.0331–1.0828)	0220, 0222, 0229 with source = 911[g]

Source: National Safety Council.
Note: n/a means comparability ratio not calculated or does not meet standards of reliability or precision.
[a]WHO (1977).
[b]WHO (1992).
[c]Hoyert, Arias, Smith, et al. (2001). Table III.
[d]BLS (1992).
[e]The National Safety Council has used E800–E949 for unintentional injuries. The code group in the table omits complications and misadventures of surgical and medical care (E870–E879) and adverse effects of drugs in therapeutic use (E930–E949).
[f]Figures in parentheses are the 95% confidence interval for the comparability ratio.
[g]Struck by flying object where the source of injury was a bullet.

Berkowitz, M., & Burton, J.F., Jr. (1987). *Permanent Disability Benefits in Workers' Compensation.* Kalamazoo, MI: W.E. Upjohn Institute for Employment Research.

Blincoe, L.J., & Faigin, B.M. (1992). *Economic Cost of Motor Vehicle Crashes,* 1990. Springfield, VA: National Technical Information Service.

Bureau of Labor Statistics [BLS]. (1992). *Occupational Injury & Illness Classification Manual.* Itasca, IL: National Safety Council.

Bureau of Labor Statistics [BLS]. (2006, October 19). *Workplace Injuries and Illnesses in 2005.* Press release USDL-06-1816.

Hensler, D.R., Marquis, M.S., Abrahamse, A.F., Berry, S.H., Ebener, P.A., Lewis, E.D., Lind, E.A., MacCoun, R.J., Manning, W.G., Rogowski, J.A., & Vaiana, M.E. (1991). *Compensation for Accidental Injuries in the United States.* Santa Monica, CA: The RAND Corporation.

Hoyert, D.L., Arias, E., Smith, B.L., Murphy, S.L., & Kochanek, K.D. (2001). Deaths: final data for 1999. *National Vital Statistics Reports, 49*(8).

Kakalik, J.S., & Pace, N. (1986). *Costs and Compensation Paid in Tort Litigation.* R-3391-ICJ. Santa Monica, CA: The RAND Corporation.

Landes, S.R., Ginsburg, K.M., Hoskin, A.F., & Miller, T.A. (1990). *Estimating Nonfatal Injuries.* Itasca, IL: Statistics Department, National Safety Council.

Miller, T., Viner, J., Rossman, S., Pindus, N., Gellert, W., Douglass, J., Dillingham, A., & Blomquist, G. (1991). *The Costs of Highway Crashes.* Springfield, VA: National Technical Information Service.

Miller, T.R., Brigham, P.A., Cohen, M.A., Douglass, J.B., Galbraith, M.S., Lestina, D.C., Nelkin, V.S., Pindus, N.M., & Smith-Regojo, P. (1993a). Estimating the costs to society of cigarette fire injuries. *Report to Congress in Response to the Fire Safe Cigarette Act of 1990.* Washington, DC: U.S. Consumer Product Safety Commission.

Miller, T.R., Pindus, N.M., Douglass, J.B., & Rossman, S.B. (1993b). *Nonfatal Injury Incidence, Costs, and Consequences: A Data Book.* Washington, DC: The Urban Institute Press.

Rice, D.P., & MacKenzie, E.J. (1989). *Cost of Injury in the United States: A Report to Congress.* Atlanta, GA: Centers for Disease Control and Prevention.

Schiller, J.S., Adams, P.F., & Coriaty Nelson Z. (2005). Summary health statistics for the U.S. population: National health interview survey, 2003. *Vital and Health Statistics, Series 10, No. 224.* Hyattsville, MD: National Center for Health Statistics.

Toscano, G., & Windau, J. (1994). The changing character of fatal work injuries. *Monthly Labor Review, 117*(10), 17–28.

World Health Organization. (1977). *Manual of the International Statistical Classification of Diseases, Injuries, and Causes of Death.* Geneva, Switzerland: Author.

World Health Organization. (1992). *International Statistical Classification of Diseases and Related Health Problems — Tenth Revision.* Geneva, Switzerland: Author.

OTHER SOURCES

The following organizations may be useful for obtaining more current data or more detailed information on various subjects in *Injury Facts®*.

American Association of Poison Control Centers
3201 New Mexico Avenue, Suite 330
Washington, DC 20016
(202) 362-7217
www.aapcc.org
info@aapcc.org

Bureau of Labor Statistics
U.S. Department of Labor
2 Massachusetts Avenue, NE
Washington, DC 20212
(202) 691-5200
www.bls.gov
blsdata_staff@bls.gov

Bureau of the Census
U.S. Department of Commerce
Public Information Office
Washington, DC 20233-0001
(800) 321-1995
www.census.gov

Bureau of Justice Statistics
810 7th Street, NW
Washington, DC 20531
(202) 307-0765
www.ojp.usdoj.gov/bjs
askbjs@usdoj.gov

Bureau of Transportation Statistics
U.S. Department of Transportation
400 7th Street, SW, Room 3430
Washington, DC 20590
(800) 853-1351
www.bts.gov
answers@bts.gov

Centers for Disease Control and Prevention
1600 Clifton Road
Atlanta, GA 30333
(800) 311-3435
www.cdc.gov

Chemical Safety Board
2175 K Street, NW, Suite 400
Washington, DC 20037
(202) 261-7600
www.chemsafety.gov
info@csb.gov

Eno Transportation Foundation
1634 I Street, NW, Suite 500
Washington, DC 20006
(202) 879-4700
www.enotrans.com

Environmental Protection Agency, U.S.
1200 Pennsylvania Avenue, NW
Washington, DC 20460
(202) 272-0167
www.epa.gov

European Agency for Safety and Health at Work
Gran Via, 33
E-48009 Bilbao, Spain
Phone: +34 944-794-360
Fax: +34 944-794-383
http://europe.osha.eu.int
information@osha.eu.int

Federal Aviation Administration
U.S. Department of Transportation
National Aviation Safety Data Analysis Center
800 Independence Avenue, SW
Washington, DC 20591
(866) 835-5322
www.faa.gov

Federal Bureau of Investigation
935 Pennsylvania Avenue, NW
Washington, DC 20535-0001
(202) 324-3000
www.fbi.gov

Federal Highway Administration
U.S. Department of Transportation
400 7th Street, SW
Washington, DC 20590
(202) 366-0660
www.fhwa.dot.gov
execsecretariat.fhwa@fhwa.dot.gov

Federal Motor Carrier Safety Administration
U.S. Department of Transportation
400 7th Street, SW
Washington, DC 20590
(800) 832-5660
www.fmcsa.dot.gov

Federal Railroad Administration
U.S. Department of Transportation
1120 Vermont Avenue, NW
Washington, DC 20590
(202) 493-6000
www.fra.dot.gov

Federal Transit Administration
400 7th Street, SW
Washington, DC 20590
www.fta.dot.gov

FedStats
Gateway to official statistical information available to the public from more than 100 federal agencies.
www.fedstats.gov

FirstGov
Gateway to federal, state, local, tribal, and international government websites.
www.firstgov.gov

Insurance Information Institute
110 William Street
New York, NY 10038
(212) 346-5500
www.iii.org

Insurance Institute for Highway Safety
1005 N. Glebe Road, Suite 800
Arlington, VA 22201
(703) 247-1500
www.highwaysafety.org

International Hunter Education Association
P.O. Box 490
Wellington, CO 80549-0490
(970) 568-7954
www.ihea.com
info@ihea.com

International Labour Office
4, rue des Morillons
CH-1211 Geneva 22
Switzerland
Phone: +41-22-799-6111
Fax: +41-22-798-8685
www.ilo.org
ilo@ilo.org

Mine Safety and Health Administration
1100 Wilson Boulevard, 21st Floor
Arlington, VA 22209-3939
(202) 693-9400
www.msha.gov

Motorcycle Safety Foundation
2 Jenner Street, Suite 150
Irvine, CA 92718-3812
(714) 727-3227
www.msf-usa.org

National Academy of Social Insurance
1776 Massachusetts Avenue, NW, Suite 615
Washington, DC 20036-1904
(202) 452-8097
www.nasi.org
nasi@nasi.org

National Center for Education Statistics
U.S. Department of Education
1990 K Street, NW
Washington, DC 20006
(202) 502-7300
http://nces.ed.gov

National Center for Health Statistics
3311 Toledo Road, Room 2217
Hyattsville, MD 20782
(301) 458-4000
www.cdc.gov/nchs

National Center for Injury Prevention and Control
Office Of Communication Resources, Mail Stop K65
4770 Buford Highway, NE
Atlanta, GA 30341-3724
(770) 488-1506
www.cdc.gov/ncipc
ohcinfo@cdc.gov

National Clearinghouse for Alcohol and Drug Information
P.O. Box 2345
Rockville, MD 20847-2345
(301) 468-2600 or (800) 729-6686
www.health.org

National Climatic Data Center
151 Patton Avenue
Asheville, NC 28801-5001
(828) 271-4800
www.ncdc.noaa.gov/oa/ncdc.html
ncdc.info@noaa.gov

National Collegiate Athletic Association
700 W. Washington Street
P.O. Box 6222
Indianapolis, IN 46206-6222
(317) 917-6222
www.ncaa.org

National Council on Compensation Insurance
901 Peninsula Corporate Circle
Boca Raton, FL 33487
(800) NCCI-123 (800-622-4123)
www.ncci.com

National Fire Protection Association
P.O. Box 9101
Batterymarch Park
Quincy, MA 02269-0910
(617) 770-3000 or (800) 344-3555
www.nfpa.org
osds@nfpa.org

National Highway Traffic Safety Administration
U.S. Department of Transportation
400 7th Street, SW
Washington, DC 20590
(888) 327-4236
www.nhtsa.dot.gov
  National Center for Statistics and Analysis (NPO-121)
  (202) 366-4198 or (800) 934-8517
  NCSAweb@nhtsa.dot.gov

National Institute for Occupational Safety and Health
Clearinghouse for Occupational Safety and Health
  Information
4676 Columbia Parkway
Cincinnati, OH 45226
(800) 356-4674
www.cdc.gov/niosh
eidtechinfo@cdc.gov

National Spinal Cord Injury Association
6701 Democracy Boulevard, Suite 300-9
Bethesda, MD 20817
(301) 214-4006
www.spinalcord.org
info@spinalcord.org

National Sporting Goods Association
1601 Feehanville Drive, Suite 300
Mt. Prospect, IL 60056
(800) 815-5422
www.nsga.org
info@nsga.org

National Transportation Safety Board
490 L'Enfant Plaza East, SW
Washington, DC 20594
(202) 314-6000
www.ntsb.gov

Occupational Safety and Health Administration
U.S. Department of Labor
Office of Statistics
200 Constitution Avenue, NW
Washington, DC 20210
(800) 321-OSHA (6742)
www.osha.gov

Prevent Blindness America
211 W. Wacker Dr., Suite 1700
Chicago, IL 60606
(800) 331-2020
www.preventblindness.org
info@preventblindness.org

Transportation Research Board
500 5th Street, NW
Washington, DC 20001
(202) 334-2934
www.nas.edu/trb

U.S. Coast Guard
2100 2nd Street, SW
Washington, DC 20593-0001
(800) 368-5647
www.uscgboating.org
uscginfoline@gcrm.com

U.S. Consumer Product Safety Commission
National Injury Information Clearinghouse
Washington, DC 20207-0001
(301) 504-7921
www.cpsc.gov
clearinghouse@cpsc.gov

World Health Organization
20, avenue Appia
CH-1211 Geneva 27
Switzerland
Phone: +41-22-791-2111
Fax: +41-22-791-3111
www.who.int
info@who.int

Accident is that occurrence in a sequence of events that produces unintended injury, death, or property damage. *Accident* refers to the event, not the result of the event (see *Unintentional injury*).

Death from accident is a death that occurs within one year of the accident.

Disabling injury is an injury causing death, permanent disability, or any degree of temporary total disability beyond the day of the injury.

Fatal accident is an accident that results in one or more deaths within one year.

Home is a dwelling and its premises within the property lines including single-family dwellings and apartment houses, duplex dwellings, boarding and rooming houses, and seasonal cottages. Excluded from *home* are barracks, dormitories, and resident institutions.

Incidence rate, as defined by OSHA, is the number of occupational injuries and/or illnesses or lost workdays per 100 full-time employees (see formula on page 61).

Injury is physical harm or damage to the body resulting from an exchange, usually acute, of mechanical, chemical, thermal, or other environmental energy that exceeds the body's tolerance.

Motor vehicle is any mechanically or electrically powered device not operated on rails, upon which or by which any person or property may be transported upon a land highway. The load on a motor vehicle or trailer attached to it is considered part of the vehicle. Tractors and motorized machinery are included while self-propelled in transit or used for transportation. *Nonmotor vehicle* is any road vehicle other than a motor vehicle, such as a bicycle or animal-drawn vehicle, except a coaster wagon, child's sled, child's tricycle, child's carriage, and similar means of transportation; persons using these latter means of transportation are considered pedestrians.

Motor-vehicle accident is an unstabilized situation that includes at least one harmful event (injury or property damage) involving a motor vehicle in transport (in motion, in readiness for motion, or on a roadway but not parked in a designated parking area) that does not result from discharge of a firearm or explosive device and does not directly result from a cataclysm. [See Committee on Motor Vehicle Traffic Accident Classification (1997), *Manual on Classification of Motor Vehicle Traffic Accidents*, ANSI D16.1-1996, Itasca, IL: National Safety Council.]

Motor-vehicle traffic accident is a motor-vehicle accident that occurs on a trafficway — a way or place, any part of which is open to the use of the public for the purposes of vehicular traffic. *Motor-vehicle nontraffic accident* is any motor-vehicle accident that occurs entirely in any place other than a trafficway.

Nonfatal injury accident is an accident in which at least one person is injured and no injury results in death.

Occupational illness is any abnormal condition or disorder other than one resulting from an occupational injury caused by exposure to environmental factors associated with employment. It includes acute and chronic illnesses or diseases that may be caused by inhalation, absorption, ingestion, or direct contact (see also page 61).

Occupational injury is any injury such as a cut, fracture, sprain, amputation, etc., which results from a work accident or from a single instantaneous exposure in the work environment (see also page 61).

Pedalcycle is a vehicle propelled by human power and operated solely by pedals; excludes mopeds.

Pedestrian is any person involved in a motor-vehicle accident who is not in or upon a motor vehicle or nonmotor vehicle. Includes persons injured while using a coaster wagon, child's tricycle, roller skates, etc. Excludes persons boarding, alighting, jumping, or falling from a motor vehicle in transport who are considered occupants of the vehicle.

Permanent disability (or permanent impairment) includes any degree of permanent nonfatal injury. It includes any injury that results in the loss or complete loss of use of any part of the body or in any permanent impairment of functions of the body or a part thereof.

Property damage accident is an accident that results in property damage but in which no person is injured.

Public accident is any accident other than motor-vehicle that occurs in the public use of any premises. Includes deaths in recreation (swimming, hunting, etc.), in transportation except motor-vehicle, public buildings, etc., and from widespread natural disasters even though some may have happened on home premises. Excludes accidents to persons in the course of gainful employment.

Source of injury is the principal object such as tool, machine, or equipment involved in the accident and is usually the object inflicting injury or property damage. Also called *agency* or *agent*.

Temporary total disability is an injury that does not result in death or permanent disability but that renders the injured person unable to perform regular duties or activities on one or more full calendar days after the day of the injury.

Total cases include all work-related deaths and illnesses and those work-related injuries that result in loss of consciousness, restriction of work or motion, or transfer to another job, or require medical treatment other than first aid.

Unintentional injury is the preferred term for accidental injury in the public health community. It refers to the *result* of an accident.

Work hours are the total number of hours worked by all employees. They are usually compiled for various levels, such as an establishment, a company, or an industry. A work hour is the equivalent of one employee working one hour.

Work injuries (including occupational illnesses) are those that arise out of and in the course of gainful employment regardless of where the accident or exposure occurs. Excluded are work injuries to private household workers and injuries occurring in connection with farm chores that are classified as home injuries.

Workers are all persons gainfully employed, including owners, managers, other paid employees, the self-employed, and unpaid family workers but excluding private household workers.

Work/Motor-vehicle duplication includes *work injuries* that occur in *motor-vehicle accidents* (see *Work injuries* and *Motor-vehicle accident*).